SYSTEM IN CRISIS: THE CASE FOR HEALTH CARE REFORM

SYSTEM IN CRISIS: THE CASE FOR HEALTH CARE REFORM

Editors

Robert J. Blendon, Sc.D.
Jennifer N. Edwards, M.H.S.

A collaborative work of
Harvard School of Public Health
Louis Harris and Associates, Inc.
Institute for the Future

FAULKNER & GRAY
A JPT PUBLISHING GROUP COMPANY

Faulkner & Gray, Inc., New York
Healthcare Information Center, Washington DC

System in Crisis: The Case for Health Care Reform

Copyright © 1991

Faulkner & Gray, Inc.

Library of Congress Cataloguing-in-Publication Data

Blendon, Robert.
    System in Crisis: The Case for Health Care Reform /
edited by Robert J. Blendon, Jennifer N. Edwards.

Index included

1. Medical care—United States—Forecasting.
2. Medical policy—United States—Decisionmaking.
3. Health planning—United States.
4. Medical care—Public opinion.

ISBN 0-9624775-8-3

The sponsoring editor was Luci S. Koizumi; production director
was Thomas W. Chambers. Design and production by Jodi Nussbaum.
Editorial assistance by Virginia Vitzthum. The cover was designed by
Susan Namovicz. Science Press was the printer.

Published by Faulkner & Gray's
Healthcare Information Center

1133 Fifteenth Street, NW
Washington DC 20005

PRINTED IN THE UNITED STATES OF AMERICA

THE AUTHORS

Harvard School of Public Health

Robert J. Blendon, Sc.D.
Roger I. Lee Professor and Chairman
Department of Health Policy and Management
Harvard School of Public Health

Robert J. Blendon is Roger I. Lee Professor and Chairman of the Department of Health Policy and Management of the Harvard School of Public Health. Prior to his Harvard appointment, Dr. Blendon was Senior Vice President at The Robert Wood Johnson Foundation, where he worked for 15 years. He is probably best known for his research on access to health care, satisfaction with national health care systems, AIDS and discrimination, and public opinion on health care.

Jennifer N. Edwards, M.H.S.
Research Specialist
Department of Health Policy and Management
Harvard School of Public Health

Jennifer N. Edwards is a research specialist in the Department of Health Policy and Management at the Harvard School of Public Health. Previously Ms. Edwards was Senior Health Policy Analyst for Ford Motor Company. She received her Master of Health Science degree from Johns Hopkins and is currently a Pew Doctoral Fellow at the University of Michigan School of Public Health.

Joanna E. Siegel, Sc.D.
Assistant Professor
Department of Health Policy and Management
Harvard School of Public Health

Joanna E. Siegel is an Assistant Professor in the Department of Health Policy and Management at the Harvard School of Public Health. Dr. Siegel's research interests in AIDS policy include pharmaceutical policy related to AIDS drugs and prevention programs for intravenous drug users. Other research interests include health care financing for the uninsured and the cost-effectiveness of medical interventions.

Karen Donelan
Research Specialist
Department of Health Policy and Management
Harvard School of Public Health

Karen Donelan is a research specialist in the Department of Health Policy and Management at the Harvard School of Public Health. She has co-authored a number of articles on public opinion and health care with Dr. Robert J. Blendon. Ms. Donelan is pursuing doctoral studies in health policy at the School of Public Health.

Louis Harris and Associates, Inc.

Humphrey Taylor
President and Chief Operating Officer
Louis Harris and Associates, Inc.

Humphrey Taylor is President and Chief Operating Officer of Louis Harris and Associates, Inc., the international market and opinion research firm. He has overall responsibility for more than 4,000 surveys in 70 countries for governments, corporations, and foundations on health care and such subjects as housing, insurance, transportation, welfare planning, marketing, communications, banking, and industrial relations. He has testified before congressional committees and subcommittees on Social Security, health care cost containment, Medicare, aging, policies affecting disabled people, drug exports, the taxation of employee benefits, and privacy. Mr. Taylor has published many articles and papers on survey research and public policy, and appears frequently on radio and television.

Robert Leitman
Senior Vice President
Louis Harris and Associates, Inc.

Robert Leitman is Senior Vice President of the international survey research firm, Louis Harris and Associates, Inc. Since joining the Harris firm in 1988, Mr. Leitman has had overall responsibility for surveys in public policy and futures forecasting. His work, conducted for corporations, foundations, not-for-profit organizations, and government agencies, has focused on health care, education, the elderly, and other public policy issues. Prior to joining Louis Harris and Associates, Mr. Leitman spent several years in the Mayor's Office in New York City and was Executive Director of the New York City Commission on the Year 2000.

Institute for the Future

J. Ian Morrison, Ph.D.
President and Director, Health Care Program
Institute for the Future

J. Ian Morrison is President of the Institute for the Future, Menlo Park, CA, and director of the Institute's health care research program. He specializes in long term forecasting and planning with particular emphasis on health care. Dr. Morrison holds an interdisciplinary doctorate in urban studies from the University of British Columbia, and a master's degree in geography from the University of Edinburgh, Scotland. He has written, lectured, and consulted on health care and strategic planning topics for government, industry, hospitals, physicians, and a variety of nonprofit agencies.

Gregory Schmid, Ph.D.
Senior Research Fellow
Institute for the Future

Gregory Schmid is a Senior Research Fellow at the Institute for the Future. Since joining the Institute in 1974, Dr. Schmid has directed projects in both the corporate and public policy areas. Among his major research interests is the preparation of the Institute's annual *Ten-Year Forecast*, a comprehensive look at the U.S. business environment. Dr. Schmid holds a doctorate in economics from Columbia University. Following his studies, he spent more than five years with the Federal Reserve Bank of New York, first as an economist and later as chief of one of its research divisions.

Ellen M. Morrison, Ph.D.
Research Fellow
Institute for the Future

Ellen M. Morrison is a Research Fellow at the Institute for the Future. She devotes virtually all of her time to health care projects, analyzing the forces that make change difficult, as well as those that make change inevitable for the U.S. health care system. Dr. Morrison holds a master's and a doctoral degree in sociology from the University of Chicago. She has written articles, books, and book chapters based on in-depth studies of health care organizations.

TABLE OF CONTENTS

INTRODUCTION

This book is written in response to the growing perception that America's health care system is in need of change. At the time of publication of this book, nine out of ten Americans believe there is a health care crisis in the United States (see Figure 1), and 85 percent think our health care system needs reform.[1]

What will this groundswell of public support for health care reform mean for the future? Will it lead to major changes in the way our hospitals and physicians practice and are paid, the role played by private insurers and employers, and the choices Americans have in purchasing and receiving their health care?

How we have chosen to answer this question, we believe, is unique. Our response is not based on our perspectives as health care experts or academics. Rather, we present the views of more than 50,000 people, including the public, the elderly, major employers, union leaders, insurers, physicians, hospital CEOs, and state and federal health officials, who were interviewed about health care reform. What we asked of these many and diverse groups is: (1) how do they see our health care problems? (2) what are they doing either personally or in their jobs to respond to cost, access, or quality concerns? and (3) what public or private sector health care initiatives do they feel are worthy of their support?

We add to our conclusions, drawn from these many surveys, the results of an analysis of key economic, demographic, political, and health care trends. Here we examine what voters, business executives, physicians, hospitals, patients, and politicians have been doing in recent years in response to increasing pressure to improve the health care system.

The focus of this book differs from that of many others on the United States health care crisis. Its intent is not to present an idealized vision of what major health care reform could lead to in the United States, but rather to provide a realistic assessment of the forces and trends that are likely to shape the delivery of medical care over the next five years. For the reader who is charged with setting the agenda of institutions, this book has been designed to aid in strategic planning by identifying the most probable changes in the health care system that will emerge from this period of ferment and change. Our aim is very pragmatic: to help decisionmakers identify the major changes in America's health care system that are likely to occur in the near future (three to five years) from those that are not.

1

Our conclusions about the future of health care reform are presented tentatively. Forecasting future events has proved to be an imperfect science. For example, in the area of new technology development, many experts inaccurately predicted fundamental changes in our lives that would result from emerging scientific discoveries that later proved to be of no practical, material use. In the mid 1960s, well-known forecasters predicted widespread use of mass-produced, low-cost modular housing by the mid-1980s; the launching of a solar power plant in space by 1983; and a revolution in air travel to be brought about by the use of personal vertical take-off aircraft by 1977.[2,3] In medicine, a 1970 article in the *New England Journal of Medicine* anticipated that by the year 2000, computers would become the mainstay for providing the basic diagnostic and treatment recommendations for large numbers of patients, replacing the current means of clinical decisionmaking by doctors.[4] Each case mistakenly overestimated the practicality of new technological discoveries.

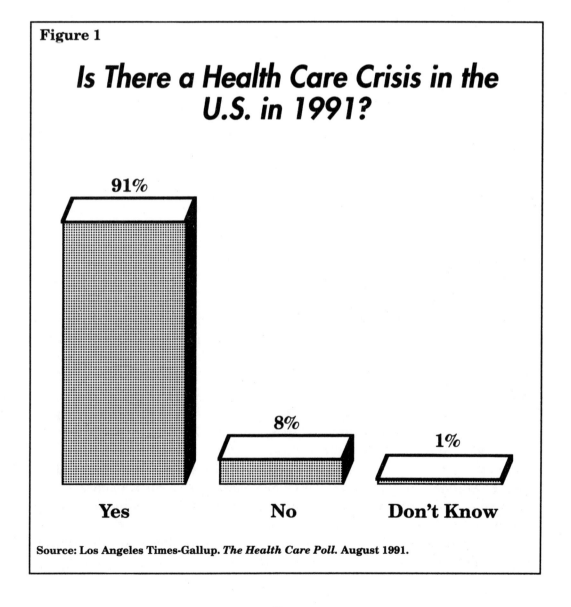

Figure 1

Is There a Health Care Crisis in the U.S. in 1991?

91%

8%

1%

Yes   No   Don't Know

Source: Los Angeles Times-Gallup. *The Health Care Poll.* August 1991.

Forecasters also have been prone to underestimate the impact of long term political and social forces. For example, experts did not foresee the decreased demand in life insurance that resulted from the increase in the number of married women in the workforce. Mothers working outside the home have improved their families' economic security and decreased the demand for substantial life insurance policies.[5]

Our response to the inherent difficulty of anticipating future trends is three-fold. First, we rely heavily on surveys that measure the actual adaptive and proactive changes that businesses, consumers, government, insurers, hospitals, and doctors are undergoing. Second, we describe trends rather than making point-in-time forecasts. We can therefore update the forecasts regularly as new information becomes available about these trends. Third, we look at both the accuracies and errors in past forecasts to improve our forecasts. We start the book with an example, written by Robert J. Blendon and Jennifer N. Edwards of the Harvard School of Public Health, of how re-examining older forecasts can be helpful. Chapter 1 is about the lessons to be learned from the efforts of health care experts in the late 1970s to predict changes to hospitals in the 1990s.

Chapters 2 and 3 identify forces external to health care that will shape the nation's health care in the 1990s. In Chapter 2, Gregory Schmid of the Institute for the Future describes the key demographic, social, and economic trends in the United States. These include the graying of the baby-boomers, the diminishing household size, a shrinking middle class, shortages of new workers entering the labor force, and the impact of changing capital formation patterns.

To complement the discussion of economic and social changes, Humphrey Taylor and Robert Leitman of Louis Harris and Associates describe America's changing political climate as it influences health care legislation, regulations, and innovations. The authors describe shifting party loyalties, changing public priorities, and preferences for domestic policies. They provide unique insights into public attitudes toward government, business, the economy, and key institutions in our society.

The next four chapters examine health care in the 1990s from the perspective of the key participants whose behavior will shape future events. Chapter 4 examines consumers of health care services in a changing health care marketplace. Taylor and Leitman use two recent consumer surveys to identify signs of changing consumer preferences that might affect health care institutions and professionals in the years ahead.

Similarly, in Chapter 5, Ian Morrison and Ellen Morrison of the Institute for the Future and Edwards explore the attitudes and activities of large employers, their intentions toward future cost containment activity, and the implications for the changing health care marketplace. The authors' perspectives are based on a recent survey of major payers that identifies key trends in private sector efforts to contain costs and to evaluate the quality of health care for employees.

In Chapter 6, Morrison and Morrison discuss hospital administrators' views of the future of our health care system. Based on a recent survey of hospital chief executive officers, the authors describe changes hospitals anticipate in response to increasing marketplace and government regulation, including diversification of services and managed care contracting.

Chapter 7 examines these same forces but from the perspective of practicing physicians. Based on trend data and a current physician survey, Taylor, Leitman, and Edwards describe the variety of pressures on physicians to change their style of medical practice and resulting resistance from doctors.

The next three chapters look at attitudes the public and various leadership groups have toward important health care policy issues being debated in the early 1990s. In Chapter 8, Blendon and Karen Donelan of the Harvard School of Public Health explore the sudden upsurge in public interest in health care reform and national health insurance and the important implications for the future. In Chapter 9, Leitman and Edwards describe the special role of the elderly in health policy.

In Chapter 10, Taylor and Leitman present important findings of a recent national survey of key institutional leadership groups. The authors examine the question of national health care reform from the perspective of institutional leaders — employers, union officials, medical association executives, insurance executives, and federal and state government officials. The chapter focuses on how willing these leadership groups are to compromise in order to achieve the goal of national health care reform.

Chapter 11 explores the major emerging epidemiologic problem — AIDS — and its likely impact on our health care system in the next five years. In it, Joanna Siegel, Donelan, and Blendon of the Harvard School of Public Health discuss projections for the course of the AIDS epidemic and its implications for health care institutions and public policy.

We conclude the book with our view of the most important changes likely to occur in the next five years.

This is the first in a series of books about the future of American health care to be published by Faulkner & Gray. The series, and a previously published book,[6] is the product of a long term effort we have undertaken with Louis Harris and Associates and the Institute for the Future to fill a void in the strategic planning literature. It has been made possible in part by generous grants from the Pew Charitable Trusts and the Robert Wood Johnson Foundation. The perspectives on the future of health care presented in this volume are the sole responsibility of the authors under whose names they appear, and do not reflect in any way the views of the Pew Charitable Trusts or the Robert Wood Johnson Foundation. — *The Editors*

REFERENCES

1. Los Angeles Times-Gallup. *The Health Care Poll.* August 1991.

2. Schnaars SP. *Megamistakes: Forecasting and the Myth of Rapid Technological Change.* New York, NY: The Free Press; 1989.

3. Amara R. What we have learned about forecasting and planning. *Futures.* 1988; 20:385-401.

4. Schwartz WB, Patil RS, Szolorts P. Artificial intelligence in medicine: where do we stand? *New England Journal of Medicine.* 1987; 316:685-687.

5. Morrison JL, Renfro WR, Boucher WI. *Applying Methods and Techniques of Futures Research.* San Francisco: Jossey-Bass; 1983:7-8.

6. Amara R, Morrison JI, Schmid G. *Looking Ahead at American Health Care.* Washington, D.C.: McGraw-Hill; 1988.

CHAPTER 1

Looking Back at Hospital Forecasts

Robert J. Blendon and Jennifer N. Edwards
Harvard School of Public Health

INTRODUCTION

In the late 1970s and early 1980s several notable health care analysts made forecasts about the future of American hospitals based on major changes they predicted would soon occur in the health care system.[1,2,3,4,5] While most factors that shape the delivery and financing of hospital care were expected to continue at a fairly constant rate, analysts anticipated that (1) the slowdown in economic growth, (2) tighter corporate cost controls, (3) the surplus of physicians, and (4) the reimbursement changes being considered by the government would result in several major changes in the structure of hospitals and their delivery of care. These four forces,

7

coupled with the pro-competitive bent of government and businesses at the time, were expected to lead to marketplace competition, rather than regulation and planning, as the means to control costs.

The mild threats to their growth and prosperity that hospitals felt in the 1970s would become much worse in the 1980s as the economy softened and revenue for all types of human services became more constrained, the health care analysts predicted. Competitive cost containment strategies being used by governments and employers would curb the demand for expensive, inpatient care, leaving open the possibility of support for alternative sites of health care services. The shift away from hospital based care would be facilitated by a surplus of physicians and improvements in medical technology and would meet a growing patient demand for more convenient choices for a variety of health care services. Decreasing reimbursement and price competition with other types of health care facilities were expected to make the hospital sector much more responsive to market pressures. There was concern over how hospitals would be able to continue to provide even more uncompensated care to people with inadequate or no health insurance. In this constrained environment, some hospitals would be forced out of business, or at best, would reduce their capacity or merge with other hospitals.

Analysts also predicted that hospitals would turn to arrangements that would reduce their costs or improve their revenue stream, including developing relationships with other institutions. Hospitals would be able to operate more efficiently in integrated corporate chains, and these large scale entities would become the principal providers of health care services. Finally, once the cost issue was settled, hospitals would turn to quality as the basis for what was seen as internal competition for patients. These forecasts are summarized in Table 1-1.

LESSONS FROM THE PAST

With the advantage of hindsight, it is not surprising that we can look back at these predictions ten years later and find numerous examples of where they erred. But the goal in looking backwards is not to discredit the work of forecasters, but to improve our ability to make future forecasts. After reviewing the specific set of trends cited below, we find that private sector changes tend to be slower than anticipated, and government policy changes, which may take years to enact, have the swiftest and most dramatic impact on the health care system. Consumers' and physicians' preferences play a stronger role in shaping health care delivery than was previously recognized. Based on these findings, later chapters of this book emphasize the potential for government action in the future and the effects such actions might have, as well as changing public and leadership views. Each chapter also presents the ongoing trends in the private sector that, if left alone, are likely to continue and lead to gradual changes in today's health care arrangements.

Table 1-1

Major Forecasts for Hospitals in the 1980s

1. **Declining use of inpatient hospital care, resulting in closures and mergers**

2. **Growth of alternative institutions**

3. **Surplus of physicians**

4. **Increasing amount of uncompensated care**

5. **Decreasing reimbursement by government and insurers**

6. **Price competition between hospitals**

7. **Concentration of services in large health care chains**

8. **Quality as a basis for competition**

DECLINING USE OF INPATIENT HOSPITAL CARE/ CLOSURES AND MERGERS

Analysts predicted, based on growing concern about the rate of growth in health care costs, that there would soon be tighter cost restrictions on inpatient hospital payments. A more competitive environment, brought on by government and business pressures, would force hospitals to become more efficient, reduce their capacity, or, in some cases, abandon the acute care business altogether. Under these circumstances, they predicted less emphasis would be placed on inpatient hospital care by the 1990s. On this forecast, they were largely correct.

There was some decrease in the use of inpatient hospital services owing, in part, to the changes in the government payment system, government and corporate utilization review programs, and health maintenance organizations (HMOs). Hospital admissions dropped by 11 percent over the last decade, and the average length of a hospital stay dropped more than 8 percent.[6] But there has been only a small decrease in hospital system capacity. There were about 7 percent fewer hospitals in 1989 than there were in 1979, and about 5 percent

9

fewer beds.[6] Rather than close, many hospitals chose to broaden their focus to include the delivery of outpatient services such as alcohol and drug treatment, rehabilitation services, and urgent care centers. Figure 1-1 shows the growth in four types of outpatient services in just the last five years. The number of hospitals providing home health services increased 53 percent; outpatient rehabilitation grew 29 percent; and outpatient alcohol and drug treatment grew 35 percent.[6] The biggest increase is in the number of hospitals that have opened general outpatient departments — a growth of 58 percent in five years. Other hospitals converted acute care beds to skilled nursing beds suited for longer, less medically intensive hospital stays, which produce larger profit margins under Medicare.[7]

Rapid reimbursement changes threatened hospitals and their executives who were seeing admissions and patient revenue drop off rapidly. But did the changes lead to massive numbers of closures, mergers and downsizing as forecasted? If you were to believe the predictions of hospital administrators, the answer would be yes. In surveys of hospital CEOs conducted in 1986, 1988, and 1990, almost half of executives in each year reported they feared their institution might fail in the next five years.[8] The financial uncertainty was reflected in the hospital bond ratings, which worsened in the last decade. Between 1983 and 1988, Standard & Poors raised 56 hospital ratings, compared

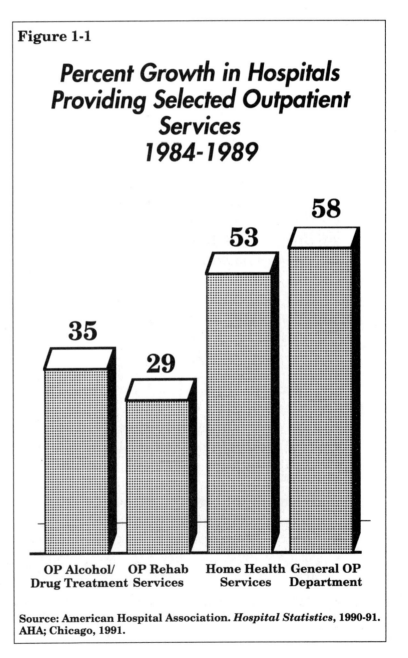

Figure 1-1

Percent Growth in Hospitals Providing Selected Outpatient Services 1984-1989

OP Alcohol/ Drug Treatment	OP Rehab Services	Home Health Services	General OP Department
35	29	53	58

Source: American Hospital Association. *Hospital Statistics*, 1990-91. AHA; Chicago, 1991.

with 280 downgrades, with the ratios of downgrades to upgrades growing from 2:1 in 1983 to 12:1 in 1988.[9] But, based on other financial indicators, the outlook is not as dismal. An analysis of hospitals' financial status found only 12 percent of hospitals were actually financially distressed in 1990, meaning their admissions, revenue, and cash flow had dropped significantly, putting them at high risk of closing.[10]

Figure 1-2

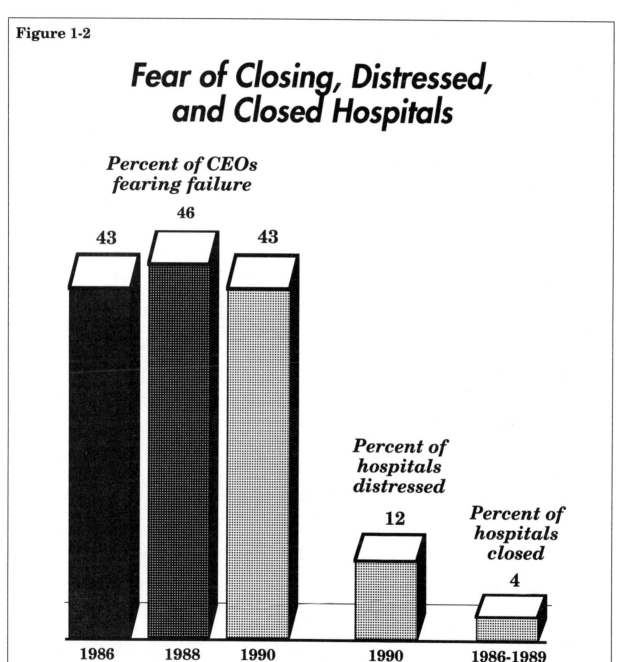

Fear of Closing, Distressed, and Closed Hospitals

Percent of CEOs fearing failure

46

43   43

Percent of hospitals distressed

12

Percent of hospitals closed

4

1986   1988   1990   1990   1986-1989

Source: Deloitte & Touche. *U.S. Hospitals and the Future of Health Care.* June 1990. HCIA. *The HCIA Distressed Hospital Quarterly.* Baltimore, Fourth Quarter 1990. AHA. *Hospital Statistics 1990-91*, AHA; Chicago, 1991.

Data on estimated closures show that both the administrators and the financial analysts were overly pessimistic. Over the entire decade, only 558 community hospitals and 203 non-community hospitals (federal, long term care, and psychiatric hospitals and chemical dependency facilities) closed[11] out of approximately 6,900 hospitals in the United States, despite many more being at risk, as shown in Figure 1-2. What both the hospital executives and the financial analysts did not take into account is the resilience of hospitals. Hospitals have been able to operate and remain viable at very low occupancy rates by using part-time staff and sharing medical equipment. Further, many had the support of their communities and considerable political influence with government because of the critical need they meet in providing care to under-served communities and individuals. In many communities, hospitals are one of the largest sources of jobs.[12]

The data on hospital closures are not conclusive. Many hospitals that report closing to the American Hospital Association (AHA) subsequently reopen under a different name or management or have merged with other hospitals. In reviewing the data, we have found that hospitals are actually much more likely to merge than to close. One study done by the AHA found that between 1980 and 1987, 231 hospitals merged into 111 new institutions, accounting for 120 reported closures.[13] The bottom line is that we have seen only a slight downsizing in the hospital industry's capacity, meaning the tightening reimbursement and competitive environment have not had the anticipated effect of driving hospitals out of business.

The lack of significant reduction in capacity can best be demonstrated by the data on employment in the hospital industry. One would expect that in an industry that is being constrained, employment would decrease as hospitals became more efficient. Hospital employment did decline somewhat in the early 1980s (a decrease of 2.3 percent between 1983 and 1986), but rebounded between 1986 and 1989 when it grew almost 7 percent.

While the overall hospital rate of growth has been slower than the economy as a whole (national employment grew 10.9 percent between 1983 and 1989), employment of some types of hospital workers increased by more than 50 percent, as shown in Table 1-2.[14] Managerial and administrative workers grew 20 percent between 1983 and 1989, outpacing technical workers who increased by about 11 percent.

The largest growth area was marketing, advertising, and public relations managers, which grew an astounding 71 percent in six years, while aides, orderlies, and attendants dropped by 27 percent.[15] Increasing the size of management and decreasing frontline workers is a very different strategy from other competitive industries where cost savings are achieved by laying off managers, not producers. The other striking staffing change during this period was the increased use of more highly skilled registered nurses as substitutes for a variety of less well paid specialized technicians and aides.

GROWTH OF ALTERNATIVE INSTITUTIONS

Many people predicted that a variety of alternative institutions would be established to meet a growing demand for lower cost, more convenient care. This shift was expected to be facilitated by a surplus of physicians, as discussed below. They were right — the growth of free-standing facilities that began as a trickle in the 1970s took off in the 1980s. There are few sources of data available to show the full range of services now available from hospitals' competitors, but where we have data, we can see the growth has been dramatic. Free-standing surgical centers, for example, have experienced almost 600 percent growth in the 1980s.

Table 1-2

Hospital Employment by Occupation, 1983-1989

	1983	1986	1989	% Change 1983-89
All Hospital Employees	4,152,360	4,055,000	4,334,590	4.4
Managerial & Administrative Workers	153,910	165,920	184,710	20.0
Professional, Para-professional & Technical Workers	2,081,910	2,101,570	2,301,730	10.6
Marketing, Advertising & Public Relations Managers	3,780	N/A	6,480	71.4
Registered Nurses	992,490	N/A	1,042,990	13.1
Licensed Practical Nurses	334,690	N/A	261,890	-21.7
Nursing Aides, Orderlies & Attendants	380,595	N/A	278,215	-26.9
Cleaning & Building Services	207,650	N/A	182,870	-11.9

Source: Anderson K, Wootton B. Changes in Hospital Staffing Patterns. *Monthly Labor Review*. 1991; 114:3-9.

As shown in Figure 1-3, most of these are independently owned, but a small number of hospitals have developed their own centers to compete with other operators.[16] Other types of new or greatly expanded facilities include urgent care centers, hospices, free-standing diagnostic centers, and home health agencies. However hospitals continue to take in the largest share of personal health care expenditures, 44 percent in 1989.[17]

SURPLUS OF PHYSICIANS

One of the driving forces in the 1980s around which many health care forecasts were based was the expected surplus of physicians. The surplus, predicted by the Graduate Medical Education National Advisory Committee (GMENAC) and debated by a variety of economists, was expected to result in doctors competing with each other and with hospitals for patients, in some cases setting up alternative facilities outside hospitals. Physicians' incomes would fall as

Figure 1-3

Ambulatory Surgical Centers by Ownership, 1987

Number of ASCs

580 — Independently owned
190 — Corporate owned
95 — Hospital owned

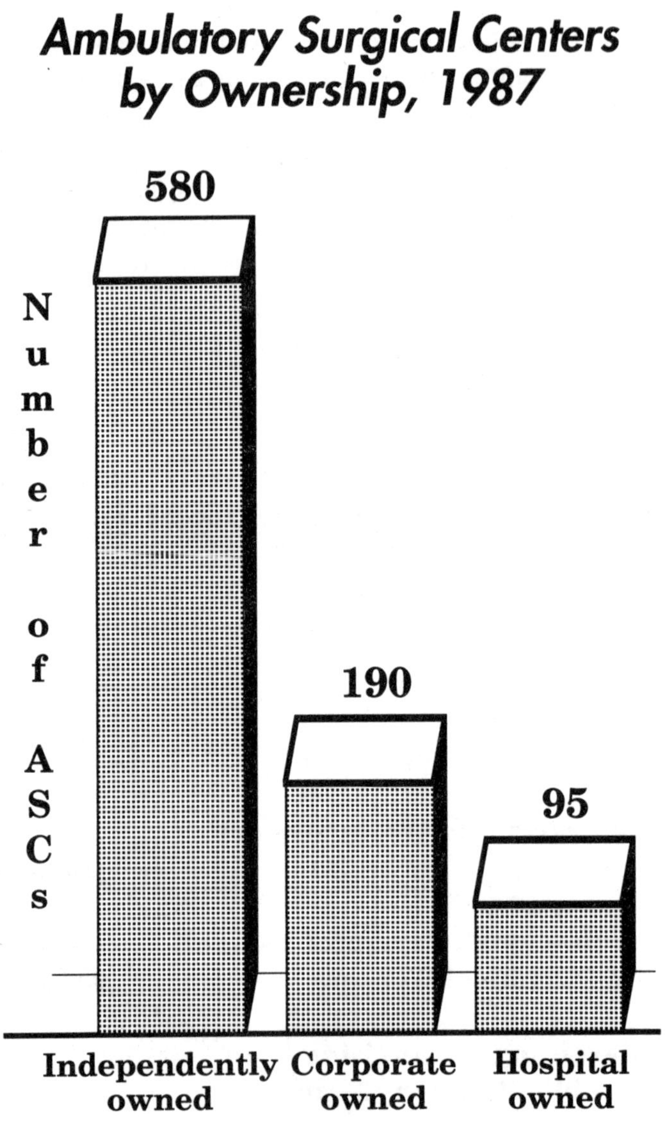

Source: Durant GD. Ambulatory Surgery Centers: Surviving, Thriving into the 1990s. *MGM Journal*, March-April 1989.

they were forced to both lower their prices to attract private patients and to accept lower rates from Medicare. More doctors would go into management and teaching rather than direct patient care.

As foreseen, there has been a large growth in the number of new physicians in the 1980s, about three times larger than the growth of the total population (19% versus 6.5%).[17] The influx of new physicians has outpaced the rate of departures from medical practice, leading to an overall growth in the physician-to-population ratio of 12 percent. In 1980 there were 193 active physicians per 100,000 civilian population, and by 1986 the ratio had climbed to 216.[19] Contrary to predictions, however, the higher ratio of doctors to patients has not caused doctors' incomes or workloads to decrease, and medicine continues to attract new college graduates each year. Despite the increased number of physicians per person, physicians have been able to maintain and even increase their real income levels, as shown in Figure 1-4.

Although their incomes have not fallen, physicians are able to detect some change in the demand for care among patients in their community. Thirty-six

Figure 1-4

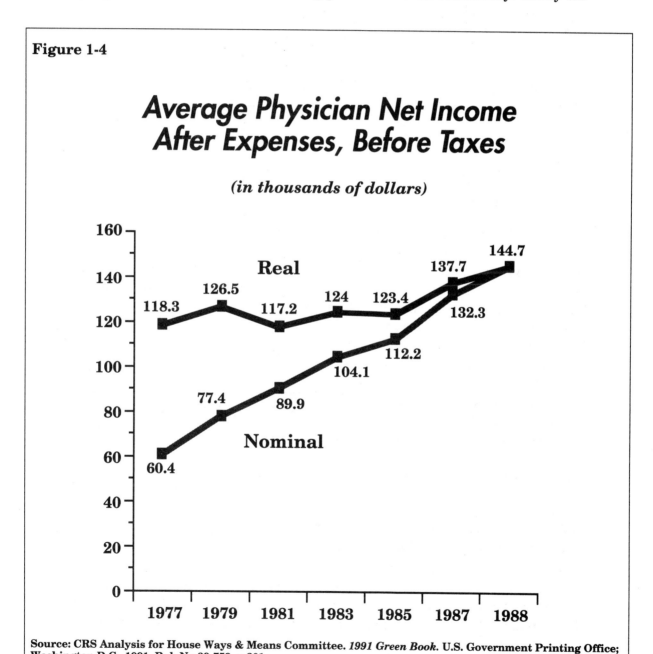

Average Physician Net Income After Expenses, Before Taxes

(in thousands of dollars)

Source: CRS Analysis for House Ways & Means Committee. *1991 Green Book*. U.S. Government Printing Office; Washington D.C., 1991. Pub No 39-759, p.301.

percent of physicians report that they are seeing more competition for patients in their communities, up from 20 percent in 1982. Still, the percent of doctors whose patient load has decreased changed only slightly over the decade, from 13 percent in 1982 to 16 percent in 1989.[6] The response of physicians to the increased competition has been to move away from solo practices into group practices where referrals are easier, but the proportion of doctors taking professional positions in non-patient care areas has not increased. The percent of non-federal physicians who practice in groups of three or more has increased from 26 percent in 1980 to 30 percent in 1988.[18] Only 8 percent of doctors reported they worked in teaching, administration, or research in 1988, no change from 1980.[19]

Rather than driving incomes down or reducing the workload as would be seen in a traditional marketplace, the growth in the supply of physicians seems to have demonstrated that physicians are able to induce demand for services and/or raise their fees without changing the setting in which most physicians practice. Over the last decade physician fees for established patients have increased about 3 percent faster than the consumer price index each year.[20] Chapter 7 provides additional information on this topic.

INCREASING AMOUNTS OF UNCOMPENSATED CARE

Analysts predicted that a variety of constraints on the health care system would leave more people without a way of paying for their hospital care. A declining amount of philanthropy, cutbacks in Medicaid coverage and eligibility, the closing of neighborhood health centers, and the growth in for-profit hospitals were expected to contribute to more people falling through the cracks in the health care system.[4]

These forces have, indeed, adversely affected people's abilities to pay for hospital care. Government reports show a 24 percent increase in the last decade in the total number of uninsured people and a 40 percent increase in the number of uninsured children.[21,22,23] While many people needing health care choose not to seek care when they are unable to pay for it,[24] a growing share of the burden of paying for care for uninsured people falls on hospitals. Figure 1-5 shows that uncompensated hospital care costs grew from $4.7 billion in 1980 to $8.8 billion in 1988.

DECREASING REIMBURSEMENT BY GOVERNMENT AND INSURERS

Analysts predicted that employers and the government would become aggressive about constraining hospital reimbursement in the early 1980s. When those predictions were made, employers had already begun to seek discounts from hospitals, and the nation's economic concerns were expected to overshadow government interest in health and human welfare programs. Analysts expected that the least efficient hospitals would not be able to cope with the new restraints and would go out of business in droves. One of the authors predicted that a thousand hospitals would close in the 1980s.[4]

Not surprisingly, analysts were unable to predict just how much hospital reimbursement did change in the 1980s. Not only was the federal government able to get lower hospital payment rates by switching to the prospective payment system, but many employers were able to negotiate lower prices through their insurance carriers. As shown in Table 1-3, the government was much more successful than other payers in reducing hospital rates of increase.

The Health Care Financing Administration (HCFA), in tracking annual national health expenditures, has reported a decline in the proportion of all health care expenditures on inpatient hospital care in the last decade. As shown in Figure 1-6, the share of total national health expenditures being spent on inpatient hospital care decreased from 29.9 percent in 1980 to 25.9 percent in 1989.[17] Taking into account the increase that would have otherwise taken place, it is estimated that inpatient days were reduced by more than 28 percent

Table 1-3

Average Annual Increases in Real Hospital Costs for Medicare and Other Payers

Year	Medicare	Other Payers
	percent change	
1976-1981	9.2	4.6
1982	10.0	8.2
1983	5.8	7.3
1984	5.0	0.8
1985	7.7	0.2
1986	3.0	5.8
1987	-2.3	8.7
1988	3.5	8.9

Source: Schwartz WB, Mendelson DN. Hospital Cost Containment in the 1980s: Hard Lessons Learned and Prospects for the 1990s. *New England Journal of Medicine*. 1991; 324:1041.

Figure 1-5

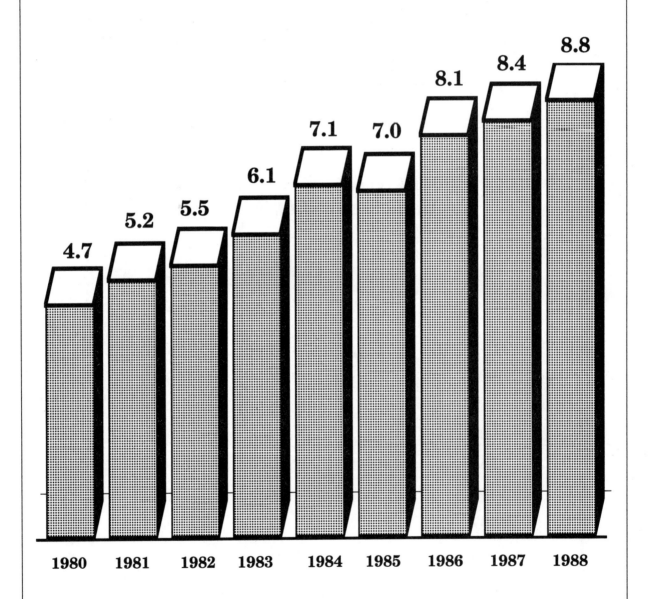

Real Uncompensated Hospital Care Costs

(in billions of dollars)

Source: Fraser I, Narcross J, Kralovec P. Hospital Care for the Poor, 1980-1989. AHA unpublished paper, July 1991.

Figure 1-6

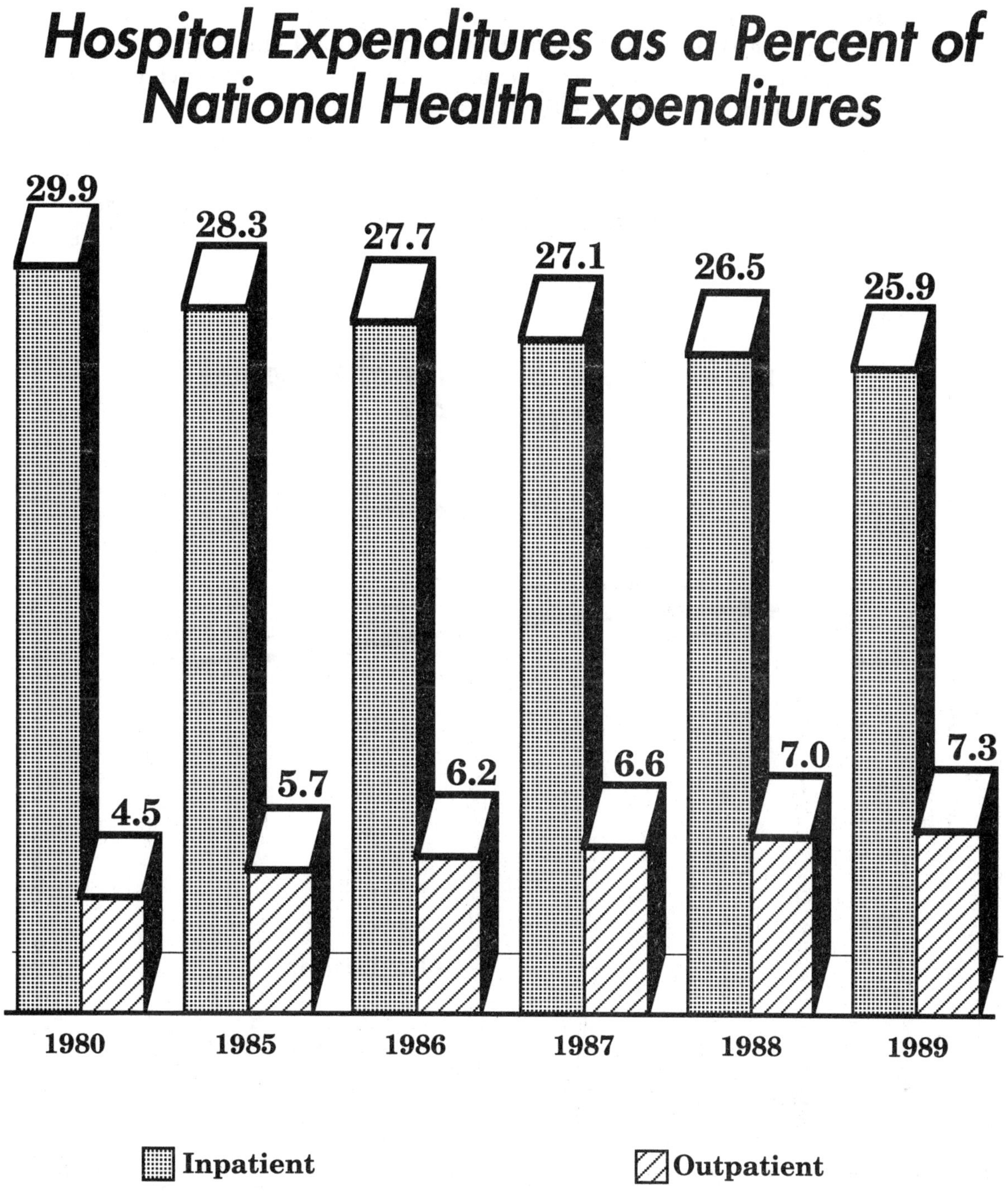

Hospital Expenditures as a Percent of National Health Expenditures

Source: Lazenby HC, Letsch SW. National Health Expenditures, 1989. *Health Care Financing Review.* Winter 1990; 12:1-26.

between 1981 and 1988.[25] Some of the loss in inpatient care was a gain by hospitals in outpatient care. The proportion of total expenditures going for outpatient hospital care increased from 4.5 percent in 1980 to 7.3 percent in 1989. By 1989, hospitals were deriving 22 percent of their patient revenue from outpatient care, up from 13 percent in 1980, as shown in Figure 1-7.[26] Overall, hospitals lost a fairly small share of the market to other types of providers and health care facilities — much less than was expected.

For the care that continues to be provided on an inpatient basis, hospitals' revenue in excess of costs — patient margins — has been decreasing. Figure 1-8 shows that patient margins have decreased in recent years to close to zero. Revenue from other sources, primarily interest income; state tax appropriations;

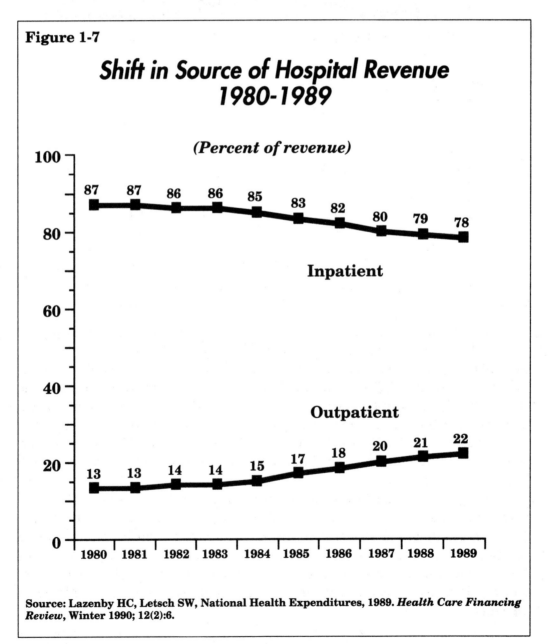

Figure 1-7

Shift in Source of Hospital Revenue 1980-1989

(Percent of revenue)

Inpatient

Outpatient

Source: Lazenby HC, Letsch SW, National Health Expenditures, 1989. *Health Care Financing Review*, Winter 1990; 12(2):6.

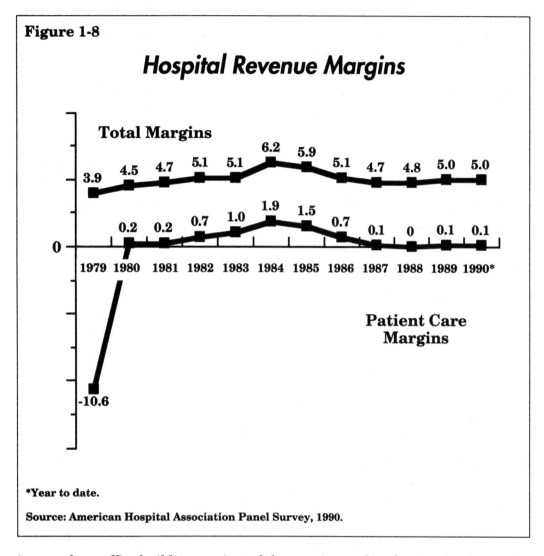

Figure 1-8

Hospital Revenue Margins

Total Margins

3.9   4.5   4.7   5.1   5.1   6.2   5.9   5.1   4.7   4.8   5.0   5.0

0.2   0.2   0.7   1.0   1.9   1.5   0.7   0.1   0   0.1   0.1

0

1979 1980 1981 1982 1983 1984 1985 1986 1987 1988 1989 1990*

Patient Care Margins

-10.6

*Year to date.

Source: American Hospital Association Panel Survey, 1990.

income from office buildings, private laboratories, and real estate investments; and grants and contributions, has allowed hospitals to maintain total margins around 5 percent. There is some debate about whether hospital margins reflect the true financial picture of hospital revenue because there is considerable flexibility in how hospitals account for revenue and expenses.[27] We show them here not because the numbers are absolute, but because they illustrate the growing pressure in the 1990s for hospitals either to accept less money for inpatient services rendered or to develop creative financing alternatives from non-hospital sources.

Margins on Medicare patients, for whom reimbursement is the most restrictive, are the lowest. Figure 1-9 shows negative patient margins for the Medicare population in the last two years, meaning that some hospitals could be losing money by treating Medicare patients and must find other revenue sources to cover the cost of their care. It is commonly believed that hospitals are able to recover their losses by cost-shifting — charging higher rates to non-Medicare patients.

PRICE COMPETITION BETWEEN HOSPITALS

Analysts predicted in the early 1980s that price would be the basis for competition for patients. Because of the surplus in the physician supply, individual physicians would lower their charges to attract patients. Other

Figure 1-9

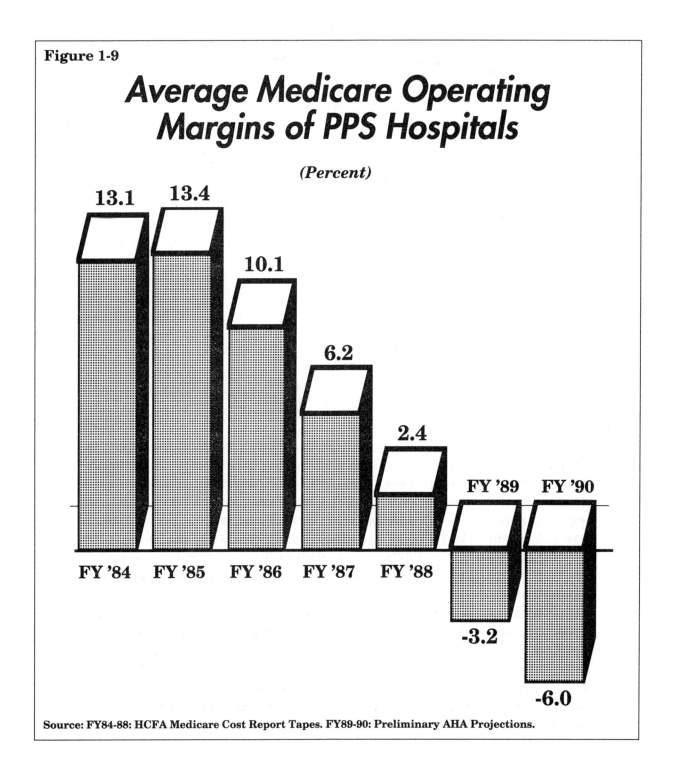

Average Medicare Operating Margins of PPS Hospitals

(Percent)

Source: FY84-88: HCFA Medicare Cost Report Tapes. FY89-90: Preliminary AHA Projections.

Table 1-4

Percent Distribution of Admissions by Hospital Size

Hospital Size	1979	1989
<100 beds	14.2%	11.3%
100-400 beds	53.0	55.5
400+ beds	32.8	33.2

Source: American Hospital Association. *AHA Hospital Statistics*, 1990-91. Chicago: AHA; 1991, xxxvi.

physicians would join well-managed, capitated delivery systems, such as closed-panel Health Maintenance Organizations (HMOs), in order to achieve efficiencies in delivering care. The expectation was that employers and the government would channel their employees and beneficiaries to lower cost providers, and consumers would support this effort by seeking providers with the lowest out-of-pocket costs.

We have not seen widespread competition based on price. The growth in group and staff model HMOs, like the Kaiser Plan, has been slow, and only a small number of people have elected to enroll in capitated plans, even though premium and out-of-pocket costs are often lower than traditional fee-for-services plans. HMO enrollment ranges from a high of 31 percent in California to a low of no HMO enrollees in Wyoming, Alaska, West Virginia, and Mississippi.[28] Nationally, about 14 percent of the population have joined an HMO, up from 4 percent in 1980, but less than half of current HMOs could be described as tightly capitated like the Kaiser Plan and the Harvard Community Health Plan. The forecast of price competition by competitive health care systems breaks down because individuals remain resistant to joining lower cost alternative health care plans. Employers, who do have the incentive to control their employees' spending, have been reluctant to direct their employees to low cost providers. Only 18 percent of medium and large firms limit their employees choice of hospitals and doctors, and 14 percent offer managed care as the only insurance plan option.[29]

Just as the enrollment in HMOs has been slower than predicted, there has not been much increased utilization of lower cost hospitals. Forecasters suggested that the new competitive arrangements would shift patients from the larger, more expensive institutions, such as teaching hospitals, to less expensive institutions. Table 1-4 shows that, over the decade, there has been very little change in the distribution of admissions between the larger, more expensive hospitals and the smaller, less expensive institutions. The share of admissions to large hospitals actually stayed nearly constant over the period. Utilization of smaller hospitals, fewer than 100 beds, decreased as a percent of total admissions.

Likewise, the predicted growth of the new "medical-industrial complex" proved to somewhat of a myth by the end of the decade.[30] For-profit hospitals, which were expected to grow in response to a competitive market, have actually shrunk as a proportion of total community hospitals since 1980. As a share of the hospital market, for-profits have dropped from 12.5 percent in 1980 to 9 percent of total community hospitals in 1989. As a percent of total beds, for-profits comprised 14 percent of beds in 1980 and 11 percent in 1989.[31] The commercialization of American hospital care is a revolution that never occurred, and with recent declines in profitability, may not occur in the future.

Finally, the notion that increased marketplace competition between hospitals would lower prices may actually be a fallacy. Research by Hadley and Swartz found that the annual growth in hospital costs was higher in communities where there were more hospitals and lower in those with fewer.[32]

CONCENTRATION OF SERVICES IN LARGE HEALTH CARE CHAINS

One of the most widely quoted predictions was that health care services ultimately would be consolidated into eight to ten very large health care systems with annual revenues in excess of $30 billion and each representing 5 percent or more of the U.S. health care marketplace.[33] These giant health care chains would be the end product of a drive toward efficiency in management and health care delivery and the demand among employers and consumers for convenient, lower cost care. By 1990, we have seen some concentration of hospitals into multi-institution systems, but the current concept of a system is still far from the model forecast. Instead of national systems, hospitals have shown a preference for regional systems that include anywhere from two to a several hundred hospitals. Some systems are made up of one hospital that owns, leases, or sponsors other services, such as home health care or ambulatory care facilities.

Currently, only 31 percent of hospital beds are in the approximately 300 systems in the U.S., although 56 percent of hospitals are affiliated with a system, as shown in Figure 1-10.[34] There has been only a small amount of integration of other services with hospital care, except in HMOs.

QUALITY AS A BASIS FOR COMPETITION

Finally, analysts predicted that, after price, quality was going to be the basis on which hospitals would compete. Consumers of health services would select their doctors and hospitals based on information about the quality of care they could expect to receive.

What we have found is that people, both consumers and payers, evaluate quality of care based on very subjective measures. Surveys show that both

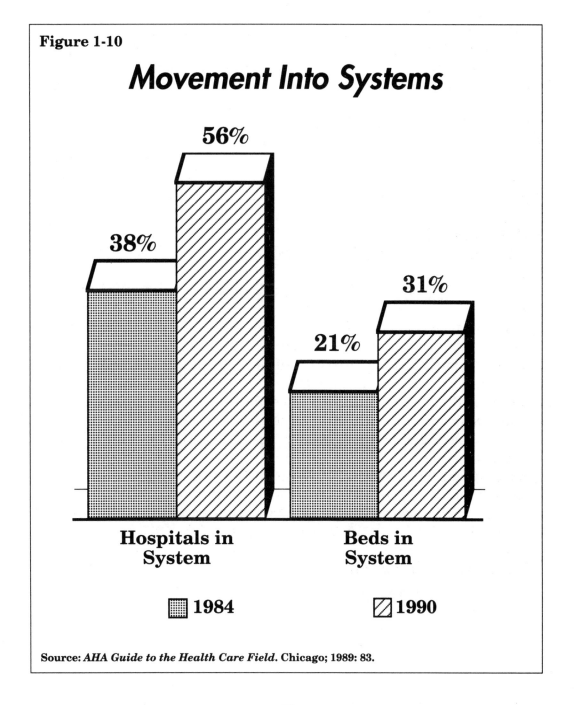

Figure 1-10

Movement Into Systems

56%

38%

31%

21%

Hospitals in System

Beds in System

■ 1984　　　　◻ 1990

Source: *AHA Guide to the Health Care Field.* Chicago; 1989: 83.

groups equate good quality with high technology care and high staff levels, both of which are typical of more expensive hospitals.[35] Employers report that they rely on non-empirical measures to evaluate quality, like feedback from employees, reputation of providers, and price (see Figure 1-11). In fact, employers state that, in general, they assume the more expensive the hospital the better its quality. Similarly, patients report that their choice of a hospital is based on reputation, location, and previous experience.[35]

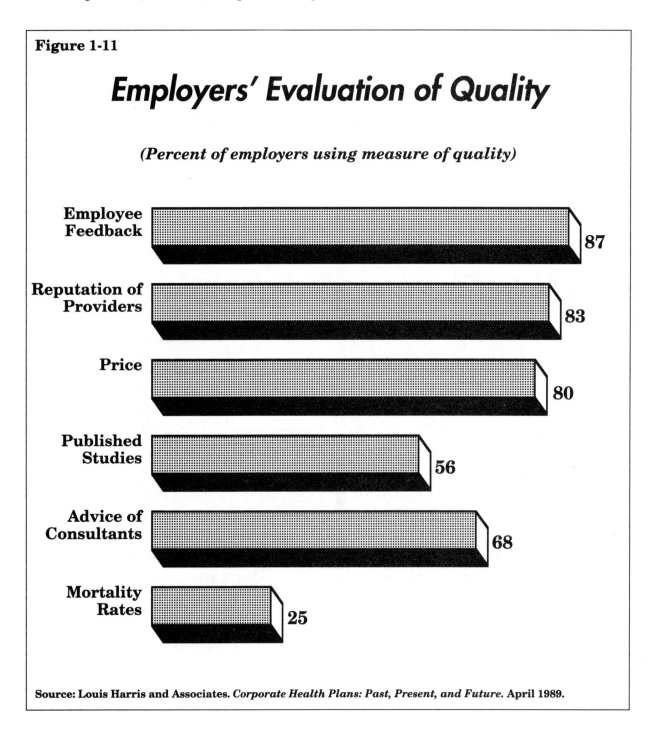

Figure 1-11

Employers' Evaluation of Quality

(Percent of employers using measure of quality)

Employee Feedback **87**

Reputation of Providers **83**

Price **80**

Published Studies **56**

Advice of Consultants **68**

Mortality Rates **25**

Source: Louis Harris and Associates. *Corporate Health Plans: Past, Present, and Future.* **April 1989.**

Objectively measuring the outcome of care and making the information available to consumers has been a much more difficult task than originally envisioned. The initial effort by HCFA to publish mortality statistics by hospital has not achieved widespread acceptance by doctors, hospitals, or the research community. As a result, this expected revolution in purchasing based on quality predicted for the 1980s has been put on hold as we focus on the need for more sophisticated measurements of outcomes of care in the 1990s.

CONCLUSION

In reviewing hospital forecasts made in the late 1970s and early 1980s, it has not been our intent to prove them in error, but instead to learn how we can be more effective in making judgments about the future of health care. Based on this analysis, we find that change occurs slowly and more gradually than predicted by experts. The often touted "revolution" in health care may be an aid in selling new books, but it is not likely to prove to be true. The lesson, which carries over to the conclusions we draw throughout this book, is that forecasters need to be cautious in making predictions in health care because consumers, doctors, and politicians, rather than traditional economic forces, influence health care decisions more than was previously realized. Changes will not occur if the public and health care professionals are not enthusiastic about them, as shown by the relatively small proportion of the population that has enrolled in health maintenance organizations. Analysts predicted nearly half the population would be in an HMO by 1990, yet most of the public has said all along that they do not want to give up their current doctor and that they prefer to maintain more freedom of choice in specialists and hospitals. So despite employees' concerns over their health care costs and their employers' interests in saving money, relatively few consumers have joined tightly managed care systems or are interested in joining in the near future (see Chapter 4). There will be examples in subsequent chapters of other cases where the public has supported or opposed changes and where public attitudes have been instrumental in the change process.

There are some events which, by the nature of their development, no one would have been able to forecast their appearance or magnitude. For example, the impact of the AIDS epidemic on the health care system of some cities has been enormous and has proven predictions about excess beds to be wrong. New York City, once an example of successful health planning, now faces a severe shortage of hospital beds as a result of previous closures.

The work in this chapter has been supported in part by a grant from the Commonwealth Fund.

REFERENCES

1. Goldsmith JC. *Can Hospitals Survive? The New Competitive Health Care Market*. 1981; Homewood, IL: Dow Jones-Irwin.

2. Ginzberg E. *The U.S. Health Care System: A Look to the 1990s*. University Medical Conference on Health Policy. 1985; New York.

3. Ellwood PM Jr., Ellwein LK. Physician glut will force hospitals to look outward. *Hospitals*. January 16, 1981;81-85.

4. Blendon RJ. Policy Choices for the 1990s: An uncertain look into America's future. in Eli Ginzberg (ed.) *The U.S. Health Care System: A Look to the 1990s*. Cornell University Medical Conference on Health Policy. 1985; New York.

5. Altman SH. Decade ahead will challenge financial viability of hospitals. *Hospitals*. January 16, 1981;87-92.

6. American Hospital Association. *AHA Hospital Statistics, 1990-91*. AHA; Chicago, 1991.

7. Hegland A. Hospital based long-term care beds on the rise. *Contemporary Long-Term Care*. February 1991;35.

8. Deloitte and Touche. *U.S. Hospitals and the Future of Health Care*. Boston, MA; Deloitte and Touche:4.

9. Moore SF. Is access to capital the next crisis for not-for-profits? *Healthcare Trends Report*. August 1989;3:16.

10. Health Care Investment Analysts. *The HCIA Distressed Hospital Quarterly*. Baltimore, MD; HCIA, Inc.:1-2.

11. American Hospital Association. Fifty community hospitals closed, 43 opened in 1990. *AHA News*. March 18, 1991;27:1.

12. Greene J. Towns breathe new life into closed hospitals. *Modern Healthcare*. March 25, 1991;24-28,30.

13. Data show number, type of mergers. *Modern Healthcare*. March 19, 1990;33.

14. Anderson K, Wootton B. Changes in hospital staffing patterns. *Monthly Labor Review*. 1991;114:3-9; and Bureau of Labor Statistics. *Employment and Wages, Annual Averages*. Washington, D.C.; May 1985, December 1987, and October 1990.

15. Anderson K, Wootton B. Changes in hospital staffing patterns. *Monthly Labor Review*. 1991;114:3-9.

16. Durant GD. Ambulatory surgical centers: surviving, thriving into the 1990s. *MGM Journal*. March-April, 1989.

17. Marder WD, et al. *Physician Supply and Utilization by Specialty: Trends and Projections*. AMA Center for Health Policy Research; Chicago, 1988:5; and U.S. Bureau of the Census. *Current Population Reports*, series P-25, No. 995.

18. Havlicek PL. *Medical Groups in the U.S.: A Survey of Practice Characteristics*. American Medical Association; Chicago: 1990.

19. Marder WD et al. *Physician Supply and Utilization by Specialty: Trends and Projections*. AMA Center for Health Policy Research; Chicago:1988.

20. *Socioeconomic Characteristics of Medical Practice 1990/1991*. AMA Center for Health Policy Research; Chicago:1991:114.

21. Walden D, Wilensky G, Kasper J. *Changes in Health Insurance Status: Full Year and Part Year Coverage: Data Preview 21*. Rockville, MD: National Center for Health Services Research;1985. US Dept of Health and Human Services publication PHS 85-3377.

22. Short P. *Estimates of the Uninsured Population, Calendar Year 1987*. Rockville, MD: Public Health Service; 1990. US Dept of Health and Human Services publication PHS 90-3469. National Medical Expenditure Survey Data Summary 2.

23. Cunningham P, Monheit A. Insuring the children: a decade of change. *Health Affairs*. Winter 1990;9:76-90.

24. Freeman H, Blendon R, Aiken L, Sudman S, Mullinex C, Corey C. Americans report on their access to health care. *Health Affairs* Spring 1987;6:13-4.

25.   Schwartz WB, Mendelson DN. Hospital Cost Containment in the 1980s: Hard Lessons Learned and Prospects for the 1990s. *New England Journal of Medicine.* 1991;324:1041.

26.   Lazenby HC, Letsch SW. National Health Expenditures, 1989. *Health Care Financing Review.* Winter 1990;12:1-26.

27.   Kane N. Hospital profits, a misleading measure of financial health. *Journal of American Health Policy.* July/August 1991;1:27-35.

28.   Marion Merrell Dow. *Managed Care Digest.* Update Edition. 1990; Kansas City.

29.   Taylor H, Leitman R. *Corporate Health Plans: Past, Present, and Future.* Louis Harris and Associates; New York, 1989.

30.   Starr P. *The Social Transformation of American Medicine.* Basic Books Inc.; New York:1982:429.

31.   American Hospital Association. *AHA Hospital Statistics, 1990-91.* AHA; Chicago, 1991:7.

32.   Hadley J, Swartz K. The impacts of hospital costs between 1980 and 1984 of hospital rate regulation, competition, and changes in health insurance coverage. *Inquiry.* Spring 1989;26:35-47.

33.   Ellwood says "supermed" concept gaining ground, expects up to 10 within decade. *FAHS Review.* March/April 1986:69-71.

34.   *American Hospital Association Guide to the Health Care Field.* Chicago; 1989:B3.

35.   Taylor H, Leitman R. *Survey of Health Care Consumers.* February 1990; and *Corporate Health Plans: Past, Present and Future.* April 1989; Louis Harris and Associates; New York.

CHAPTER 2

Demographic, Social, and Economic Changes in the 1990s

Gregory Schmid
Institute for the Future

INTRODUCTION

Day-to-day crises often hide deeper and more fundamental changes. In the midst of a debate over major restructuring of the health care system, it is easy to lose sight of the broader changes that may transform that system over the long run. The most important long term change in the United States is *demographic*. This is an aging society. Much attention has been given to the growing number of very old people, but the largest aging group during the 1990s will be the baby-boom generation, many of whom will be passing their 50th birthday. Birth rates have risen dramatically over the past two years, creating a mini-baby-boom group that will influence society for a long time. Several age cohorts actually will be shrinking. Those turning 65 will be fewer in number in the year 2000 than in 1990, but, even more important, the number of young adults will fall dramatically.[1]

Social changes will be important. Growing affluence, education, and diversity will influence the behavior of the population as workers, consumers, and patients throughout the 1990s.[2,3,4]

The demographic shifts will also affect the *labor force*. The number of young workers entering the work force during the 1990s will drop sharply.[5] Employers will have to look harder to fill positions, and more employers will have to hire those with less experience or less training and/or recruit more workers from outside our borders. The workplace will take on the more diverse look and languages of the younger generation. In the meantime, employers increasingly will use alternative means to stretch the existing labor supply: experimenting with flexible employment practices and using more capital to enhance productivity.

Demographic and labor issues will drive *economic and business* decisions. Businesses will need more capital to make up for labor shortages. There is a reasonable expectation that the real cost of capital will fall somewhat during the 1990s.[6] In addition, business will continue to restructure itself to maximize the talents of long term employees and the more flexible labor market.

Public policy choices will influence the delivery of health care. Government deficits and the encroachment of health care price increases on budgets for other social welfare spending eventually will force a major change in what services the government pays for and how the reimbursement system works.

This chapter examines 14 major demographic, social, labor, economic, and public policy trends that are likely to characterize the 1990s and the impact of each of these trends on the health care system.

DEMOGRAPHIC TRENDS

1. More Very Old

Trend. The number of people surviving past age 75 will continue to increase rapidly during the 1990s, just as it has done every decade for the past 50 years (see Figure 2-1). In fact, the average annual growth *rate* will be somewhat slower during the 1990s than during the 1980s. However, the *number* of people 75 or older will increase by almost 10 percent during the 1990s (an increase of 3.4 million people during the 1990s compared to 3.1 million during the 1980s).[7]

Because of relatively low birth rates during the years of the Great Depression, the number of people turning 65 will not grow at all during the 1990s (see Figure 2-2). This means that while the total number of people over 65 will continue to grow slightly faster than the overall population, the rate of growth will be only half of what it has been during the previous four decades.[1]

Impact. Aging has a direct impact on health care budgets. Rates of health care use rise dramatically with age. Hospital days per person for those 75 years old are twice as high as for 65 year-olds and three times as high as for 55 year-

Figure 2-1

The Number of Elderly Continues To Grow

(Average annual rate of change for people 75 years of age or older)

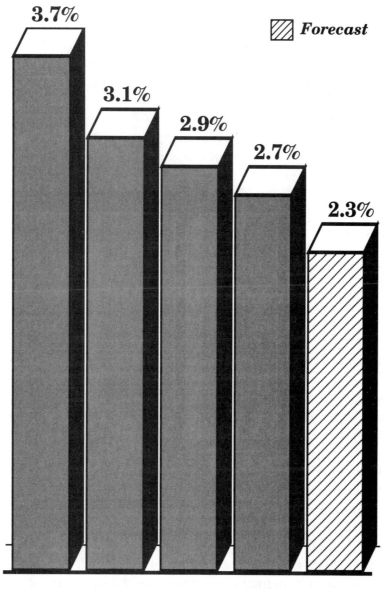

Source: U.S. Bureau of the Census, *Current Population Reports*, Series P-25, *Population Estimates and Projections*, #519, 1974; 917, 1982; 1018,1989; and 1045,1990.

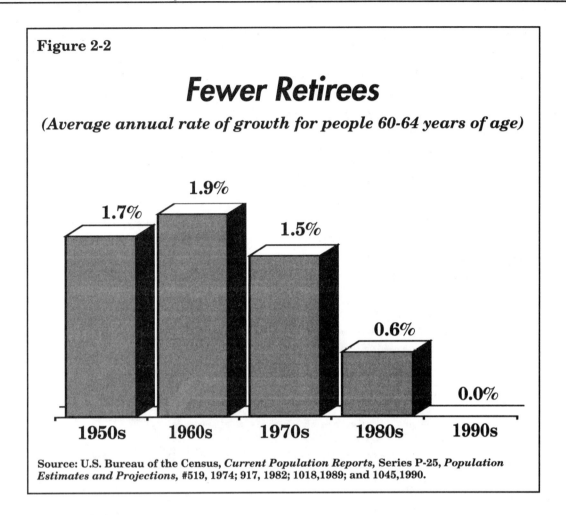

Figure 2-2

Fewer Retirees

(Average annual rate of growth for people 60-64 years of age)

1.7% 1.9% 1.5% 0.6% 0.0%

1950s 1960s 1970s 1980s 1990s

Source: U.S. Bureau of the Census, *Current Population Reports*, Series P-25, *Population Estimates and Projections*, #519, 1974; 917, 1982; 1018,1989; and 1045,1990.

olds.[7] Nursing home usage, of course, rises very rapidly after 75 years of age. There is a much smaller discrepancy by age for use of less intensive care, such as physician visits. Seventy-five year-olds will make 10 percent more physician visits per person than 65 year-olds and 25 percent more than 55 year-olds.[8] Since hospital and nursing home care is much more expensive than a physician visit, cost per person is much higher for the elderly. Thus, the increasing number of very old persons and especially their heavy use of hospitals and nursing homes will increase strain on the health care system. The projected growth in the number of elderly likely to need long term care services also will play an important role in decisions about long term care insurance.

2. More Middle Aged

Trend. The real revolution, though, will be among the middle aged. Birth rates rose very rapidly immediately after World War II, and this baby-boom generation will pass its 45th birthday in this decade. The annual rate of growth of people between the ages of 45 and 49 will rise by almost 4 percent per year during the 1990s (see Figure 2-3) — a rate of growth higher than the rate of overall population growth of any third world country. The total number of people in that age group will rise from around 14 million in 1991 to more than 19 million in 2000.[1]

Impact. People in their late 40s use health care services less than people in their 60s and 70s. But people in their late 40s and early 50s do use substantially more health care resources than do younger people. People at 55 use 45 percent more hospital services than do people at 45, who in turn use 50 percent more than people at 35, who in turn use 20 percent more than people at 25.[8] People at 55 use 20 percent more physician services than people at 45, who in turn use 20 percent more than people at 35, who in turn use 20 percent more than people at 25.[8] The tremendous increase in sheer numbers of people in their late 40s and early 50s will substantially increase total demand for services. In fact, the increase in certain areas of health care spending — prescription drugs and outpatient visits — will be higher for the middle-aged population than for the elderly because the number of middle aged is so much greater.

3. Fewer Young Adults

Trend. Birth rates fell in the mid-1960s as dramatically as they rose in the mid-1940s. This produced a relatively small cohort of people who reached their

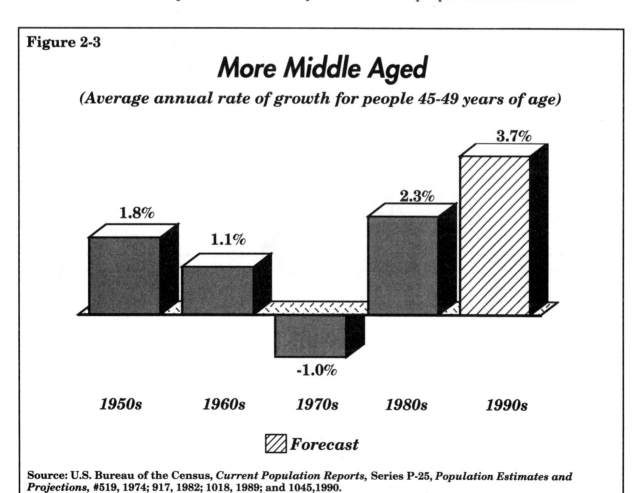

Figure 2-3

More Middle Aged

(*Average annual rate of growth for people 45-49 years of age*)

- 1.8% — 1950s
- 1.1% — 1960s
- -1.0% — 1970s
- 2.3% — 1980s
- 3.7% — 1990s

//// *Forecast*

Source: U.S. Bureau of the Census, *Current Population Reports*, Series P-25, *Population Estimates and Projections*, #519, 1974; 917, 1982; 1018, 1989; and 1045,1990.

early 20s during the late 1980s and will reach them in the 1990s. In fact, the number of people in their early 20s fell by 2.5 million during the late 1980s and will fall by another million during the 1990s (see Figure 2-4).[1]

Impact. One important impact of fewer young people is on the character of economic growth in the United States. Household growth has been a key component of economic growth because it is associated with an increase in new housing starts, new car sales, purchasing of furniture and household durables, opening of bank accounts and insurance policies, and new enrollment in health care plans. With the decline in household formation rates, the economic growth of the 1990s will be in replacement and upgrading of products within households rather than in new household formation. Business cycles may be more volatile since there will be a substantial increase in discretionary spending as opposed to spending on the basic necessities. We can expect the discretionary parts of health care spending (*e.g.*, paying for private hospital rooms and opting for convenient care over cost-saving care) to gain an increased share of total income.

Figure 2-4

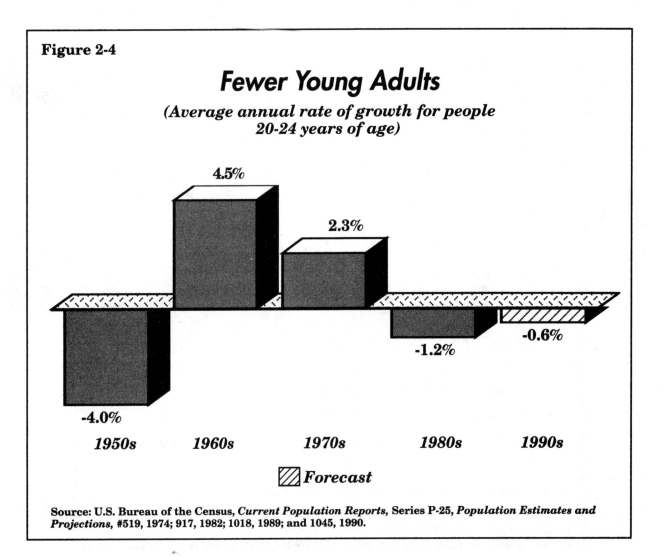

Fewer Young Adults

(Average annual rate of growth for people 20-24 years of age)

Source: U.S. Bureau of the Census, *Current Population Reports*, Series P-25, *Population Estimates and Projections*, #519, 1974; 917, 1982; 1018, 1989; and 1045, 1990.

4. A New Baby Boom?

Trend. After almost 20 years of stability, birth rates have risen dramatically in the past two years. The number of births rose substantially in the late 1980s. This increase was due not to a change in fertility rates (in fact, fertility rates — the rate of births to women between the ages of 15 and 44 — fell by more than 15 percent during the period), but to an increase in the number of women in peak child-bearing years. Over the past two years, however, fertility rates have risen to their highest levels since the early 1970s (see Table 2-1). Birth rates are rising for women of all ages and of all economic groups. During each of the past two years, births have reached more than 4 million, a number exceeded only during the peak of the baby-boom years (1956-61).[8]

Impact. A rise in fertility rates will have limited but important consequences. It will extend the echo boom for several years beyond the baby boomers' peak fertility ages. It will have impacts on women's participation in the labor force and on the support services and career paths necessary to retain family workers in the labor force and in particular career patterns. It will change the number and type of workers who need family health care coverage.

SOCIAL TRENDS

5. Growing Diversity

Trend. The 1990 census showed a clear increase in our population's diversity. There was a large increase in the number of immigrants who entered the United States during the 1980s, with almost 90 percent of the immigrants coming from non-European countries.[9] The ratio of minorities in our population

---

Table 2-1

Another Baby Boom?

	Average Annual Births (Thousands)	Fertility Rate*
1950s	4,049	117
1960s	3,881	101
1970s	3,331	71
1980s	3,749	60
1989-90	4,100	70

*Number of births per thousand women 15-44 years of age

Source: National Center for Health Statistics. Monthly Vital Statistics Report. *Annual Supplement on Final Natality Statistics,* various years.

---

is rapidly changing. Four of the largest states that are major magnets for immigrants now have minority populations that are close to or exceeding one-third of the total population (see Figure 2-5).[4] Since the immigrant population (like most minorities in the United States) is younger than the general population and has higher birth rates, minority populations will continue to grow faster than the overall population throughout the 1990s.[10] Within a decade, California and Texas are likely to find that less than 50 percent of their populations are Caucasian and of European descent.

Impact. The increases in diversity will affect both health care consumers and workers. The diverse backgrounds of consumers will influence the products and services they seek and the manner in which they shop for them. Patient

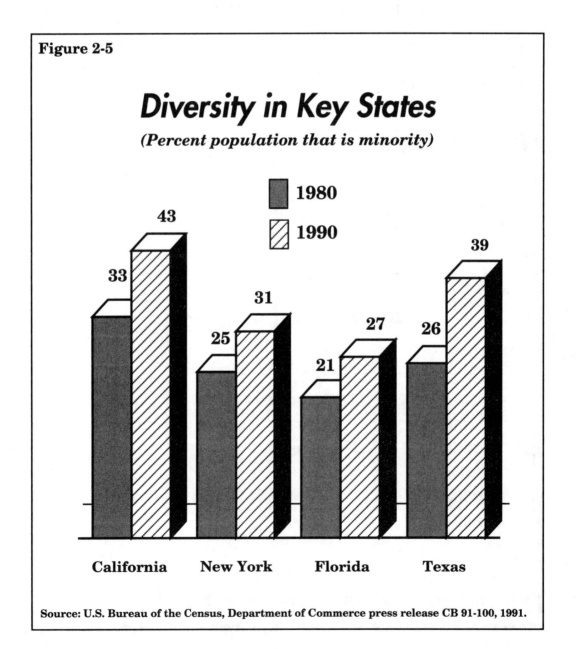

Figure 2-5

Diversity in Key States
(Percent population that is minority)

1980
1990

Source: U.S. Bureau of the Census, Department of Commerce press release CB 91-100, 1991.

preferences and their attitudes toward lifestyle changes and preventive care will require substantive changes in how hospitals, doctors, and other health care providers relate to and treat their patients.

6. Rising Levels of Education

Trend. The U.S. population is making large strides in educational attainment. In the mid- and late 1980s, the percentage of high school graduates

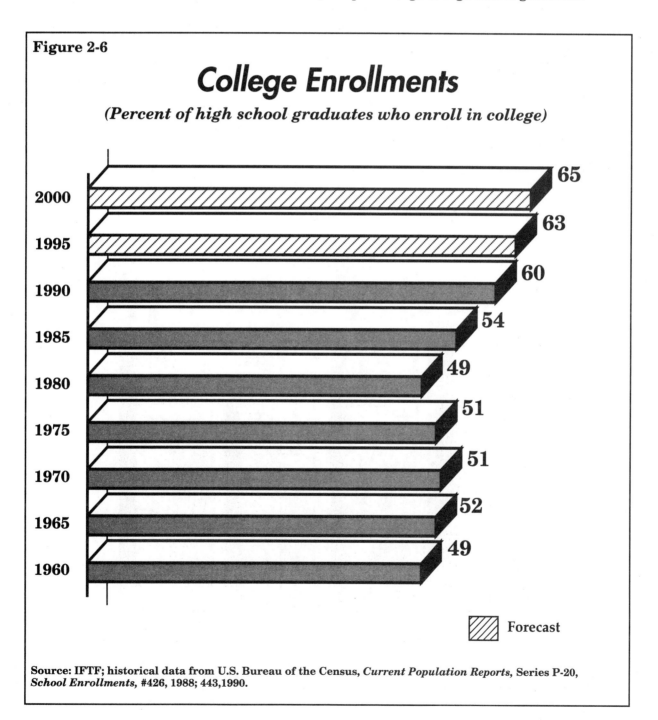

Figure 2-6

College Enrollments

(Percent of high school graduates who enroll in college)

Year	Value
2000	65
1995	63
1990	60
1985	54
1980	49
1975	51
1970	51
1965	52
1960	49

Forecast

Source: IFTF; historical data from U.S. Bureau of the Census, *Current Population Reports*, Series P-20, *School Enrollments*, #426, 1988; 443,1990.

who went on to college rose from about 50 percent to more than 60 percent (see Figure 2-6).[11] At the same time, the percentage of young adults who earned a high school diploma or its equivalency remained fairly constant at about 81 percent.[12] Thus, the number of young adults with only a high school diploma entering the labor force for full-time work is dropping precipitously, raising an alarm among employers who fear worker shortages and declining standards of entry.

Impact. Again, the impact of the movement to college will be felt both by the labor market and by the consumer side of the health care business. The shortages of high school-educated workers will be painfully evident to employers when they try to fill jobs. On the consumer side, more highly educated people will tend to be more knowledgeable about alternatives, more demanding of choice, and more concerned about their own perceptions of quality.

Figure 2-7

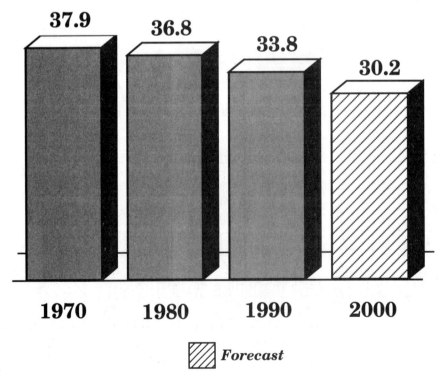

The Fading Middle

(Percent of all households with constant dollar income between $15,000 and $35,000)

37.9   36.8   33.8   30.2

1970   1980   1990   2000

Forecast

Source: IFTF; historical data from U.S. Bureau of the Census, *Current Population Reports,* **Series P-60,** *Consumer Income,* **No. 168, 1989.**

7. The Fading Middle

Trend. Over the past 20 years, the percentage of all households that could be characterized as lower middle class fell from 38 percent to just under 34 percent (see Figure 2-7).[1,2] More and more U.S. households are making it into the upper middle classes. Between 1970 and 1990, the percentage of such households rose from 36 percent to 41 percent.[13] If these trends continue through the 1990s, we will see only about 30 percent of households as members of the lower middle class. This means that while more American families make it into the affluent sector, the gap between those well off and the rest of society will be growing and, more than ever, the United States will be a two-tiered society.

Impact. Most of the middle class gets insurance through their employment or through self-purchase. Increasingly, we are seeing a split of the middle-class market into tiers, with the expanding upper income group demanding choice and quality and the shrinking lower middle group concerned about cost and access. Trying to provide the same level of services to both will create growing strains and problems during the 1990s.

LABOR TRENDS

8. Looking for Workers

Trend. The growth of the labor force will decrease sharply during the 1990s. After three decades of rapid expansion, growth rates during the 1990s

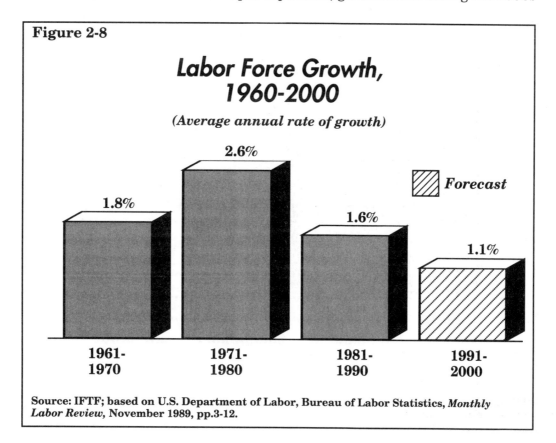

Figure 2-8

Labor Force Growth, 1960-2000

(Average annual rate of growth)

1.8% 2.6% 1.6% 1.1%

Forecast

| 1961-1970 | 1971-1980 | 1981-1990 | 1991-2000 |

Source: IFTF; based on U.S. Department of Labor, Bureau of Labor Statistics, *Monthly Labor Review,* November 1989, pp.3-12.

will fall to only about one percent per year (see Figure 2-8).[5] Two long term trends will cause this transformation. The aging of the baby-boom generation means that most of this group are already in the labor force (those born at the tail end of the baby boom in the mid-1960s are just over 25 years of age). Further, the tremendous increase in women's participation rates that was so prominent during the 1970s and 1980s likely will continue during the 1990s, but at a much slower pace.[5] Only the rate of immigration is likely to increase during the next ten years.[14] But, without a revolutionary change in immigration policy, this cannot offset the domestic factors slowing growth.

Impact. The slower growth in the labor force will force all employers—especially those in health care services that have been major employers of new workers during the past two decades—to search much harder for new workers of all types (paraprofessionals, nurses, technicians, hospital orderlies, and billing clerks). Wages are likely to go up sharply and people with lower levels of qualifications (for example, less education, less experience, less dedication to the labor force, less command of the English language) will make up more of the new hires. Since personal service is such an important part of the delivery of health care, it will be very hard to increase productivity from existing workers, and health care enterprises will have to compete for eligible workers.

9. A More Diverse Work Force

Trend. Over the past three decades, the rate of legal immigration to the United States has been rising rapidly. During the 1990s, the number of immigrants will rise again because of the immigration reform bill of 1989, which raised the quota by some 20 percent (see Table 2-2).[15,16] The economic disparities between the United States and its neighbors to the south and in the Far East, plus the shortages of young workers in the U.S., will produce more illegal immigration as well, adding another 200,000 immigrants per year. In all, close to 25 percent of new workers in each year of the 1990s will be recent immigrants.

Table 2-2

Immigration Surge

(Average annual)

1950s	**252,000**
1960s	**332,000**
1970s	**449,000**
1980s	**589,000**
1990s	**700,000**

Source: **U.S. Immigration and Naturalization Service,** *1988 Statistical Yearbook,* **Table 2. Projections by IFTF.**

Figure 2-9

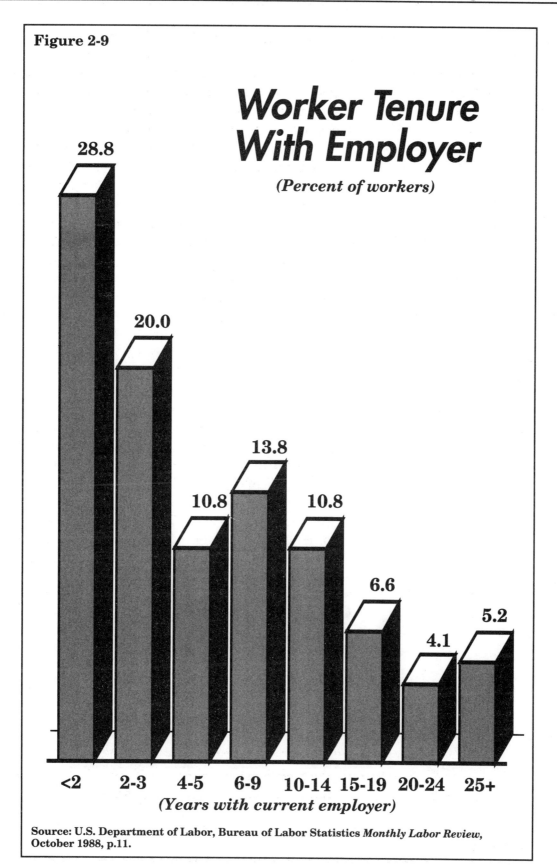

Worker Tenure With Employer

(Percent of workers)

(Years with current employer)

Source: U.S. Department of Labor, Bureau of Labor Statistics *Monthly Labor Review,* October 1988, p.11.

Impact. A large number of immigrant workers will come to the labor market with limited language skills and education levels that are well below the average U.S. worker. It will be up to the employer to provide the special training to maintain productivity and customer service. As a major employer of new workers, the health care system has been and will continue to be a large user of immigrant labor. This need will stretch from foreign workers with extensive training (physicians and nurses) to those with few skills (orderlies and kitchen workers). Hospitals and other labor-intensive facilities will be the center of much of this employment activity. To deal effectively with this new labor force, hospitals and other health care service providers need to adapt their workplaces to the special needs of the immigrant groups (*i.e.,* language and cultural sensitivity, special training, and educational programs).

10. Labor Market Adapts to Workers' Needs

Trend. The labor market has experienced a tremendous increase in the percentage of women workers. Between 1970 and 1990, the percentage of all workers who were women rose by almost 20 percent (from 38% to 46%).[17] Women, more often than men, work outside the home less than full time. While two-thirds of men are employed year-round, full-time, only one-half of women

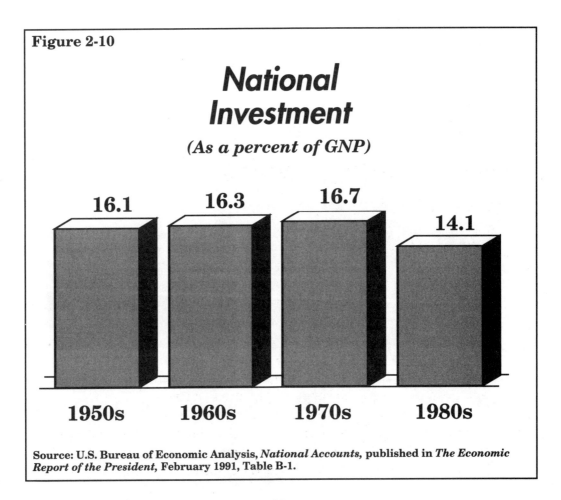

Figure 2-10

National Investment

(As a percent of GNP)

1950s	1960s	1970s	1980s
16.1	16.3	16.7	14.1

Source: U.S. Bureau of Economic Analysis, *National Accounts,* published in *The Economic Report of the President,* February 1991, Table B-1.

are. This means that as women play a more prominent role in the labor market, enterprises must adapt to workers' needs to split time between work, home, and other activities.

Workers stay with a single employer for six-and-a-half years on average. Almost 60 percent of workers have been with their current employer less than five years, and only 15 percent for 15 years or more (see Figure 2-9).[18] High turnover means that a good deal of organizational effort must be put into training and adapting people to the organization's culture. Further, high turnover rates mean recruitment from a pool of new workers that is increasingly diverse in educational and linguistic background and in work goals and needs.

Impact. The short job tenure will affect both health care benefits and health care workers. Under the Consolidated Omnibus Budget Reconciliation Act of 1985 (COBRA), employers are required to continue to make benefits available to employees who leave the firm. The administrative cost to the employer will grow as more people rely on COBRA for insurance. More workers who move from job to job or who work only part time will lose health care benefits and will be forced to pay for the health care services or health insurance they need.

Health care establishments — especially hospitals — face a real duality in their labor markets. Health care service workers currently are found at the two extremes of the divide between temporary and permanent. Physicians, nurses, and lab technicians tend to have job and occupation tenure rates that are twice the national average.[19] On the other hand, records clerks, health aides, health records technicians, and food workers have tenure rates that are between one-half and one-third of the national average.[19] Health establishments must continue to offer a variety of salary and benefits packages, as well as education and training programs that meet the diverse occupational needs of an already very diverse work force.

ECONOMIC/BUSINESS TRENDS

11. Need for Capital

Trend. Fewer young workers entering the work force means greater pressure on businesses to increase the productivity of current employees. This is especially true when businesses, such as health care services providers, do not have the option of moving the production of goods and services abroad. Productivity enhancement can come in a variety of forms: hiring more highly educated workers, training or retraining current workers, changing the way the work flow is structured, or changing the ratio of capital to labor. Given the shortages of young workers over the next decade, the primary means of enhancing productivity will be through increased spending on systems and equipment that will allow workers to produce more goods or provide more services.

The level of investment as a share of GNP decreased during the whole of the 1980s (see Figure 2-10).[19] Even during the eight-year business cycle expansion (from 1982 through 1990), investment and the buildup of real capital stocks fared poorly. Compared to past post-World War II expansions, the stock of real capital grew 14 percent more slowly during the 1982-90 expansion. Business investment fared worst of all, growing at a rate 33 percent more slowly than in previous expansions.

Impact. As we experience shortages of labor during the 1990s, the growth of the real stock of business capital will be of increasing importance. This is especially true because both of the United States' main international rivals — Japan and Germany — are increasing their capital stock at a much faster rate than the U.S. Increasing rates of productive investment is critical to long term growth rates in this country.

12. The Cost of Capital

Trend. Over the past decade, huge government deficits have forced up real

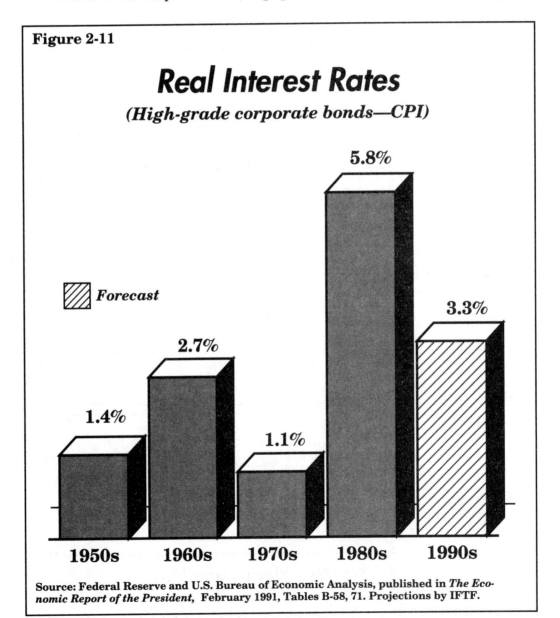

Figure 2-11

Real Interest Rates

(High-grade corporate bonds—CPI)

Source: Federal Reserve and U.S. Bureau of Economic Analysis, published in *The Economic Report of the President,* February 1991, Tables B-58, 71. Projections by IFTF.

Figure 2-12

The New Business Organization

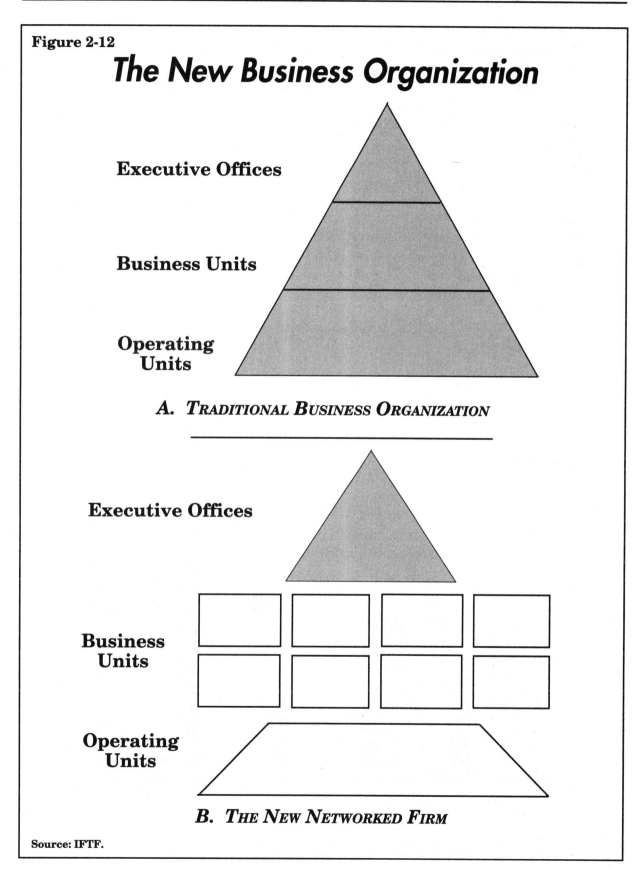

Executive Offices

Business Units

Operating Units

A. TRADITIONAL BUSINESS ORGANIZATION

Executive Offices

Business Units

Operating Units

B. THE NEW NETWORKED FIRM

Source: IFTF.

rates of interest. After averaging between 1 percent and 2 percent for 35 years, real interest rates rose to an average of almost 6 percent during the 1980s (see Figure 2-11), resulting in business investment in real dollars during the 1980s well below what it traditionally has been during the business expansion cycles.

The key to an investment surge during the 1990s will be the cost of capital. Three factors can contribute to a lowering of real interest rates during the 1990s. The first is demographic. The baby boomers are aging. As they do so, they will reach ages (about 45 or 50 years of age) when households tend to change from net borrowers to net savers,[20] increasing society's savings. In addition, the baby-boom households will be reaching their peak earning years[1] when it is easier to save more.

The second factor will be the reduction of the federal deficit. Federal deficits averaged more than 4 percent of GNP during the 1980s and remain near that level for fiscal 1992.[21] But both congressional and executive leaders have agreed to a long-term deficit reduction plan. While past deficit agreements have not been very successful, this one seems broader based than past ones and is expected to cut the deficit as the economy moves out of the recession. We look for some reduction in the federal deficit over the next few years, though not its elimination.

The third factor will be a change in the behavior of the financial sector. The plethora of new investment opportunities during the 1980s, many of them speculative in nature (mergers and acquisitions, corporate real estate, junk bonds), stimulated rapid growth in private credit aside from investment in new productive equipment. The recession and the deterioration of banks' and savings and loans' balance sheets will make financial institutions more hesitant to fund high-yielding but high-risk enterprises. Altogether, these factors are likely to produce a somewhat lower real rate of interest during the 1990s.

Impact. If real interest rates do fall, this will create opportunities to increase investment in productive (and profitable) business enterprises. A decrease in the cost of borrowing, combined with the growing cost of new workers, will lead to a preference for investing in ways to improve efficiency. For example, hospitals will find the initial investment in computerizing medical records would pay off in reduced personnel costs in a few years.

13. Reorganizing Business

Trend. Large corporate businesses have tried to enhance workers' productivity by changing the way they organize work. Starting in the late 1980s, large businesses began to use more team- or group-based activities to get their work done.[22] Use of teams allows large organizations to move away from the old hierarchy that relied on a pyramid structure and a constantly expanding pool of production-based workers. With an aging work force, businesses have had to draw on the diverse talents of current employees and find challenging and rewarding work for them to do. New network-based teams allow the flexibility to do this. Teams draw on the diverse skills and resources of different departments by taking experienced workers from a variety of departments, assigning a project that matches their unique set of abilities, and allowing them to work intensively as a group. Finally, the teams or groups often include external consultants who can add perspective and specialized expertise. The result is a change from the old pyramid-shaped hierarchy to a flatter organization with a lot of the dynamic of problem solving handled by ad hoc task-oriented work groups (see Figure 2-12).

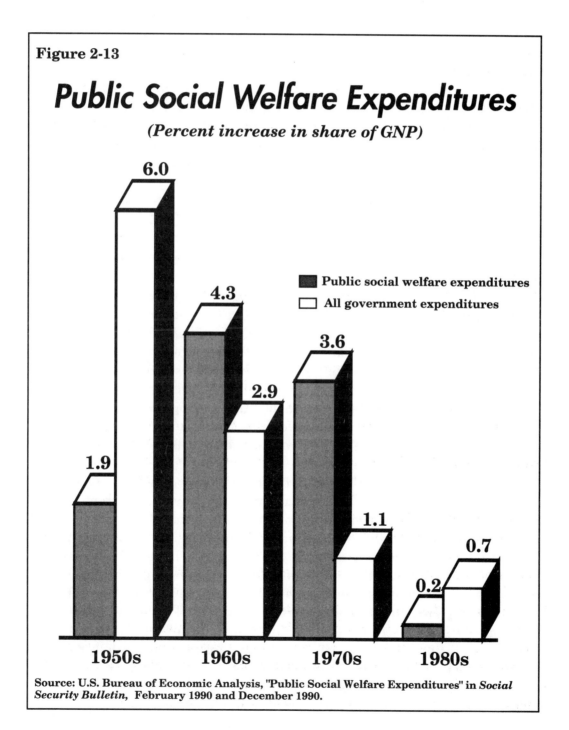

Figure 2-13

Public Social Welfare Expenditures
(Percent increase in share of GNP)

■ Public social welfare expenditures
□ All government expenditures

6.0
4.3
2.9
3.6
1.9
1.1
0.2
0.7

1950s   1960s   1970s   1980s

Source: U.S. Bureau of Economic Analysis, "Public Social Welfare Expenditures" in *Social Security Bulletin,* February 1990 and December 1990.

Impact. Health care providers should feel right at home with the organizational changes sweeping American business. For a long time, they have organized themselves on the basis of task-oriented teams delivering ad hoc services in a flexible manner. But health care organizations are not immune to the repercussions of the changes; many of the new health care provider networks are being organized much like the networked firm with close information ties established among groups of providers around a few key tasks (purchasing, insurance, patient services, and reimbursements). Further, many of the major private health care payers are networked firms. They are using many more outside consultants or part-time temporary workers and no longer provide the standard health benefits packages to large groups of both blue- and white-collar workers that they did only a short while ago. This results in a wide array of coverages for the whole spectrum of middle level workers, increasing the difficulty of budget and service planning for health care providers and the associated billing and reimbursement procedures. The rules of the game are changing rapidly for everyone.

PUBLIC POLICY TRENDS

14. Limiting Social Welfare

Trend. The budget deficits of the 1980s limit the government's ability to fund a variety of social welfare programs. Taken in its broadest definition, public social welfare includes any program that brings direct benefits to individuals and families. It includes such things as health care, education, Social Security, and welfare payments. During the 1960s and 1970s, public social welfare spending grew much faster than GNP and other government spending as the federal government implemented or expanded various programs (*i.e.* Social Security, Medicare, Medicaid, and Aid to Families with Dependent Children), while the states expanded supplemental health care programs and educational spending. The deficits of the 1980s have stopped all that. Public social welfare spending now is growing at the same rate as the GNP and slower than overall government spending (see Figure 2-13).[23]

Impact. The decline in the growth rate of public social welfare expenditures means hard times for public health care spending. Even at current costs of delivery of health care, expenditure limitations mean that the large number of uninsured and those who have access to only the most basic types of care will find little chance of improvement. Of even greater concern is the encroachment of health care spending on other public social welfare spending. Because health care costs are rising twice as fast as overall costs in the United States,[5] health care is taking an ever increasing portion of the total public social welfare spending. This increased share is not translating into any increase in access or improvement in quality. In the short run, this is tolerable; in the long run, it is not sustainable. If health care costs continue to rise much more quickly than other costs, look for major government initiatives to control spending on health care.

50

APPENDIX

The forecasts used in this chapter come from the Institute for the Future's *Ten-Year Forecast* database. Most of the forecasts are based on the extrapolative forecasting models of government agencies such as the Bureau of the Census and the Department of Labor or our own models. Where we modify a trend or examine impacts, we rely heavily on group judgment of experts, usually gathered in workshops or panels, as well as our own monitoring of key trends and relationships among trends.

REFERENCES

1. U.S. Bureau of the Census. Current Population Reports, Series P-25. *Population Estimates and Projections.* 1974:519; 1982:917; 1989:1018; 1990:1045.

2. U.S. Bureau of the Census. Current Population Reports, Series P-60. *Consumer Income.* 1989; No. 168. Projections by IFTF.

3. U.S. Bureau of the Census. Current Population Reports, Series P-20. *School Enrollments.* 1988:426; 1990:443. Projections by IFTF.

4. U.S. Bureau of the Census, Department of Commerce Press Release, 1991:CB 91-100.

5. U.S. Department of Labor, Bureau of Labor Statistics. *Monthly Labor Review.* 1989:3-12. Projections by IFTF.

6. Board of Governors of the Federal Reserve System; Trends projected by IFTF.

7. Arnett RH, McKusick DR, Sonnefeld ST, Cowell CS. Projections of Health Care Spending. *Health Care Financing Review,* Spring 1986;7:1-36.

8. National Center for Health Statistics. Monthly Vital Statistics Report. *Annual Supplement on Final Natality Statistics,* various years.

9. U.S. Immigration and Naturalization Service. *1988 Statistical Yearbook,* Table 2. Projections by IFTF.

10. U.S. Bureau of the Census. Current Population Reports, Series P-25. *Population Estimates and Projections.* 1989:1018.

11. U.S. Bureau of the Census. Current Population Reports, Series P-20. *School Enrollments.* 1988:426; 1990:443.

12. U.S. Bureau of the Census. Current Population Reports, Series P-20. *School Enrollments.* 1990:443, Table A7. Projections by IFTF.

13. U.S. Bureau of the Census. Current Population Reports, Series P-60, *Consumer Income.* 1989:168.

14. IFTF projection based on the Immigration Act of 1990.

15. U.S. Immigration. *1988 Statistical Yearbook.* Table 2. Projections by IFTF.

16. Population Reference Bureau. *Population Today.* Dec. 1990;18:3.

17. U.S. Department of Labor, Bureau of Labor Statistics. *Employment and Earnings.* February 1991, and *Handbook of Labor Statistics.* August 1989.

18. U.S. Department of Labor, Bureau of Labor Statistics. *Monthly Labor Review,* Oct. 1988:11.

19. U.S. Department of Labor, Bureau of Labor Statistics; U.S. Department of Commerce, Bureau of Economic Analysis. National Accounts. Published in *The Economic Report of the President.* Feb. 1991: Table B-1.

20. Federal Reserve Board. Survey of Consumer Finances. *Federal Reserve Bulletin.* Sept. 1984.

21. U.S. Department of Labor, Bureau of Labor Statistics; U.S. Department of Commerce, Bureau of Economic Analysis. *National Accounts.* Feb. 1991. Table B-1 and Table B-79.

22. Johansen R. *Groupware: Computer Support for Business Teams.* New York: The Free Press, 1988.

23. U.S. Bureau of Economic Analysis. Public Social Welfare Expenditures. *Social Security Bulletin.* Feb. 1990 and Dec. 1990.

CHAPTER 3

The (Un)changing Political Landscape

Humphrey Taylor and Robert Leitman
Louis Harris and Associates

INTRODUCTION

Movements in the electorate come like changes in the ocean: in tides, waves, ripples, and squalls. The movement of the population from the Northeast and Midwest to the South and West and the steady growth of the black, Hispanic and Asian populations are long term, slow moving tides. Changes in party identification or the impact of economic cycles are the waves. The savings and loan scandal and last fall's battle over budget deficit reduction are ripples. The Gulf War was a short, sharp, and wholly unexpected squall.

One common misunderstanding is the belief that polls predict change. They do not; they only measure it. The belief that they predict comes from the fact that measurements of voting intentions immediately before elections are often quite accurate predictors of voting behavior on election day itself.

The pollsters who work for politicians and parties earn their fees not merely from knowing what to measure and how to measure it. Of equal, or even more, importance to their candidates is their ability to make sound judgments about how opinion may change and how it can be influenced. In so far as pollsters actually predict anything other than an immediate election, they base their judgments not just on the survey data but on history and their understanding of political forces and the electoral process. If measuring opinion is more or less a science, using survey data to make forecasts is an art.

POLLS CAN BE UNRELIABLE GUIDES TO FUTURE OPINION

Politicians who read the polls (and which ones do not?) in deciding which policies to support can get into a lot of trouble. While well-conducted polls are the only reliable way to measure current public opinion, they are unreliable predictors of future opinion.

This lesson was strongly reinforced by the Gulf War. No doubt many members of Congress who voted on January 12 against authorization of the war did so for honorable reasons. But some surely did so with one eye on the polls.

Six different national polling organizations that conducted surveys just before January 15, when the war started, reported that less than 50 percent (between 44 and 49%) of the public favored immediate military action, while a similar or slightly higher proportion favored allowing more time for sanctions to work.[1] Immediately after the air war began, public opinion changed dramatically. The polls reported between 68 and 84 percent of the public approving the decision to go to war, while those who favored waiting had dropped to between 13 and 26 percent.[2]

Just before the ground war began, the public preferred a continuation of the air war to an invasion. For example, a CBS/New York Times poll reported that a massive 79 percent majority wanted the coalition to "continue mainly bombing from the air," while only 11 percent favored "beginning the ground war soon."[3] But 11 days later another CBS/New York Times poll reported a huge 75 to 19 percent majority believed that it was "right to start the ground war" when it was started.[4] Events, not the public's previous opinions, shaped public opinion. In politics, as in much else, nothing succeeds like success.

This is not to say that politicians should, or could afford to, ignore public opinion. Success in politics — that is, re-election — depends in large measure on how the people perceive your record, on whether or not they think you did right by them. The key to re-election is to distinguish between what the public thinks is right today and what it will think when the next election comes around. That can mean persuading the public to change its mind. Since the Gulf War, some politicians may be more aware of this difference — the difference between leading and following — and that the key to success in politics is giving people not the policies they want, but the results.

DEMOGRAPHIC CHANGES

One long term, slow moving tide in the electorate is the growth of the black and Hispanic populations and the relative decline of white populations, as is shown in Table 3-1. By the year 2050, demographers believe half the U.S. population (but substantially less than half the voting age population) will be non-white or Hispanic. Non-Hispanic whites will become a minority, albeit the largest minority. While the political impact of this tide over the long term will be enormous, in the short and even the medium term it will be relatively modest.

One factor which tends to reduce the political impact of the slow but continuing growth of black and Hispanic potential voters is that they are less likely to vote than are whites. Hispanics in particular tend not to vote (Table 3-2).

In recent elections very large majorities of blacks and smaller majorities of Hispanics have voted Democratic. Theoretically, if this were to continue, growth would clearly be very beneficial to the Democrats. But it may not continue. Already it is clear that middle class and more affluent Hispanics (particularly Cubans) often vote Republican. As more blacks and Hispanics, particularly second and third generation Hispanics, become more affluent, the Democratic advantage among these groups may well diminish.

Table 3-1

Voting Age Population by Race and Ethnicity, 1980-2000

	1980	*1990*	*2000*
White	87.7%	85.4%	84.2%
Black	10.4	11.4	12.1
Other			
(including Asian, Native American)	1.9	3.2	3.7
Hispanic	5.2	6.7	8.2

Source: U.S. Bureau of the Census. *Statistical Abstract of the United States.* 1990: 16, 262.

REDISTRICTING

The impact of new electoral districts, based on the distribution of population found in the 1990 Census, will be seen in the 1992 House elections and the Electoral College votes. Eight states, all in the South and West, will gain House seats. Thirteen states in the North East and Mid-West will lose seats. As the numbers of House seats change, so will electoral votes, swinging more political power from the Rust and Frost belts to the Sunbelt.

On paper, this should be good news for the Republicans, giving them more electoral votes and more House seats. In practice, these changes may help the Republicans more in the Presidential race than in the House elections. In most of the states involved, the Democrats are in control of the redistricting process and will presumably try to gerrymander the district boundaries to their advantage. However, to judge by history, this is much harder to achieve than most people believe.

In his recent book *The Electoral Origins Of Divided Government*, University of California (San Diego) political scientist Gary Jacobson concludes that redistricting has, at most, a very modest impact on House elections. He points out that successful gerrymandering requires predictable partisan loyalties when, in fact, they are not at all stable.[5] Furthermore, incumbents try to protect their large majorities, thus reducing the parties' abilities to move enough supporters into neighboring districts to make a difference. Jacobson points out that attempts to gerrymander districts in California (by the Democrats) and Indiana (by the Republicans) in 1981 were completely unsuccessful.

Table 3-2

Claimed Turnout in Presidential Elections by Different Racial/Ethnic Groups: 1984, 1988 Presidential Elections

(As percent of voting age population)

	1984	*1988*
White	61.4	59.1
Black	55.8	51.5
Hispanic	32.6	28.8

Note: The *actual* turnout was lower than the claimed turnout. However, this *difference* between groups, and over time, almost certainly reflects real differences.

Source: U.S. Bureau of the Census. *Statistical Abstract of the United States.* 1990:262.

One byproduct of redistricting welcomed by Republicans is the creation of new districts with no incumbents, thereby — given the power of incumbency — giving Republican candidates more hope of reducing the Democratic majority in the House. Here again Jacobson's findings may surprise them. Since 1968, Democrats have won slightly more of such open seats from the Republicans (62) than Republicans have taken from Democrats (60).

One reason why Republicans have not done better in these new districts, Jacobson argues, is that "Republicans . . . have fielded inferior candidates on the wrong side of issues that are important to voters in House elections."[5] Republicans, he believes, field weak candidates in part because their preference is to be in business, unlike Democrats who are much more attracted to electoral politics.

One other reason for uncertainty about the impact of redistricting is that many of these new districts are going to states with rapidly-growing Hispanic populations. If they voted in large numbers, and if they voted very strongly Democratic (and there is much uncertainty about these two "ifs"), Hispanics might change the political cast of these states.

In the Presidential race, the effect of redistricting is much more certain. In 1988, President Bush won seven of the eight states that are gaining electoral votes with 57 percent of the vote. In the 13 states losing votes he won only 52 percent of the vote. So, whatever the impact of redistricting on House elections, political power continues to flow Southwest to the advantage of Republican presidential candidates.

CHANGES IN PARTY IDENTIFICATION

Party identification — the feeling that one is a Republican or a Democrat — is an important and relatively slow moving measure of the underlying power-base of the parties. Over the last decade, Republicans have made major gains in this area and have greatly reduced what used to be a huge Democratic advantage. Different polls measure party identification in different ways, but the trend in all of them has been the same. Using the average for seven major national polls over the last 11 years, Table 3-3 shows a fall of 17 percentage points in the Democratic lead. If this trend continues at this speed, the two parties will be equal in party identification by 1994 or 1995. However, there is nothing inevitable about the direction or the speed of this trend. Events and leadership could change it substantially.

What is also clear from these data is that party identification is, at best, only a marginal guide to voting behavior. Voting in both presidential and congressional races is, of course, dependent on the candidates and their campaigns, regardless of their parties.

Another telling measure is self-definition of political philosophy. Since 1975, a plurality of 38-to-42 percent of Americans have identified themselves as moderates, while only 17-to-20 percent self-identified as liberals. The major shift has been an increase in the proportion of Americans who see themselves as conservatives. In the years surrounding the election of Jimmy Carter, only 30-to-31 percent of the American public said they were conservatives. In the year prior to the election of Ronald Reagan, that proportion reached 35 percent and it has been around 38 percent since the year President Bush was elected (see Table 3-3). If liberals vote Democratic and conservatives vote Republican, as they tend to, this puts the Democrats in the unenviable position of having to win about three-fourths of the moderate voters to win a majority in a Presidential election.

Table 3-3

Party Identification and Political Philosophy 1980-1991

	Average Democratic Advantage in Party Identification*	Average Conservative Advantage Over Liberal in Political Philosophy***
1980	**22%**	**17%**
1981	**15**	**21**
1982	**17**	**18**
1983	**17**	**18**
1984	**12**	**17**
1985	**8**	**20**
1986	**8**	**19**
1987	**10**	**18**
1988	**10**	**20**
1989	**7**	**20**
1990	**6**	**20**
1991**	**5**	**20**

* Based on averages for ABC/WP, CBS/NYT, NBC, Gallup, Harris, Roper & Yankelovich polls.
** January through April, 1991.
*** Based on averages for Harris polls.

GENERATIONAL DIFFERENCES IN PARTY IDENTIFICATION

A recent analysis of all the national Gallup political surveys conducted over an 18-month period reveals the clear difference between different cohorts of voters, depending on when they first voted or were eligible to vote.[6]

The Democrats do best among voters aged 51 to 78, although the oldest voters who came of age politically in 1926 or earlier are quite strongly Republican. Republicans, on the other hand, do much better among voters aged 30 or less, as shown in Table 3-4.

Historically, voting cohorts have tended to become more conservative as they age. If new young voters continue to go Republican, future prospects for the Democrats are very poor. These new voters will replace those (mainly Democratic) voters who will die over the next two decades.

OTHER MEDIUM-TERM TRENDS IN PARTY STRENGTH

Paralleling their gains in party identification over the last decade, the Republicans have substantially improved their image, relative to the Democrats, on two other key measures. However, these differences between the parties have fluctuated more violently, buffeted by short term events.

At the time of writing, the Republicans enjoy substantial advantages as the party trusted "to do a better job" generally and as the party thought "to do a better job of keeping the country prosperous" (see Tables 3-5 and 3-6). However, the Republicans' positive ratings appear to have benefitted sharply from the Gulf War. How quickly they will fade may depend on the economy. A look back at the numbers in 1982 and 1983 suggest that continued bad economic times could quickly reverse recent Republican gains.[7]

CURRENT STRENGTHS AND WEAKNESSES OF THE PARTIES

A recent ABC/Washington Post poll provides a clear picture of the strengths and weaknesses of the two parties. As shown in Table 3-7, the Republicans do best on defense, international influence, foreign affairs and making U.S. industry more competitive. The Democrats do best on helping the poor, the elderly, and the homeless and at protecting Social Security.[8]

In other words, the Republicans are seen as the party of the "haves." Competence is their long suit, while the Democrats are seen as the party of the "have-nots," weak on management but strong on compassion. It is "head versus heart." Presidential elections over the last 20 years suggest that while the "heart" issues may move people, the "head" issues are more decisive in the polling place. Congressional elections, on the other hand, may be more influenced by domestic and "heart" issues.

Table 3-4

Strong Generational Patterns

The Depression Generation Went Democratic...and Stayed There. The Eighties Generation Is Republican.

Age in 1991	Years When Came of Age Politically	Party Identification		Republican Lead Over Democrats
		Republican	Democrat	
19 - 22	1987 - '90	38%	26%	+12
23 - 26	1983 - '86	37	28	+ 9
27 - 30	1979 - '82	36	26	+10
31 - 34	1975 - '78	34	31	+ 3
35 - 38	1971 - '74	30	35	- 5
39 - 42	1967 - '70	31	34	- 3
43 - 46	1963 - '66	29	31	- 2
47 - 50	1959 - '62	31	33	- 2
51 - 54	1955 - '58	31	37	- 6
55 - 58	1951 - '54	31	37	- 6
59 - 62	1947 - '50	27	38	-11
63 - 66	1943 - '46	33	38	- 5
67 - 70	1939 - '42	28	43	-15
71 - 74	1935 - '38	32	45	-13
75 - 78	1931 - '34	32	48	-16
79 - 82	1927 - '30	41	40	+ 1
83+	1926 and earlier	50	35	+15
All ages		33	34	- 1

Source: Gallup Organization. Combined Gallup polls. *Newsweek.* October 1989 - March 1991. Storrs, CT: Roper Center for Public Opinion Research, 1991.

Where does health care fit within the two party competition? This question was not asked as part of the former survey. It was, however, queried of registered voters in 1991 by Hart and Teeter.[9] Health care was seen as an issue where Democrats had a moderate advantage. The results show 47 percent of registered voters see the Democratic party as doing the best job on this issue. Fourteen percent identified Republicans as most capable, while 39 percent remained uncertain about which party would be the most effective for providing the nation with better health care. The large proportion of undecided registered voters on this issue provides an opportunity for one or both of the political parties to expand their image identification as the best for health care concerns.

THE GULF EFFECT

It is not always easy to measure the long term impact of events on elections and the public mood. Political scientists in Britain, using the same poll data, disagree on the long term electoral benefits to Margaret Thatcher from the Falklands War. There was no doubt about the huge short term benefit. Whether

---

Table 3-5

Party Trusted To Do Better Job 1982-1991

(Republican lead over Democrats)

1982	-7
1983	-5
1984	+1
1985	+9
1986	+7
1987	-7
1988	-4
1989	+1
1990	+2
1991	+13

Source: ABC News/*Washington Post*. Average of polls: 10/11/82; 9/13/82; 12/13/83; 8/1/83; 7/18/84; 2/15/84; 1/17/84; 6/22/85; 6/22/85; 2/26/85; 1/16/85; 10/28/85; 9/23/85; 7/29/85; 9/8/86; 6/23/86; 3/24/86; 2/12/86; 12/17/87; 10/19/87; 6/1/87; 3/9/87; 11/4/90; 10/14/90; 5/21/90; 1/16/90; 6/21/91; 3/4/91.

or not, or how much, it contributed to her subsequent re-election victory is less clear, even if the conventional wisdom is that it contributed a lot.

President Bush is clearly the beneficiary of a huge dividend of popular support from the Gulf War. Shortly before it began, following the acrimonious and unedifying battles over the budget deficit reduction in the fall, there was more talk of the President's weakness on "the vision thing" and "the wimp thing." As Table 3-8 illustrates, the Gulf War has put a stop to "the wimp thing" — for the time being at least. He may still face "the vision thing" in 1992 if a more clearly defined domestic agenda does not emerge.

HISTORICAL PRECEDENTS FOR THE 1992 PRESIDENTIAL ELECTION

A review of the popularity ratings of eight presidents before George Bush confirms the current assumption that he will be almost impossible to defeat in 1992. In the several hundred Gallup ratings of these Presidents, only one (President Truman's rating shortly after he was sworn in to replace President

Table 3-6

Party Thought To Do Better Job of Keeping Country Prosperous (1980-1990)
(Republican lead over Democrats)

1980	- 6
1981	+13
1982	-10
1983	- 7
1984	+ 8
1985	+16
1986	+18
1987	+ 1
1988	+ 7
1989	+21
1990	+ 2
March 1991	+24

Source: Gallup Organization.

Table 3-7

Republican and Democratic Advantages on the Issues: March 1991

Question: Which political party, the Republicans or Democrats, do you trust to do a better job...?

Democratic Party　　　　　　　　　　　　　**Republican Party**

STRONG REPUBLICAN ADVANTAGE

Democratic	Issue	Republican
17%	Maintaining a strong national defense	68%
26%	Increasing U.S. influence overseas	60%
23%	Handling foreign affairs	59%
26%	Making U.S. industry competitive overseas	55%

MODERATE REPUBLICAN ADVANTAGE

Democratic	Issue	Republican
32%	Handling the nation's economy	49%
34%	Controlling inflation	49%
26%	Reducing the problem of illegal drugs	48%
28%	Handling the crime problem	46%
35%	Holding taxes down	44%
34%	Reducing the threat of nuclear war	43%
35%	Reducing the federal budget deficit	43%

NEITHER PARTY HAS ADVANTAGE

Democratic	Issue	Republican
39%	Improving education and the schools	41%
42%	Keeping the U.S. out of war	37%
40%	Protecting the environment	35%

MODERATE DEMOCRATIC ADVANTAGE

Democratic	Issue	Republican
45%	Keeping unemployment down	38%
48%	Helping the middle class	34%

STRONG DEMOCRATIC ADVANTAGE

Democratic	Issue	Republican
52%	Protecting the Social Security system	29%
54%	Handling the homeless problem	27%
60%	Helping the elderly	24%
64%	Helping the poor	22%

Source: Survey by ABC News/*Washington Post*, March 4-6, 1991.

Roosevelt) produced a higher rating than George Bush's rating immediately after the Gulf War (Table 3-9). President Bush's lowest rating to date is also better than the lowest first term ratings of five Presidents; of the three who did better, Eisenhower and Johnson went on to re-election while Kennedy did not live to run again.

While Bush's ratings have slipped since the Gulf War, it is difficult to imagine a scenario which could prevent Bush's re-election for a second term. As Table 3-9 shows, no other President in modern times has stood so high in the polls after 27 months in office.[10]

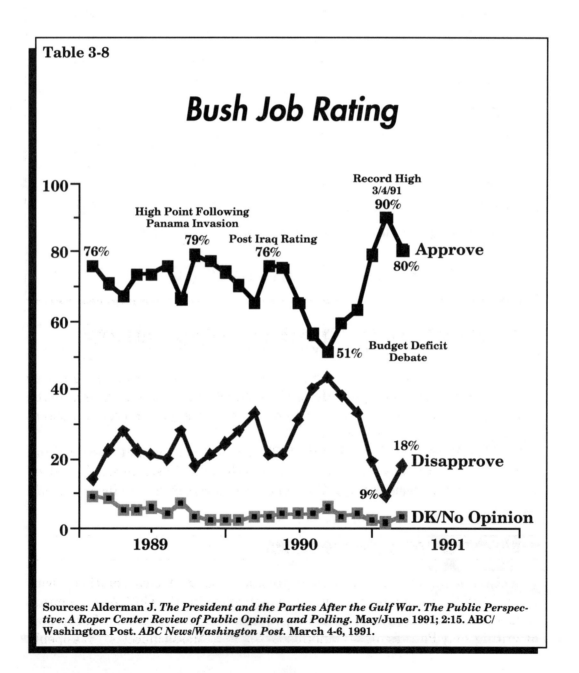

Table 3-8

Bush Job Rating

Record High
3/4/91
90%

High Point Following
Panama Invasion
79%

Post Iraq Rating
76%

76%

Approve
80%

51%   Budget Deficit
Debate

18% **Disapprove**

9%

DK/No Opinion

1989   1990   1991

Sources: Alderman J. *The President and the Parties After the Gulf War. The Public Perspective: A Roper Center Review of Public Opinion and Polling.* May/June 1991; 2:15. ABC/Washington Post. *ABC News/Washington Post.* March 4-6, 1991.

Table 3-9

First Term Ratings of Presidents

	Highest	Lowest	Rating After 27 Months In Office
Truman	+84	-21	+21
Eisenhower	+66	+34	+50
Kennedy	+68	+26	+44
Johnson	+71	+61	*
Nixon	+56	+ 9	+1
Ford	+68	- 6	*
Carter	+66	-31	-6
Reagan	+49	-21	-8
Bush	+81	+16	+71

Note: No ratings are included here for second terms.
*Johnson and Ford did not serve 27 months in their first terms.

Source: Gallup Organization. Trend data, 1935-1988. Storrs, CT: Roper Center for Public Opinion Research.

PRESIDENT BUSH'S RATINGS ON THE ISSUES

President Bush's exceptionally high standing in the spring of 1991 was based almost entirely on his handling of the Gulf War and foreign affairs. On the economy, the recession, and domestic problems generally, he received substantial negative ratings (Table 3-10).

The Democrats' best hope for 1992, however slim, is that memories are short, that the economy will deteriorate, and that the President will be judged mainly on his domestic record. There is not much reason to believe this will happen.

DEMOCRATIC CONTENDERS

One of the oldest adages in politics is, "you can't beat somebody with nobody." With President Bush riding so high following the Gulf War, potential Democratic contenders have been very reluctant to enter the lists. At the time of writing, only Paul Tsongas ("another Greek from Massachusetts") has openly declared himself a candidate. At this time in previous election cycles, the Iowa farmers and the burghers of New Hampshire were already under political siege from Presidential hopefuls.

For what they are worth as measures of recent opinion rather than future election results, the polls in March and April 1991 showed Governor Mario Cuomo and the Reverend Jesse Jackson as frontrunners followed by Senator Lloyd Bentsen and Representative Dick Gephardt (see Table 3-11). But polls taken at this time have usually been a very bad guide to elections. In the spring of 1975, Jimmy Carter was almost invisible in the polls.

One of the characteristics of American presidential politics is that new faces can emerge with remarkable speed. If the leading Democratic contenders do not throw their hats into the ring, we can expect to see one or more new faces in 1992.

THE QUAYLE FACTOR

Arguably President Bush's greatest vulnerability is Dan Quayle. Many people — Republicans and Democrats alike — who feel that the President made an unfortunate, but understandable, mistake in 1988 will find it much harder to accept his reluctance to admit and correct that mistake in 1992.

The President's apparent reluctance to change his Vice President probably has several causes. (1) He does not want to admit to making a mistake. (2) He likes Quayle, who has by most accounts performed adequately as Vice President. (3) If he drops him, he opens up a can of worms; if his replacement is less conservative, right-wingers who never trusted Bush may go after him. (4) The choice of an alternative may upset those who were passed over.

Table 3-10

President Bush's Ratings on Handling Different Issues: March 1991

	Percent
The Gulf War	**+84**
Foreign affairs	**+64**
The economy	**-17**
Recession	**-20**
Domestic problems	**-30**

Source: *The Harris Poll.* New York: Louis Harris and Associates, 3/15-19/91; 3/29/91-4/2/91.

Table 3-11

Leading Democratic Contenders for Presidency, Early 1991

(Polls of Democratic and Independent voters)

	Hart & Teeter March 1991	Gallup April 1991
	Percent	Percent
Mario Cuomo	18	23
Jesse Jackson	16	14
Lloyd Bentsen	12	9
Richard Gephardt	7	11
Sam Nunn	7	*
Albert Gore	6	9
Douglas Wilder	3	3
Bob Kerrey	1	*
George McGovern	*	8
Charles Robb	*	4
George Mitchell	*	3
Paul Tsongas	*	1
Bill Clinton	*	1

*Not listed.

Sources: Gallup Organization. *Gallup Poll.* 5/4/91; and Hart & Teeter Research Companies. NBC News/*Wall Street Journal*, 3/29/91.

Table 3-12

Ratings of Vice Presidents

	Highest	Lowest
	(Favorable minus unfavorable rating)	
Richard Nixon (1953-1961)	+62	+20
Lyndon Johnson (1961-1963)	+48	(only one rating)
Hubert Humphrey (1965-1969)	+43	+15
Spiro Agnew (1969-1973)	+43	+12
Nelson Rockefeller (1974-1977)	+12	(only one rating)
Walter Mondale (1977-1981)	+48	+39
George Bush (1981-1989)	+51	+29
Dan Quayle (1989 -	+22	+14

If President Bush completes another four years in office, the Vice Presidency will not matter much, except in its influence on the Republican nomination in 1996. But concern about the President's health could make the Vice Presidency an important issue. A recent Harris poll found that keeping Quayle on the ticket (as opposed to not referring to any running mate) might reduce Bush's majority by as much as 8 percentage points.[11] As shown in Table 3-12, Quayle's ratings on the job he is doing as Vice President are worse than almost all previous Vice Presidents.

TOPICAL SALIENT ISSUES

Table 3-13 lists the issues mentioned by the public as being "the most important" or the top priority for the government. Those at the top of the list are rather familiar — the economy and employment (which, but for the Gulf War, could have hurt President Bush). On some polls (and the answers to open-ended questions vary notoriously from one research firm to another, based partly on how the question is asked), homelessness and poverty come up quite high and

Table 3-13

Most Important Problems Facing the Country

CBS/New York Times:	April 1991 (open ended) Percent
Economy, general	20
Jobs/employment	12
Gulf/Mideast	3
Other foreign policy	5
Homelessness	5
Education	5
Crime	4
Poverty	4
Budget deficit	4

Source: CBS News/New York Times. CBS News/*New York Times*. 4/6/91.

Gallup:	April 1991 (open ended) Percent
Economy, general	20
Poverty, homelessness	13
Drugs	10
Jobs/unemployment	8
Budget deficit	6
Environment	6
Ethics, morals	4
Health care	1

Source: Gallup Organization. *Gallup Poll.* 5/4/91.

Table 3-14

One Domestic Issue Which Federal Government Should Do Something About

March 1991 (List read)

	Percent
Education	26
Poverty and homelessness	18
Crime	14
Health care	9
Drugs	9
The environment	7
Abortion	3
Mass transit, roads, highways	2

Source: **Hart & Teeter Research Companies. NBC News/***The Wall Street Journal.* **3/29/91.**

may encourage the Democrats who do very well on such issues. Education and the environment are second tier issues. Health care as an issue is scarcely mentioned at all on these open-ended questions.[12]

In the end, the Democrats' most potent theme could be "whose side are you on?" Health care could become important as the symbol of a "caring" Democratic party and a "heartless" Republican party, if the Democrats could fashion a policy that does not look like it will lead to a Massachusetts-like fiscal debacle.

A recent Hart & Teeter poll asked people to choose from a list of domestic issues one which the Federal Government should address. As shown in Table 3-14, education topped the list followed by poverty and homelessness (together) and crime. Health care mentioned by 9 percent came fourth equal with drugs, just above the environment.[13] While other surveys show that health care reform is potentially a quite powerful issue, it will not become more prominent unless some very visible politician chooses to develop a major campaign around it.

THE SAVINGS & LOAN SCANDAL

The collapse of the savings and loan institutions is arguably one of the worst financial disasters in the history of this country. It occurred when the Reagan-Bush team was in charge, resulting from the ideologically-motivated deregulation of the thrifts. It will eventually cost taxpayers several hundreds of billions of dollars and has already wiped out any hope of a peace dividend.

The Democrats have not yet been able to make anything of this issue politically, despite President Bush's consistently unfavorable rating on this issue and the involvement of his son.[14] Quite apart from their possible reluctance to attack the President on this issue when he is still riding so high in the post-Gulf period, the Democrats themselves have been players. Ex-Speaker Jim Wright resigned owing to his involvement in Texas savings and loans and ex-Representative Tony Coelho left the House before he had to face similar accusations. The problems of the four Democratic Senators among the Keating five may be preventing the Democrats from exploiting what could otherwise have been an important election issue.

TURNOUT

The exceptionally low and declining turnout of American voters compared to those almost everywhere else is well known. The highest voter turnout in the last 15 Presidential elections was in 1960, when almost 63 percent of the voting age population voted (Table 3-15). Except for 1984, it has fallen every election since then, down to a low point of just over 50 percent in 1988.[15]

While one often expects trends as steady as this 28-year trend to continue, history suggests a continued decline is far from inevitable. In 1936 and again in

---

Table 3-15

Voter Turnout in Presidential Elections

(As percentage of voting age population)

	Percent			Percent
1932	52.4		1960	62.8
1936	56.0		1964	61.9
1940	58.9		1968	60.9
1944	56.0		1972	55.2
1948	51.1		1976	53.5
1952	61.6		1980	52.6
1956	59.3		1984	53.1
			1988	50.2

Source: U.S. Congress, Clerk of the House. *Statistics of the Presidential and Congressional Election.* 1932-1988: biennial.

1952, the Presidential elections somehow triggered the interest or the passion of enough people to produce a sharp increase compared to a low turnout in the previous race.

At the time of writing, there is no evidence to suggest that 1992 will see much change in overall turnout. That will depend on the clash of candidates and issues in the election campaign itself, and the ability of the parties' machineries to bring out key groups. For the Democrats, important voters will be the elderly, blacks, and the poor. For Republicans, it will be those better off, residents of the Sunbelt, and business people.

PREFERENCES FOR DIVIDED GOVERNMENT

Party politics as we know it was not something the Founding Fathers considered, but it is an idea most Americans have come to expect. Americans are not bothered by the split in which the White House and the two Houses of Congress are controlled by different parties. (The word "controlled" is, of course,

---

Table 3-16

Preference for Divided Government

Q.: **In recent years, whenever a Republican president has been in the White House there usually has been a Congress controlled by the Democrats. Do you think it is better or worse for the country to have a president of one party and Congress controlled by the other party, or don't you think it makes much difference?**

	1984 Percent	1988 Percent	1991 Percent
Better to have divided government	32	34	36
Worse to have divided government	25	24	22
No difference	38	38	40
Not sure	5	4	2

Source: *The Harris Poll.* New York: Louis Harris and Associates, 5/9-15/91.

misleading. Congressmen's votes are frequently out of the control of their parties.) Less than a quarter believe it is worse to have a divided government than one in which one party controls the executive and legislative branches of government.[16] Like the Founding Fathers, many Americans believe in strong checks and balances.

Some political scientists have suggested that voters consciously split their votes to bring about a divided government, but there is no survey evidence to support their hypothesis. There has been a growing salience for foreign policy and defense issues in presidential elections and for domestic issues in Congressional elections. Relatively few voters now vote the straight party ticket. Rather, people vote on issues and for candidates. Americans are likely to vote for four more years of divided government in November 1992 unless something very unexpected happens between now and then.

CONCLUSION

At the moment, President Bush looks like a shoo-in for re-election in 1992, and the Republicans look strong beyond 1992. However, having seen the impact of Watergate on the 1976 election and the Gulf War on President Bush's popularity, we should not underestimate the impact of squalls.

Possible squalls that could hurt the President's 1992 re-election chances include: the Gulf War aftermath getting much uglier; further revelations about the 1980 negotiations with Iran to slow the release of the hostages; President Bush's health getting scarier, while Vice President Quayle stays on the ticket; and the economy getting worse in 1992 with no sign of recovery. Each of these seems possible but unlikely. And, of course, some other unforeseen event may have even greater impact.

The likeliest outcome is that President Bush will be re-elected in 1992 and will continue to confront a Democratic Congress. The net result for domestic policy is likely to be a continuing incremental minimalism at the federal level, and greater pressure on the states and localities to address the local impact of national problems.

REFERENCES

1. Taylor H. Polls, Politics, and the Gulf War. *National Review.* May 13, 1991;43:38.

2. ABC News/Washington Post. ABC News/*Washington Post.* 1/16/91. CBS News. *CBS News.* 1/29/91. CBS News/New York Times. CBS News/*New York Times.* 1/17/91. Gallup Organization. *Gallup Poll.* 1/17/91. Los Angeles Times. *Los Angeles Times.* 1/17/91. Yankelovich Clancy Shulman. Time/CNN/Yankelovich Clancy Shulman. 1/24/91.

3.   New York Times/CBS, poll. February 12-13, 1991.

4.   New York Times/CBS, poll. February 24, 1991.

5.   Jacobson, Gary. *The Electoral Origins of Divided Government.* Boulder, CO: Westview Press, 1990.

6.   Gallup Organization. Combined Gallup Polls. *Newsweek.* October 1989 - March 1991. Storrs, CT: Roper Center for Public Opinion Research, 1991.

7.   ABC News/*Washington Post.* Average of polls: 10/11/82; 9/13/83; 12/13/83; 8/1/83.

8.   ABC News/Washington Post. ABC News/*Washington Post.* March 4-6, 1991.

9.   Hart and Teeter, NBC News/*Wall Street Journal*, March 29, 1991.

10. Gallup Organization. Trend data, 1935 - 1988. Storrs, CT: Roper Center for Public Opinion Research.

11. *The Harris Poll.* New York: Louis Harris and Associates, 5/19/91;5/9-15/91.

12. CBS News/New York Times. CBS News/*New York Times.* 4/6/91 and Gallup Organization. *Gallup Poll.* 5/4/91.

13. Hart & Teeter Research Companies. NBC News/*The Wall Street Journal.* 3/29/91

14. Gallup Organization. *Gallup Poll.* 3/13/91.

15. U.S. Congress, Clerk of the House. *Statistics of the Presidential and Congressional Election.* 1932-1988:biennial.

16. *The Harris Poll.* New York: Louis Harris and Associates, 5/9-15/91.

CHAPTER 4

Consumers' Satisfaction With Their Health Care

Humphrey Taylor and Robert Leitman
Louis Harris and Associates

INTRODUCTION

The United States, probably more than any other country, is a consumer-oriented society. A whole industry has been created to figure out what Americans want, how much they would be willing to pay for it, and what drives these preferences. Health care is one of the larger categories of goods and services people buy, yet little is known about the health care preferences of individuals. This may be because historically, physicians, not patients, have driven much of the decisionmaking about health care. Since the 1970s, however, health care consumerism has greatly increased.

Table 4-1

Satisfaction With Services

Q.: Overall, how do you feel about the health care services that you and your family have used in the last few years? Would you say you are very satisfied, somewhat satisfied, somewhat dissatisfied, or very dissatisfied?

	1987	1990
Base	1,250	1,250
	%	%
Very satisfied	44	35
Somewhat satisfied	40	44
Somewhat dissatisfied	8	12
Very dissatisfied	5	6
Not sure	3	3

Source: Louis Harris and Associates. *Survey of Health Care Consumers.* February 1990.

This chapter describes changing consumer views about the health services these individuals and their families receive. It also presents data on the acceptability of many of the changes being considered by insurance companies and corporate employee benefits departments and identifies areas for future innovations. Pace-setting executives and institutions in the 1990s will be those who can see a shift in consumer preferences and values and respond to it.

This chapter is based primarily on trends drawn from the results of two consumer surveys conducted by Louis Harris and Associates in 1987 and 1990.* Supplemental data is from surveys sponsored by the American Medical Association, the Employee Benefits Research Institute, and the Conference Board. Together, these surveys provide the most complete description available of how consumer behavior and attitudes are changing, and the important implications for health care providers, insurers and corporations providing health benefits.

SATISFACTION WITH HEALTH CARE

Despite the high levels of dissatisfaction with the health care system described in Chapter 8, most Americans continue to be satisfied with their own personal health care, although there has been a small decline in consumer

---

* Consumer phone surveys were conducted by Louis Harris and Associates of a randomly selected sample of 1,250 adult Americans. The margin of error on each is ±4%.

satisfaction in recent years. As can be seen in Table 4-1, most Americans are satisfied with the health care they and their families receive. In fact, 35 percent of Americans surveyed are very satisfied with the health care services they or their families received in the last few years, down from 44 percent in 1987. There has been a small increase in the number of dissatisfied people. Currently, 18 percent are dissatisfied, compared with 13 percent in 1987.[1]

In further probing the reasons behind their dissatisfaction, we find that the high cost of health care is more of a problem for this group than for the others surveyed. As shown in Table 4-2, people without health insurance are more likely to be dissatisfied than individuals with either private or public insurance. Twenty-nine percent of people without health insurance are dissatisfied, compared to 17 percent of all insured people. Relative to this response, we found that people who report their health care costs are causing them difficulty are more dissatisfied with the health care they receive. Twenty-four percent of people who report their costs are out of control are dissatisfied with their care, while only 3

Table 4-2

Effect of Insurance on Satisfaction With Services

Q.: Overall, how do you feel about the health care services that you and your family have used in the last few years? Would you say you are very satisfied, somewhat satisfied, somewhat dissatisfied, or very dissatisfied?

			Insurance		
	Total	**Private**	**Medicare**	**Medicaid**	**None**
Base	1,250	1,093	248	76	87
	%	%	%	%	%
Very satisfied	35	36	36	33	29
Somewhat satisfied	44	46	40	42	39
Somewhat dissatisfied	12	11	11	16	17
Very dissatisfied	8	5	8	6	12
Not sure	2	2	4	3	3

Source: Louis Harris and Associates. *Survey of Health Care Consumers.* February 1990.

Table 4-3

Control Over Health Care Costs and Satisfaction With Care

Satisfaction With Care	Percent Reporting Costs Are Under Control		
	Completely	Somewhat	Out of Control
Base	113	395	739
	%	%	%
Very satisfied	67	41	27
Somewhat satisfied	28	47	46
Dissatisfied	3	10	24

Source: Louis Harris and Associates. *Survey of Health Care Consumers.* February 1990.

percent of people whose costs are under control report themselves dissatisfied (Table 4-3). Given the growing number of uninsured in this country and reported increases in cost-sharing between employers and consumers, the increase in dissatisfaction over this three-year period is not surprising.

HOW THE SYSTEM IS RATED ON COST, ACCESS, AND QUALITY

The question of the public's satisfaction with their health care has been a source of confusion for many. We believe the reason for this confusion is that Americans give their health care a mixed rating: Americans are dissatisfied with the cost of their health care, but happy with access (phrased during the interview as, "the ability of people to get the health care services they need") and with the quality of care they receive. This is reflected in Table 4-4, which reports respondents' rankings of cost, access and quality. Costs are rated very poorly, while access scores in the middle. Quality is rated somewhat higher, although not as high as might be expected.

The Harris surveys also considered which aspect of health care costs most concerns people. Table 4-5 reports satisfaction with people's own health insurance, total system costs, and personal out-of-pocket costs by income level. We find consumers are concerned about both their own out-of-pocket costs and the total system costs. Fifty-one percent are dissatisfied with the total cost of health care, while 45 percent are dissatisfied with their out-of-pocket health care costs.

People are more satisfied with their health insurance coverage than they are with system and out-of-pocket costs. Seventy-one percent report being satisfied with their health insurance benefits, while only 48 percent are satisfied with total costs, and 54 percent are satisfied with their out-of-pocket costs.

Dissatisfaction with health care costs is prevalent at all levels of income. Slightly more than one-half of people at income levels up to $50,000 per year express dissatisfaction, and fully 45 percent of those with annual incomes above $50,000 are dissatisfied with the total cost of health care. Higher-income people are somewhat happier with their health insurance benefits and with their out-of-pocket health costs than those with lower income. However, it is significant to find that even among people with annual incomes of more than $50,000, 37 percent are dissatisfied with their out-of-pocket health care costs, and 22 percent are unhappy with their health insurance benefits.

Table 4-4

Americans' Ratings of the American Health Care System's Cost, Access, and Quality

Q.: How would you rate each of these aspects of the health care system on a scale of 1 to 5 where 1 means very bad and 5 means perfect?

| | Very Bad | | | | Perfect |
	1	**2**	**3**	**4**	**5**
The total cost of health care	32%	28%	25%	10%	4%
The ability of people to get the health care services they need	12	22	38	20	6
The quality of care patients receive	4	13	45	31	7

Source: Louis Harris and Associates. *Survey of Health Care Consumers.* February 1990.

Table 4-5

Satisfaction With Cost of Care and Insurance by Income

Q.: I will mention various elements of health care services that are available to you and your family. Please say for each one whether you are very satisfied, somewhat satisfied, somewhat dissatisfied, or very dissatisfied with that service.

		Income				
	Total	$15,000 or Less	$15,001-$25,000	$25,000-$35,000	$35,001-$50,000	$50,001 and Above
Base	1,250	228	240	218	258	229
	%	%	%	%	%	%
The total cost of health care, including what both you and your insurance pay						
Very satisfied	16	16	18	12	10	19
Somewhat satisfied	32	30	28	34	34	36
Somewhat dissatisfied	28	28	25	30	31	30
Very dissatisfied	23	24	28	23	24	15
Not sure	1	2	1	—	2	1
Your health insurance benefits						
Very satisfied	29	27	26	29	29	35
Somewhat satisfied	42	38	42	46	46	45
Somewhat dissatisfied	17	17	20	14	16	16
Very dissatisfied	9	13	10	16	7	6
Not sure	1	3	*	—	*	—
Your out-of-pocket cost of health care						
Very satisfied	20	19	21	16	17	25
Somewhat satisfied	34	28	30	39	42	38
Somewhat dissatisfied	25	28	28	22	25	19
Very dissatisfied	20	24	20	23	15	18

*Less than 0.5%

Source: Louis Harris and Associates. *Survey of Health Care Consumers*. February 1990.

Table 4-6

Satisfaction With Own Care

Q.: Thinking about your most recent visit to a medical doctor, would you say you were very satisfied, somewhat satisfied, somewhat dissatisfied, or very dissatisfied with...

	Percent Saying Very or Somewhat Satisfied			
	1978	**1982**	**1987**	**1989**
The medical care you received	88%	93%	92%	85%
The way the doctor explained things to you	85	89	87	89
The amount of time you had to wait for an appointment	81	89	81	75
The amount of time you had to wait before seeing the doctor	74	82	77	69

Source: Louis Harris and Associates. *Survey of Health Care Consumers.* February 1990.

SATISFACTION WITH ELEMENTS OF HEALTH CARE SERVICES

Despite the decline in overall satisfaction with our health system, satisfaction with specific elements of health care services has remained virtually unchanged since 1987. People remain satisfied with their access to a doctor. Forty-six percent of consumers in 1990, just as in 1987, are very satisfied with their ability to see a doctor whenever needed (compared to 35 percent who are very satisfied with their services in general). An additional 33 percent are somewhat satisfied and 20 percent are dissatisfied. Thirty-six percent report being very satisfied with their access to high quality medical technology, and 42 percent are somewhat satisfied. About a fifth of the population is dissatisfied.

The AMA has conducted surveys of the public since 1972 about attitudes toward physicians and the medical profession. These surveys also find Ameri-

Figure 4-1

The Public's View of the Medical Profession as a Whole

(Percent of respondents who agree)

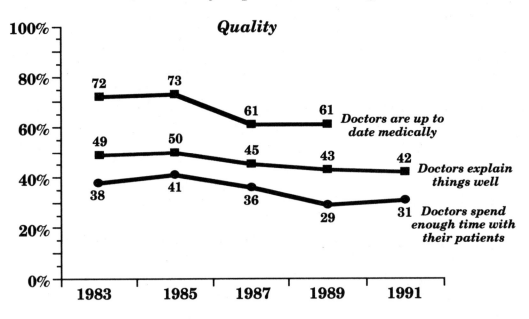

Quality

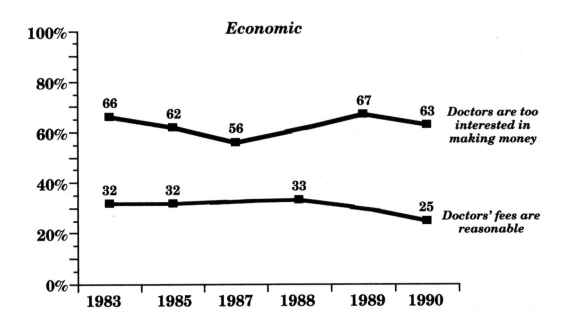

Economic

Source: Harvey L. *Survey of Public Opinion on Health Care Issues.* American Medical Association, Chicago, March 1991.

cans satisfied with the care they receive from their physicians. On a variety of measures shown in Table 4-6, two-thirds or more of Americans report favorably about their last visit to a doctor. Though satisfaction has decreased slightly since 1987, 85 percent still report they are satisfied with the medical care they received in 1990. Eighty-nine percent of people are satisfied with the way the doctor explained things to them. Two-thirds to three-quarters are satisfied with the time it took to get an appointment and to see the doctor.[2]

When asked how they felt about the medical profession as a whole, people do not give such favorable reviews. As shown in Figure 4-1, consumers believe quality of care is declining. Only 61 percent believe doctors are up to date medically, and less than half believe doctors explain things well (42 %) or spend enough time with their patients (31%). Most Americans believe doctors are too interested in financial rewards (63%), and only 25 percent believe physicians' fees are reasonable.[1] The gap between attitudes toward one's personal physician and attitudes toward the medical profession as a whole is similar to consumers' impressions of other leadership groups: people like the individual with whom they interact, but think the system, as a whole, is flawed. For example, 55 percent of people like their own Congressional representative, but only 26 percent like the Congress and the political process.[3] A result of these attitudes is that consumers support changes affecting the medical profession as a whole (such as physician payment reform) but do not support changes they believe might negatively affect the care they receive or their relationship with their physician.

SELECTING A PHYSICIAN

One indicator of consumers' attitudes toward physicians is the criteria on which they base their choice of a physician (see Table 4-7). Most patients report this is a personal decision, and they rely on the recommendation of a friend or family member (19%) or another professional (17%) more often than any other source of information.[1] When asked what other criteria they use, in addition to these reasons, people report they base their decision on convenient location, inclusion of the physician in the patient's health plan, the hospital the doctor uses, and how long the doctor has been practicing in the community. Less widely-used means are telephone directories, the doctor's gender, and what they know about the doctors' fees.[1] So, although people are very unhappy with the cost of physician care, they are not basing their choice of doctors on his or her charges. In fact, only 30 percent of people report ever having compared the price of a specific medical procedure between two or more different physicians. This finding relates to the discussion in the first chapter: unlike with other consumer goods, individuals do not want price to play a major role in their health care buying decisions.

ATTITUDES TOWARD HOSPITALS

As with the care they receive from their doctors, Americans are generally satisfied with their care when hospitalized. Only 9 percent report being dissat-

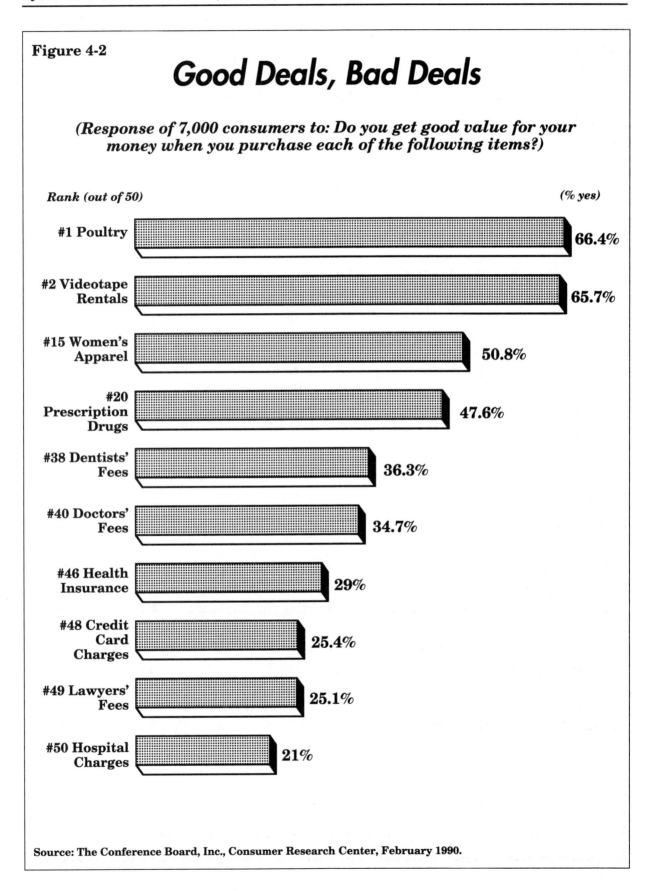

Figure 4-2

Good Deals, Bad Deals

(Response of 7,000 consumers to: Do you get good value for your money when you purchase each of the following items?)

Rank (out of 50)   *(% yes)*

#1 Poultry — **66.4%**

#2 Videotape Rentals — **65.7%**

#15 Women's Apparel — **50.8%**

#20 Prescription Drugs — **47.6%**

#38 Dentists' Fees — **36.3%**

#40 Doctors' Fees — **34.7%**

#46 Health Insurance — **29%**

#48 Credit Card Charges — **25.4%**

#49 Lawyers' Fees — **25.1%**

#50 Hospital Charges — **21%**

Source: The Conference Board, Inc., Consumer Research Center, February 1990.

Table 4-7

Physician Choice

Q.: In selecting a doctor, did any of these things affect your decision?

	Yes	No
	%	%
Whether or not the doctor has office hours in the evening or on weekends	23	75
Where the doctor's office is located	51	48
What friends or relatives told you about the doctor	50	47
What you learned about the doctor from brochures or other publications	17	80
Whether the doctor is a man or woman	12	86
What you learned about the doctor from a Yellow Pages listing in the phone book	8	90
What you heard about the doctor's fees and charges	20	77
What you heard about which hospital the doctor uses	37	60
How long the doctor has been practicing in the community	36	60
Whether or not the doctor is on a list of doctors provided by your health plan	39	58

Source: Louis Harris and Associates. *Survey of Health Care Consumers.* February 1990.

isfied, while 24 percent state they are somewhat satisfied. Nearly seven in ten (67%) report they are satisfied with their last hospitalization.[1] Many fewer are happy with care they received during their most recent emergency room visit. Less than half were very satisfied (45%), 28 percent were somewhat satisfied, and 26 percent were not at all satisfied.[4]

The quality of services received in hospital care is not the problem for the public. Instead, the high level of public dissatisfaction is with the perceived high cost of care. Comparing Americans' views on hospital spending to those of Canadians or Germans, only Americans think we spend too much on hospitals. Seventy-nine percent of Americans hold this belief, compared to 18 percent of Canadians and 19 percent of Germans.[5] Not only do Americans think we spend too much, but they do not think hospital care gives them sufficient value for the money spent. In a survey of 7,000 consumers, only 21 percent believe hospital charges are a good value for their money, ranking hospitals last on a list of 50 common consumer items (Figure 4-2).[6] Poultry and videotape rentals top the list as good values, while other health services rate near the bottom.

Table 4-8

The Importance of Health Insurance Benefits to Parents

Q.: In deciding to change jobs or work for a particular employer, are the health benefits offered very important, somewhat important, or not important at all?

	Total	Number of Children		
		None	1 or 2	3 or More
Base	1,250	710	420	118
	%	%	%	%
Very important	67	60	75	73
Somewhat important	21	23	19	21
Not important at all	6	9	4	2
Not sure	6	9	2	4

Source: Louis Harris and Associates. *Survey of Health Care Consumers.* February 1990.

Table 4-9

Insurance Preferences

Q.: If you were given a choice between health insurance that protects you from catastrophic health expenses only (at a lower premium), and coverage for routine health expenses at a higher premium, which would you choose?

	Total	3 or More Children
Base	1,250	118
	%	%
Insurance which protects against catastrophic health expenses only at lower premium	44	31
Insurance to cover the costs of routine health care at a higher premium	50	67
Not sure	6	2

Source: Louis Harris and Associates. *Survey of Health Care Consumers.* February 1990.

ATTITUDES TOWARD HEALTH INSURANCE

A recent survey found that a majority of Americans believe health insurance is the most important fringe benefit an employer provides. Consistent with the finding that people are concerned about their health care costs, 61 percent of adults rank health care above all other benefits in importance.[7] Two-thirds of Americans (67%) say health benefits are very important in deciding whether or not to change jobs or to work for a particular employer. Health benefits are even more important to parents than to single people. Seventy-three to 75 percent of parents say health benefits are very important compared to 60 percent of nonparents (Table 4-8). When given a choice between $2,500 in health benefits or a $2,500 pay increase, fully 78 percent prefer to receive health benefits.[6]

Americans are divided on what type of health insurance is most important to them. Given the choice between purchasing a policy to cover routine health

Table 4-10

Those Who Want Versus Those Who Have No Insurance Coverage

	% Saying Very Important to Them	% Who Have Coverage
Base	1,250	1,163
	%	%
Hospitalization	92	88
Long term care	79	58
Catastrophic health expenses	77	61
Doctors' visits	76	75
Prescription drugs	71	64
Routine check-ups	69	62
Dental care	69	50
Vision care and eyeglasses	59	40
Mental health services	44	49
Alcohol and drug abuse treatment	36	38

Source: Louis Harris and Associates. *Survey of Health Care Consumers.* February 1990.

expenses at a higher premium and a policy which protects against catastrophic health expenses at a lower premium, half would select coverage for routine care, and 44 percent would choose catastrophic protection (Table 4-9). Parents of larger families are more concerned about insuring their family's routine use of care. Fully two-thirds (67%) of people with three or more dependent children prefer insurance to cover the routine costs of care, 17 percentage points more than the public as a whole.

While Americans are split on which general type of coverage is important to them, there is no ambiguity about what priority they place on specific services to be covered by their policy. Virtually all consumers (92%) say that hospitalization coverage is very important to them, followed by long-term care (79%), catastrophic-related health expenses (77%), and physician visits (76%). The next highest priorities are prescription drugs (71%), routine check-ups (69%), and dental care (69%), followed by vision care and eyeglasses (59%); 44 percent want mental health services and 36 percent want alcohol and drug abuse treatment covered.[2]

As shown in Table 4-10, consumer preferences differ from actual coverage in several important ways. Many more people say long term care and catastrophic health insurance are very important to them than actually have such coverage (79 percent versus 58 percent for long term care and 77 percent versus 61 percent for catastrophic coverage). Similar divergence is true for dental insurance (69 percent say it is very important to them but only 50 percent have it), and vision care and eyeglasses (59 percent say it is very important, but only 40 percent have the coverage). At the other extreme, slightly more people have coverage for mental health and alcohol and drug abuse treatment than say it is very important to them (49 percent have mental health coverage, but only 44 percent consider it very important, and 38 percent have substance abuse treatment coverage, but only 36 percent consider it very important).[1] An obvious implication of these data is that a sizable, untapped market exists for long term care and catastrophic insurance, as well as for dental insurance and for vision care and eyeglass coverage.

Table 4-11

Interest in Paying for Nursing Home Insurance

Q: How interested would you be in paying an additional insurance premium of approximately $60.00 a month — each year until age 65 — to cover you at any time in your life — would you be very interested, somewhat interested, not very interested, not at all interested?

	Total		Health			Income
	1987	1990	Excellent	Good	Fair or Poor	$50,001 and Above
Base	1,250	1,250	498	539	211	229
	%	%	%	%	%	%
Very interested	6	11	12	9	16	15
Somewhat interested	18	28	31	27	23	35
Not very interested	20	18	21	21	13	20
Not interested at all	29	47	30	31	25	25
Already 65 or older	12	12	5	11	22	4

Source: Louis Harris and Associates. *Survey of Health Care Consumers.* February 1990.

Table 4-12

Interest in Paying for In-Home Long Term Care Insurance

Q: How interested would you be in paying an additional insurance premium of approximately $60.00 a month — each year until age 65 — to cover you at any time in your life — would you be very interested, somewhat interested, not very interested, not at all interested?

	Total		Health			Income
	1987	**1990**	**Excellent**	**Good**	**Fair or Poor**	**$50,001 and Above**
Base	1,250	1,250	498	539	211	229
	%	%	%	%	%	%
Very interested	6	17	19	13	23	24
Somewhat interested	28	33	34	36	24	36
Not very interested	15	16	16	16	9	16
Not interested at all	24	34	26	24	20	20
Already 65 or older	12	11	5	10	22	2

Source: Louis Harris and Associates. *Survey of Health Care Consumers.* February 1990.

LONG TERM CARE

For survey research to provide useful information about a product or service, it has to answer two questions: (1) how interested is the consumer in the product and (2) how much is he or she willing to pay for it? This latter question is rarely asked. In this survey, we find interest in long term care diminishes somewhat as the question of how to pay for it comes to the fore. While more than three in four Americans, many of whom do not presently have long term care and catastrophic coverage, say such coverage is very important to them, less than half of these (39%) say they'd be willing to pay $60 a month until age 65 to cover all nursing home costs they might incur at any point during their lifetimes.[1] Still, this is a large increase since 1987, when only 24 percent said they would be interested in paying $60 a month (the average cost of a private policy at that time) for nursing home coverage including only 6 percent who said they would be very interested (Table 4-11). This large increase in interest cuts across all age groups and income levels.

As shown in Table 4-12, a similarly large increase is evident in willingness to pay $60 a month until age 65 to cover *in-home*, long term health care. In 1987, only 34 percent were interested, including 6 percent who were very interested. Today, 50 percent are interested, including 17 percent who are very interested. Here too, the large increase holds true across all age groups and income levels.[1]

The people most concerned about the long term care needs of the elderly are the adult children of the elderly. About one-third of Americans with one or both parents living are willing to pay $200 a month for nursing home insurance for their parents, while almost half (45 percent) are willing to pay the same amount for in-home, long term care coverage for their parents. While this was relatively unchanged between 1987 and 1990, the number of people who say they are willing to pay a substantial amount of money ($2,400 a year) for their parents' long term care is notable (Table 4-13).

Table 4-13

Interest in Paying for Long Term Care Insurance for Parents

Q.: How interested would you be in paying an additional insurance premium of approximately $200 a month each year for nursing home care or in-home care for one or both of your parents? Would you be very interested, somewhat interested, not very interested, not at all interested in paying such a premium?

	Nursing Home Care		In-Home Care	
	1987	**1990**	**1987**	**1990**
Base	1,250	1,250	1,250	1,250
	%	%	%	%
Very interested	9	10	11	14
Somewhat interested	22	22	30	31
Not very interested	21	25	19	20
Not interested at all	48	43	39	35

Source: Louis Harris and Associates. *Survey of Health Care Consumers*. February 1990.

Table 4-14

HMO Membership

By Age

	18-29		30-39		40-49		50-64		65 & Over	
	1987	1990	1987	1990	1987	1990	1987	1990	1987	1990
Base	314	281	327	324	202	221	212	252	188	169
	%	%	%	%	%	%	%	%	%	%
Yes	10	14	12	14	9	19	6	14	6	4
No	89	85	88	85	91	80	94	85	93	95

By Income

	$15,000 or Less		$15,000-$25,000		$25,001-$35,000		$35,001-$50,000		$50,001 or More	
	1987	1990	1987	1990	1987	1990	1987	1990	1987	1990
Base	271	228	263	240	245	218	206	258	184	229
	%	%	%	%	%	%	%	%	%	%
Yes	5	6	9	15	11	15	15	18	7	18
No	94	91	85	91	88	82	84	81	90	80

Source: Louis Harris and Associates. *Survey of Health Care Consumers.* Febraury 1990.

THE CONSUMER AND MANAGED CARE

HMO enrollment, as a share of America's total population, continues to grow relatively slowly, from 9 percent of the American public in 1987 to 15 percent today, despite increasing satisfaction among HMO members. Forty-four percent of members report being very satisfied, up slightly from 41 percent in 1987.[1] The biggest increases in enrollment are among people in their forties (up to 19 percent from 9 percent) and aged people 50-64 (up to 14 percent from 6 percent). There has been a similar increase in enrollment among upper-income people; the rate of HMO membership among people with household incomes of more than $50,000 is up to 18 percent from only seven percent in 1987 (see Table 4-14). College graduates continue to join HMOs at a slightly higher rate than consumers with lower education levels. Eighteen percent of college graduates are members of HMOs, up from 11 percent in 1987.

At the same time, there is a slight decline in the rate of people saying they definitely expect to renew their membership in their HMO. In 1987, 90 percent of HMO members said they certainly (63%) or probably (27%) would renew their membership. Today 87 percent say they will renew, although only 55 percent say renewal is certain (Table 4-15). The proportion of nonmembers who say they would be interested in joining an HMO remains at 36 percent — unchanged from 1987.[1] Unless more employers require their employees to join HMOs, these numbers suggest slower growth for HMOs in the future.

Table 4-15

Interest in Renewing or Joining HMOs

Q.: Do you think you and your family certainly will, probably will, probably will not, or certainly will not renew your membership in the HMO?

	1987	1990
Base	1,250	1,250
	%	%
Certainly will	63	55
Probably will	27	32
Probably will not	6	8
Certainly will not	1	4

Q.: From what you know now about health maintenance organizations, would you be very interested, somewhat interested, hardly interested, or not at all interested in joining an HMO?

	1987	1990
Base	1,250	1,250
	%	%
Very interested	6	7
Somewhat interested	30	29
Hardly interested	17	20
Not at all interested	44	43

Source: Louis Harris and Associates. *Survey of Health Care Consumers.* February 1990.

These data also support the argument that there is a potential problem with adverse selection in HMOs. A much higher proportion of HMO members who are in excellent or good health report they are certain to renew their membership than those in fair or poor health. As reflected in Table 4-16, in 1987 there was only an 8 percentage point difference between the certain renewal rates of people in excellent health and people in fair or poor health.[1] The difference in 1990 is up to 24 percentage points — 61 percent of people in excellent health say they certainly will renew their membership compared with only 37 percent of people in fair or poor health. If this trend holds, HMOs may end up serving healthier people, leaving sicker people who need more expensive care in traditional indemnity plans. These plans could experience greater cost increases as the rates reflect the higher use of care by their sicker enrollees.

A small number of people have chosen to enroll in Preferred Provider Organizations (PPOs), health insurance plans that limit patients' choices of hospitals and doctors while providing care at a less expensive or discounted rate. PPO membership remains lower than HMO membership but has grown more rapidly over the last three years — from 6 percent in 1987 to 11 percent today. As with HMOs, the proportion of nonmembers interested in joining remains

---

Table 4-16

The Effect of Health on HMO Renewal

Q.: Do you think you and your family certainly will, probably will, probably will not, or certainly will not renew your membership in the HMO?

	Total		1987 Health			1990 Health		
	1987	1990	Excellent	Good	Fair or Poor	Excellent	Good	Fair or Poor
Base	120	178	55	51	14	80	81	17
	%	%	%	%	%	%	%	%
Certainly will	63	55	67	62	59	61	54	37
Probably will	27	32	23	33	17	32	33	30
Probably will not	6	8	8	2	16	4	7	23
Certainly will not	1	4	1	—	7	3	3	—

Caution: Many of the subsamples are very small.

Source: Louis Harris and Associates. *Survey of Health Care Consumers.* February 1990.

Table 4-17

Restricting Doctors' Freedom To Contain Costs

Q.: In order to make health care services more efficient and less expensive, some hospitals and insurance companies are reducing the freedom of doctors to prescribe different treatments and procedures. Do you feel this is very acceptable, somewhat acceptable, not very acceptable, or not at all acceptable?

	1987	1990
Base	1,250	1,250
	%	%
Very acceptable	9	8
Somewhat acceptable	48	45
Not very acceptable	23	25
Not acceptable at all	17	19
Not sure	2	3

Source: Louis Harris and Associates. *Survey of Health Care Consumers.* February 1990.

virtually unchanged: 6 percent say they are very interested and another 31 percent (up from 27 percent) are somewhat interested.[1]

AMERICANS ARE NOT READY TO RESTRICT TREATMENTS

One way to reduce the cost of health care is to restrict financial access to certain high cost procedures. As shown in Table 4-17, more than half of the American public (53%) believe that it is very (8%) or somewhat (45%) acceptable for hospitals and insurance companies to reduce the freedom of doctors to prescribe different treatments and procedures in order to make health services more efficient and less expensive. This is virtually unchanged from 1987 when 57 percent found this acceptable.[1]

While this suggests a willingness to place controls over access to unnecessary and very expensive treatments, the egalitarian tradition in America makes

Table 4-18

Public Opinion of Equality and Expensive Treatments

Q.: I will read you some statements about health insurance. Please tell me, for each one, if you tend to agree or disagree with it...

Health insurance should pay for any treatments which will save lives, even if it costs a million dollars to save one life.

	Total		Education		Income	
	1987	**1990**	**Not High School Grad.**	**College Grad.**	**$15,000 or Less**	**$50,001 or More**
Base	1,250	1,250	147	380	228	229
	%	%	%	%	%	%
Agree	71	75	84	60	84	61
Disagree	26	22	14	36	13	36

Everybody should have the right to get the best possible health care — as good as the treatment a millionaire gets.

	Total		Education		Income	
	1987	**1990**	**Not High School Grad.**	**College Grad.**	**$15,000 or Less**	**$50,001 or More**
Base	1,250	1,250	147	380	228	229
	%	%	%	%	%	%
Agree	91	90	95	77	95	85
Disagree	8	9	4	22	5	15

Source: Louis Harris and Associates. *Survey of Health Care Consumers.* February 1990.

these policies more acceptable in the abstract than in the specific. For example, as shown in Table 4-18, 90 percent of Americans agree that "everybody should have the right to get the best possible health care — as good as the treatment a millionaire gets." Three in four Americans (75%), up from 71 percent in 1987, agree that health insurance should pay for any treatments which will save lives, even if it costs a million dollars to save one life. Less-educated and lower-income people are likelier to agree with these statements than are college graduates and higher-income people.[1]

As shown in Table 4-19, fewer Americans now than in 1987 think "there are so many new, expensive treatments, surgical procedures, transplants, and medical devices that it is impossible for any health insurance plan to pay for all of them." In 1987, 68 percent of Americans agreed with this statement — today, 62 percent agree.[1] This reflects growing (not shrinking) consumer expectations for health insurance coverage.

Perhaps the most extreme finding in this regard is the continued belief among about a fourth of Americans that insurers should pay for very expensive

---

Table 4-19

Public Opinion of Insurers' Ability To Pay

Q.: I will read you some statements about health insurance. Please tell me, for each one, if you tend to agree or disagree with it . . .

There are so many new, expensive treatments, surgical procedures, transplants and medical devices that it is impossible for any health insurance plan to pay for all of them.

	Total	
	1987	**1990**
Base	1,250	1,250
	%	%
Agree	68	62
Disagree	30	36

Source: Louis Harris and Associates. *Survey of Health Care Consumers*, February 1990.

Table 4-20

Beliefs About Future Cost and Quality

Q.: **Do you agree or disagree with following statements?**

In the next five years people will be paying much more out of their pockets for health care.

	Top Managers	Public		
	1989	**Total**	**College Graduate or More**	**Income of $50,001 Or More**
Base	1,250	1,250	380	229
	%	%	%	%
Agree	88	91	91	78
Disagree	11	8	9	20

Total health costs in this country can't be significantly reduced without a sacrifice of quality.

	Top Managers	Public		
	1989	**Total**	**College Graduate or More**	**Income of $50,001 Or More**
Base	1,250	1,250	380	229
	%	%	%	%
Agree	42	32	37	27
Disagree	56	68	62	71

Source: Louis Harris and Associates. *Survey of Health Care Consumers.* February 1990.

surgery even if the patient's doctor says it is unneeded. This is a sign of Americans' continued desire to have a right to any kind of health care *they* deem necessary.

HOW FAR CAN THE CONSUMER BE PUSHED?

As described in Chapter 5, frustration with rising health care costs is likely to lead to more cost shifting by employers. Table 4-20 shows the public is well aware of this trend. Virtually all of the corporate executives (88%) and the public (91%) expect personal out-of-pocket payments for health care will be much higher over the next five years. They anticipate this even though a majority of both groups (68% of the public and 56% of top managers) do not believe quality care must, by necessity, be at high cost in this country. Among college graduates (62%) and upper-income people (71%), cynicism about the necessity of high-cost health care is even more prevalent.[1]

One way for employers to contain health care costs while maintaining employee choice is to place a limit on the amount of money contributed to the employee's health policy and allow the employee to pick the benefits he or she wants within this budget constraint. As shown in Table 4-21, 76 percent of consumers say they would find this acceptable, including 28 percent who say it

---

Table 4-21

Public Acceptance of a Capped Defined Contribution With Employee Choice of Benefits

Q.: If an employer capped the amount of money he contributed to your employee benefits and allowed you to pick which benefits you wanted to be paid for, would that be very acceptable, somewhat acceptable, not very acceptable, or not acceptable at all to you?

	Total
Base	1,250
	%
Very acceptable	28
Somewhat acceptable	48
Not very acceptable	12
Not at all acceptable	9

Source: Louis Harris and Associates. *Survey of Health Care Consumers.* February 1990

Table 4-22

Public Acceptance of Case Management, Cost-Sharing, and Restrictions on Choice

Q.: Many employers are taking steps to control their health care costs. How acceptable would it be as part of your health plan if ...

Base: 1,250

	Very Acceptable	Moderately Acceptable	Very Acceptable	Not at All Acceptable	Not Sure
	%	%	%	%	%
You were required to see your family doctor for authorization before you saw a specialist physician for non-emergency care	24	41	16	19	1
You were required to consult with a health plan representative when making decisions about non-emergency care after your health care expenses exceeded $2,000 a year	9	40	24	26	1
A health plan representative had to certify that non-emergency hospitalization is necessary before you are hospitalized	8	36	27	28	1
Your co-payments (payment for every doctor's visit) was increased by $10	7	34	28	30	1
Your annual deductible increased by $200	7	27	30	34	2
Your contribution to your health insurance premium increased by $200 a year	6	30	31	33	1
Your choice of general practitioner was restricted	4	24	27	43	2
Your choice of specialist physicians was restricted	3	21	31	44	1

Source: Louis Harris and Associates. *Survey of Health Care Consumers.* February 1990.

would be very acceptable. However, it may well be that consumer willingness to accept this option today is based, in part, on a failure to understand its likely consequences —*i.e.*, greatly increased employee costs for their own insurance over time.

The American public is becoming somewhat accustomed to facing required approvals (preadmission certification) before more specialized and costly levels of care can be reimbursed by insurers. Nearly two-thirds (65%) say it would be acceptable if their health plan required them to see their family doctor for authorization before seeing a specialist for nonemergency care, including 24 percent who say this would be very acceptable. Nearly one-half (49%) say they would find it acceptable to be required to consult with a health plan representative when making decisions about nonemergency care when health expenses exceeded $2,000 in one year. However, although only 9 percent say this would be very acceptable, and 26 percent say it would be not acceptable at all. Finally, 44 percent say that it would be acceptable if a health plan representative had to pre-certify the necessity of non-emergency hospitalization. Only 8 percent say this is very acceptable while 28 percent view it as not acceptable at all.

As presented in Table 4-22, far less acceptable to the public are several ways to increase out-of-pocket costs for health care. Majorities say that it would be unacceptable for their health plan to:

◆ Increase their co-payment per doctor's visit by $10 — 58 percent find this unacceptable, including 30 percent who find it totally unacceptable.

◆ Increase their annual deductible by $200 — 64 percent say it would be unacceptable with 34 percent saying it is not acceptable at all;

◆ Increase their contribution to their premium by $200 per year — 64 percent say it would be unacceptable, including 33 percent who say it would not be at all acceptable.

What emerges is a basic conflict between consumers and employers which could have a profound effect on the American health care system. As revealed in our 1989 survey of employers, the main cost containment strategy of many employers is to shift costs onto the employee. The resultant rising out-of-pocket expense has been a consistent source of consumer dissatisfaction with health care. By continuing down this path, employers are likely, not only to increase specific employee resistance to their cost-shifting efforts, but also to increase the general public's dissatisfaction with the system as a whole. Substantially increasing cost-shifting to the employee-consumer could hasten more dramatic reform of the American health care system. For those who wish to forestall rapid and dramatic change, increasing cost-shifting in the absence of other effective cost controls can be considered a self-destructive act, eventually resulting in a public outcry for major, governmental intervention.

Even less acceptable to consumers is absolute restriction of choice of doctors — whether of general practitioners or of specialists. Fully three-fourths (75%) would find restricting their choice of specialists unacceptable, including 44 percent who would find it totally unacceptable. Nearly as many (70%) would find restricting their choice of general practitioner unacceptable, including 43 percent who say it would be not at all acceptable.[1]

Our survey results suggest that the issue of restricting choice of physicians can be more acceptable under certain circumstances. When presented to employers and consumers as "restricted choice," few in either group say they are willing to accept such policies. Presented more positively, as "allowing you to choose your doctors from a pre-selected list," it is acceptable to many more people.[1]

CONCLUSION

Reviewing the changes in consumer satisfaction and attitudes between 1987 and 1990 shows a public basically satisfied with personal health care but unhappy with the health care system. Much of the dissatisfaction is associated with increased cost and inadequate insurance coverage to protect against rising expenses.

Nonetheless, these surveys find an American public unwilling to accept tough cost containment measures, particularly if such measures are seen as having a direct effect on their own personal care. Furthermore, concerned as they are about health costs, Americans still desire more insurance coverage for themselves in the future.

REFERENCES

1. Louis Harris and Associates. *Survey of Health Care Consumers.* February 1990.

2. Harvey L. *Survey of Public Opinion on Health Care Issues.* American Medical Association. Chicago, March 1991.

3. The Roper Center. The Public's Critique of Congress. *The Public Perspective.* 1991:2:82-83.

4. Los Angeles Times - Gallup, *Health Care Poll,* August 1, 1991.

5. Harvard Community Health Plan. *An International Comparison of Health Care Systems.* December 1990.

6. The Conference Board, Inc. Consumer Research Center, February 1990.

7. Employee Benefits in Total Compensation. *EBRI Issue Brief.* Number 111, February 1991.

CHAPTER 5

Large Employers and Employee Benefits: Priorities for the 1990s

J. Ian Morrison, Ellen M. Morrison
Institute for the Future
and
Jennifer N. Edwards
Harvard School of Public Health

INTRODUCTION

Today, eight out of ten working Americans obtain their health insurance from their place of employment where their employers pay, on average, 70 percent of the cost on their behalf.[1] While the cost of insurance has recently become quite burdensome, this has not always been the case. Employers began offering health insurance benefits as a fringe benefit for their employees when it was much less expensive than additional wages or other benefits. As shown in Table 5-1, health benefit spending by employers has risen in constant dollars from $656 per full-time employee in 1970 to $1,722 in 1989, a much more rapid increase than in other

Table 5-1

Employer Spending for Employee Compensation 1970-1989

Spending per Full-Time Equivalent Employee in Constant 1989 Dollars

Item	1970	1989	% Change
Wages and salaries	$24,768	$24,884	+ 1
Retirement benefits	1,808	2,390	+ 32
Other fringe benefits	507	729	+ 44
Health benefits	656	1,722	+163

Source: Piacentini JS, Anzick MA. Employee Benefits in Total Compensation. *EBRI Issue Brief.* February 1991; 111:4.

forms of compensation. Health benefits grew by 163 percent in constant dollars while wages and salaries grew just one percent, retirement benefits grew 32 percent, and other fringe benefits grew 44 percent.[1]

Businesses are playing a larger role in insuring the U.S. population than ever before. Businesses' share of total health care spending has increased from

Table 5-2

Business and Health Care
(Billions of 1989 dollars)

	Total Health Expenditures	Business Spending on Health	Share of Total Expenditures
1970	$237.8	$48.3	20.3%
1980	374.9	101.7	27.1
1989	604.1	173.4	28.7
2000	1,018.0	305.4	30.0

Source: IFTF; Historical data from Levit KR, Cowan CA. The Burden of Health Care Costs: Business, Households and Governments. *Health Care Financing Review.* Winter 1990; 12:127-137; and Lazenby HC, Letsch SW. National Health Expenditures, 1989. *Health Care Financing Review.* Winter 1990; 12:1-26.

Table 5-3

Medium and Large Employers Offering Health Insurance Benefits

	1980	1982	1984	1986	1988
Health insurance	97%	97%	97%	95%	92%
Employee coverage:					
wholly employer financed	72	71	62	54	51
partly employer financed	25	26	35	41	41
Family coverage:					
wholly employer financed	51	46	41	35	34
partly employer financed	43	47	56	60	58

Source: U.S. Department of Labor, Bureau of Labor Statistics, *Employee Benefits in Medium and Large Firms, 1980, 1982, 1984, 1986, and 1988.* Government Printing Office. Washington D.C.

20 percent in 1970 to almost 29 percent in 1989, and this share is forecasted to continue increasing over the next decade, as shown in Table 5-2.[2]

The rise in health care costs is becoming a significant burden for employers. Health benefits represented almost 20 percent of corporate profits in 1970. Today they are more than one-half the value of business pre-tax profits (see Figure 5-1).[2] By the year 2000, assuming no major expansions in business coverage of health care and careful controls on existing insurance programs, health care spending will be the equivalent of almost three-fourths of corporate profits.[3]

The most cost-effective response to this sharp escalation would be for employers to discontinue or reduce their share of employee health benefits. In fact, some are doing just that. As shown in Table 5-3, 92 percent of medium and large employers now provide health insurance benefits, down from 97 percent in 1980.[4] An approach less drastic than dropping coverage entirely is to reduce the share of benefits they finance. In 1980, 72 percent of employers were paying the total cost of their employees' health insurance. By 1988, this percentage had dropped to 51 percent. Likewise, wholly employer-financed contributions to family coverage fell from 51 percent of employers paying the entire cost in 1980 to 34 percent in 1988.

The number of firms that continue to offer health benefits indicates that benefits managers do take into account the importance of benefits to current and potential employees and their unions. As shown in Table 5-4, 61 percent of the

Figure 5-1

Health Care Costs and Profits

Business Spending on Health as a Percent of Pre-Tax Profits

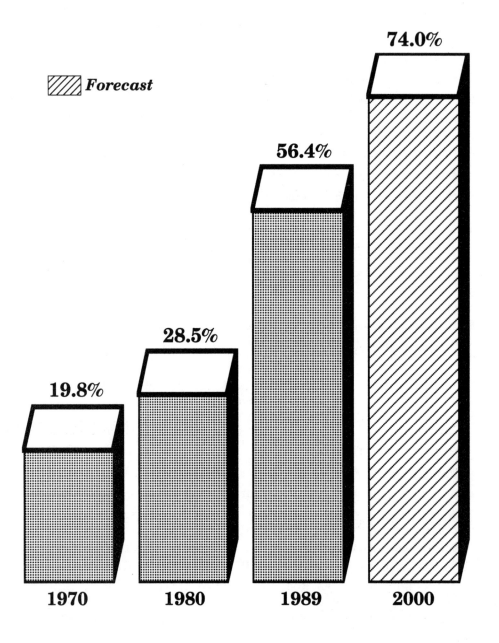

Source: IFTF; historical data from Levit, KR, Cowan, CA. The burden of health care costs: business, households, and governments. *Health Care Financing Review*. Winter 1990;12(2):127-137.

adults surveyed say that health insurance is the most important employer-provided benefit. Six out of ten report they would not accept a job if it did not come with health insurance. Seven out of ten employed adults report that if their employer gave them a choice of receiving a cash payment as an alternative to their health benefits, they would prefer their employer's contribution to their health insurance over a cash payment.[1] In making this trade-off, respondents are making the better economic choice, because health benefits, unlike wages, are not taxed. Further, the cost of buying insurance inside the workplace is likely to be much lower than buying an individual policy, because of the size of the pool over which risk can be spread and the economies of scale achieved in administering a group policy.

It appears then, that as long as employers want a stable, qualified workforce they are compelled to provide health insurance as a paid benefit. What are major employers likely to do in the 1990s, when they are caught between the needs of their employees and rapidly rising costs?

This chapter seeks to answer this question, drawing on results of three surveys conducted by Louis Harris and Associates in conjunction with the Institute for the Future and the Harvard School of Public Health. The 1989 and 1987 Corporate Health Plans surveys interviewed representative samples of 500 benefits managers in companies of 100 or more employees, with the 1989 survey

---

Table 5-4

Percentage of Adults Selecting a Particular Employee Benefit as Most Important to Them, 1990

Benefit	Most Important
Health benefits	61%
Pensions	17
Disability insurance	5
Long term care insurance	4
Life insurance	4
Child care	3
Annual leave	2
Parental leave	1

Source: Piacentini JS, Anzick MA. Employee Benefits in Total Compensation. *EBRI Issue Brief.* February 1991; 111:1-25.

interviewing an additional 200 executives in the same firms.[5,6,7] The third survey, conducted in 1990, interviewed "elite payers" — a unique sample (or more accurately, a census) of the largest payers and insurers in America.* The respondents were 50 executives of the largest corporations in the country, 52 benefits managers from those same corporations, 25 of the largest U.S. health insurers, 25 managers of the largest HMOs, 25 managers of the largest PPOs, 25 senior executives of the largest benefits consulting firms, 20 Health Care Financing Administration officials, and the Medicaid administrator and health insurance commissioner from the 10 most populous states. This population was selected to provide insights into the cutting edge of health care benefits and purchasing decisions, because these institutions are presumed to be ahead of other health care payers with respect to foresight and innovation.

EMPLOYERS' AND PAYERS' VIEWS OF THE HEALTH CARE SYSTEM

As was true for consumers, corporate benefits managers' dissatisfaction with the health care system has increased over the last several years as health care costs have risen. In 1989, only 18 percent of benefits managers expressed the belief that the system works pretty well with only minor changes needed, down from 29 percent in 1987 (see Table 5-5). This is a view shared by corporate executives, though fewer executives are prepared to completely rebuild the system.[5] Elite payers are the most dissatisfied; only 9 percent believe the system works fairly well.[7] At the same time that satisfaction has dropped, health care costs have increased. A Hay\Huggins study found that health insurance premiums have increased by 9 to 20 percent in each of the last five years.[8] Among the corporations we sampled in 1987 and 1989, health care costs increased from $1,358 to $1,944 per active employee — a 40 percent increase in two years (see Figure 5-2) This increase has contributed to the perception among many employers and elite payers that their health care costs are at least somewhat out of control (see Table 5-6).[5,6,7] The proportion of employers who think their costs are under control has decreased from 65 percent in 1987 to about half in 1989. Only one-third of their benefits managers, though, think health care inflation is under control.[5,6]

Nor do employers think a solution is just around the corner. There is a strong sense among employers that they will not soon get costs back under control. Ninety-four percent of employers anticipate that, despite their best efforts, their health care costs will rise dramatically over the next five years. Seventy-six percent expect their employees will be paying much more out-of-pocket as well.[5]

Elite payers, like the federal and state legislators surveyed in previous years, see escalation in health care costs as inevitable (see Figure 5-3).[7] Although

---

*Employer samples were stratified by three levels of size: 100-249; 250-999; and 1,000 and over. Responses were weighted to correspond to the proportion of total United States companies of these sizes. The margin of error is approximately +4 percent.

Table 5-5

Overall View of Health Care System

Q.: Which of the following statements comes closest to express-ing your overall view of the American health care system?

	Corporate Managers		Corporate Benefits Officers		
	1990	1989	1990	1989	1987
Base	50	200	52	500	500
On the whole, the health care system works pretty well, and only minor changes are necessary to make it work better	10%	21%	13%	18%	29%
There are some good things in our health care system, but fundamental changes are needed to make it work better	72	69	77	66	62
The American health care system has so much wrong with it that we need to completely rebuild it	18	10	10	15	9
Not sure	—	—	—	2	1

Source: Louis Harris and Associates, Elite Payers Survey, 1990; and Louis Harris and Associates, Survey of Employers, 1987 and 1989.

these data should not be interpreted as literal forecasts, the graphic representation shows the respondents' sense of futility in attempting to exercise control over health care spending.

EMPLOYERS' PRIORITIES FOR THEIR HEALTH PLANS

With all the attention recently given to employer health care costs, we were surprised to find employers continue to report that making sure their employees can get the health services they need is their highest priority. Forty-seven percent of benefits managers say this is their highest priority, compared to 37 percent who cite keeping the cost of care down and 15 percent who want to improve the quality of health services as their first priority (see Table 5-7).[5]

Large employers have expanded their coverage over the last few years, so that there is now almost universal coverage of hospitalization, inpatient and outpatient surgeries, physician visits, diagnostic x-ray and laboratory care, prescription drugs, mental health benefits, and in-home nursing visits.[4] As shown in Table 5-8, larger companies are more likely to offer the more specialized

Figure 5-2

Composite Health Cost per Active Employee

(In current dollars)

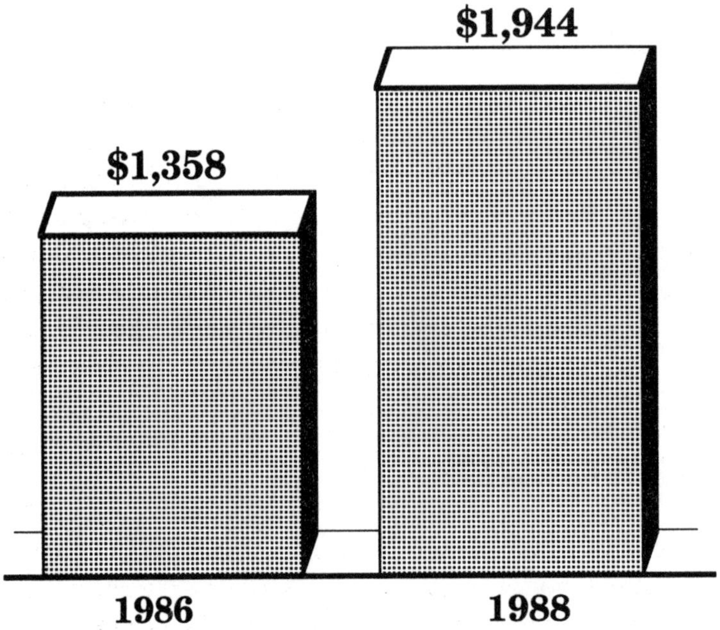

Source: Louis Harris and Associates, Employer Surveys, 1987 and 1989.

Table 5-6

Employers' Views of Their Control Over Costs

	Employers		Elite Payers, 1990	
	1987	1989	Top Manage- ment	Corporate Benefits Officers
Completely out of control	7%	10%	4%	6%
Somewhat out of control	27	41	56	31
Somewhat under control	58	45	36	63
Completely under control	7	4	4	—

Source: Louis Harris and Associates, Employer Surveys, 1987 and 1989; Louis Harris and Associates, Elite Payers Survey, 1990.

services than are smaller companies. At many companies, long term care may be the next benefit added to the list. Fully 40 percent of benefits officers say their company may offer long term care as a flexible or optional benefit over the next five years. Five percent of employers currently do offer long term care insurance, and only 14 percent say it is not at all likely that their company will offer this benefit within the next five years.[5]

Employers also intend to offer their employees more choices of health care plans. Sixteen percent of the companies not currently offering HMO plans will make one available to their employees within the next two years, and one in five that currently do not offer a PPO will make one available. About one-fifth of employers already offering HMOs and PPOs will add more plans to the options their employees already have. Employees have the most influence over their benefits when allowed to make choices not only between health plans, but also in trading credits between different types of fringe benefits. Thirty-two percent of benefits managers expect to offer a cafeteria plan or a flexible benefit plan within the next two years.[5]

CONTROLLING COSTS

We were interested in understanding why health care costs, the favorite topic of health care analysts, did not top the list of employers' problems. Table 5-9 shows that, while 56 percent of employers say health benefit costs are very important, the quality of their products and of their workforces are even more important than either wages or benefits.[5] Furthermore, 45 percent of corporate executives believe that, "human resources and employee benefits are just more costs that have to be managed effectively." About one-quarter of these executives agree with each of the two alternative viewpoints: (1) keeping total labor costs down is crucial to the company's profitability, so they must control benefit costs; and (2) human resources are so critical to the company that they would never consider a major reduction in benefits.[5] Clearly, more than cost goes into businesses' decisions to maintain their level of employee benefits. It is not surprising, then, that employee benefits managers have not been under a great deal of pressure to contain costs during the late 1980s (see Table 5-10).

Figure 5-3

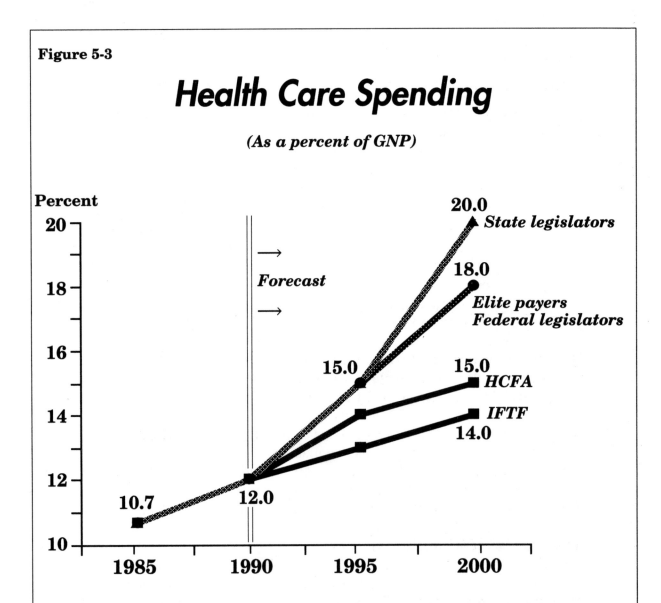

Health Care Spending

(As a percent of GNP)

Source: Louis Harris and Associates, State Legislator Survey, 1989; Federal Legislator Survey, 1989; Elite Payers Survey, 1990; HCFA estimate from Division of National Cost Estimates, Office of the Actuary, Health Care Financing Administration, National Health Expenditures, 1986-2000. *Health Care Financing Review.* Summer 1987;8(4):1-36.

Although most senior executives were only beginning to recognize the health care cost issue as a strategic priority in 1989, elite payers already believe costs are totally out of control. Since elite payers are the largest, most sophisticated employers, this concern about costs is likely to trickle down to medium-sized firms with 100 to 1,000 employees over the next several years. Indeed, employee benefits managers in these firms do anticipate that cost-containment pressures will significantly increase. As many as 76 percent of these managers anticipate that their efforts to contain costs will intensify over the next three years, up from only 45 percent in 1987.[5,6]

The following section will examine the reasons why employers believe health care costs are rising, what employers plan to do about rising costs, and what they believe will work.

WHY ARE COSTS RISING?

Employers are able to identify particular elements of the health care system they believe are responsible for rising health care costs. As shown in Figure 5-4, inpatient hospital prices tops the list, with 77 percent of employers responding that it is a major cause of rising costs, and an additional 20 percent saying it is a minor cause. Employers are likely to blame both *prices* and *utilization* for increasing costs.[5]

Table 5-7

Employers' Health Care Plan Priorities

Q.: Which one of the following is the single most important priority for the health plan provided by your company?

	1987	1989
Base	500	500
Keeping the cost of care down	38%	37%
Making sure employees can get health care services they need	45	47
Improving the quality of health care services	17	15

Source: Taylor H, Leitman R. *Corporate Health Plans: Past, Present, and Future.* Louis Harris and Associates; April 1989.

113

Table 5-8

Provision of Special Services

Q.: Does the plan that covers most of your employees cover or offer optional coverage for:

	Total	Company Size		
		100-249	250-999	1,000+
Base	500	140	160	200
Mental health	91%	85%	91%	95%
Substance abuse	88	81	88	93
Preventive medicine programs	42	39	44	41
Prescription drugs	89	87	91	94

Source: Taylor H, Leitman R. *Corporate Health Plans: Past, Present, and Future.*
Louis Harris and Associates: April 1989.

WHAT WILL EMPLOYERS DO TO CONTROL COSTS?

Logically, then, we would expect that employers would want to target both price and utilization in their cost containment strategy. In fact, these are two of four approaches used by large businesses** to contain costs. The first is to reduce the company's overall contribution to the employees' health insurance, either by paying less of the premium for the employee, and therefore increasing co-payments and deductibles, or by limiting the coverage of certain high-cost services. As portrayed in Table 5-11, 57 percent of companies have introduced co-payments and deductibles and 48 percent are considering adding or expanding these in the near future. One-third (34%) of respondents limit transplants or some high-technology treatments in their benefits coverage with an additional 6 percent expecting to use such a limitation in the future. In addition, in Table 5-3, we previously showed that over the last decade, approximately one in three large employers who had fully paid their employees' insurance premium had changed their corporate policy to one of only partial financing.

**Most of these strategies can only be implemented by large employers or insurance companies on behalf of smaller employers because they require some leverage with hospitals and doctors, or they require a large enough group of beneficiaries to be able to spread the risk.

The second strategy for containing a business' share of health care costs is to lower the administrative costs of the company's insurance plan. One approach is to self-insure, which allows businesses to avoid state insurance taxes (present in most jurisdictions), and provides the option to buy, on a competitive basis, various elements of third party billing and reimbursement processing, and to investigate duplicative insurance coverage, etc. A second approach is to shop around for an insurer with lower overhead costs or one who will share the risk of health care cost through a contractual arrangement. We found 54 percent of our large companies already self-insure, and another 25 percent expect to do so in the near future. The current turbulence of the insurance market is reflected in our finding that more than half (54%) of the companies surveyed envision changing carriers in the coming years.

The third strategy we nicknamed "litely" managed care. The intent of these efforts is for employees to get their medical care in the most cost-effective way, while minimizing interference with most of the decisions made by physicians. These cost-saving approaches include utilization review of expensive outpatient claims; offering a less costly HMO or PPO or a point-of-service (POS) HMO; negotiating discounts with local hospitals and doctors; and encouraging the use of generic drugs. Our survey found "litely" managed care was the strategy used most frequently by employers. As shown in Table 5-11, utilization review is the most common cost control activity in this category (60%) and direct negotiations with providers is the least common (27%).

Table 5-9

Top Managers' Views of Employee Benefits

Q.: How important a problem is each for your company?

	Very Important	Somewhat Important	Not Very Important	Not at All Important	Not Sure
Quality of products	82%	5%	2%	7%	3%
Quality of labor	73	22	2	3	—
Wage and salary costs	70	27	2	1	—
Employee benefits costs	56	37	5	1	—
Foreign and domestic competition	40	16	18	22	3

Source: Taylor H, Leitman R. *Corporate Health Plans: Past, Present, and Future.* Louis Harris and Associates: April 1989.

Table 5-10

Pressure Felt From Top Management To Contain Costs

	1987	1989
A great deal of pressure	19%	26%
Some pressure	38	46
Not much pressure	26	17
No pressure at all	17	10
Not sure	1	1

Source: Louis Harris and Associates, Employer Surveys, 1987 and 1989.

Strategy four is the most intrusive of the cost containment approaches available. Employers adopt policies that substantially alter the health care available to employees and their families by limiting their choices to lower-cost providers and facilities. This strategy includes the use of gatekeeper primary care physicians, whom employees must see to be referred to a specialist. Our survey found 17 percent of companies use this policy, and another 10 percent anticipate its adoption in the future.

A more stringent policy still is to limit employees' choice of physicians or hospitals based on price. Currently, 18 percent use this approach, and another 14 percent of companies plan to do so in the years ahead.

Similarly, firms can require all their employees to enroll in a less costly, tightly managed care plan. We find 14 percent of companies now do so, and almost one in four is considering this as a way to contain their costs in the future. More than one-fourth of the firms have negotiated price-limited contracts with providers of mental health and substance abuse programs that are separate from the rest of their benefits. Employees may get this type of care only through the company's designated programs. Twenty-one percent will use this approach in the future.

A final type of policy is to limit prescription drug reimbursement. This may restrict the employee's choice to generic drugs or, in some cases, to lower-cost therapeutic substitutes — drugs with similar chemical composition available at a lower price. Few companies (9%) have decided to influence physician prescribing decisions or envision doing so in the future (8%). A review of Table 5-11 clearly shows that employers are less comfortable pursuing more restrictive managed

Figure 5-4

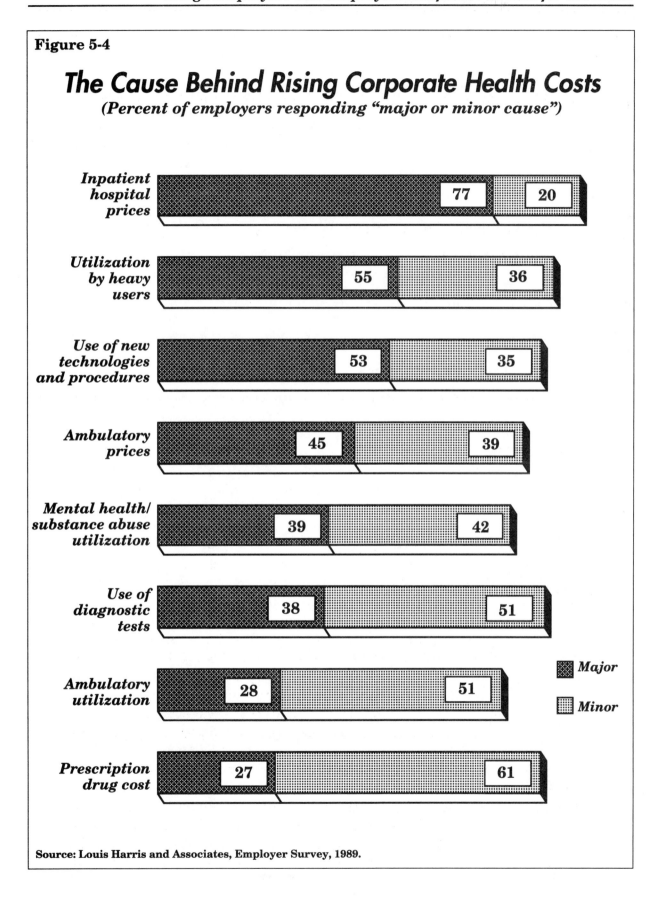

The Cause Behind Rising Corporate Health Costs
(Percent of employers responding "major or minor cause")

	Major	Minor
Inpatient hospital prices	77	20
Utilization by heavy users	55	36
Use of new technologies and procedures	53	35
Ambulatory prices	45	39
Mental health/substance abuse utilization	39	42
Use of diagnostic tests	38	51
Ambulatory utilization	28	51
Prescription drug cost	27	61

Source: Louis Harris and Associates, Employer Survey, 1989.

Table 5-11

Future Corporate Health Care Plans for Controlling Costs

	Policy in Place	Will Do or Expand in the Future
Strategy I—Reduce Company's Contribution		
◆ Increase co-payments and deductibles	57%	48%
◆ Limit transplant coverage and certain other expensive medical technologies	34	6
Strategy II—Lower Administrative Costs		
◆ Self-insure	54	25
◆ Change insurance companies	—	54
Strategy III—"Litely" Managed Care		
◆ Implement utilization review programs (OPD services)	60	32
◆ Offer HMO option	54	16
◆ Offer PPO option	30	21
◆ Encourage use of generic drugs	52	28
◆ Directly negotiate discounts with hospitals and doctors	27	31
Strategy IV—More Restrictive Managed Care		
◆ Use gatekeeper primary care physicians	17	10
◆ Limit choice of HMOs and hospitals based on price	18	14
◆ Require enrollment in managed care plans	14	22
◆ Directly contract for mental health or substance abuse services	29	21
◆ Limit choice of prescription drugs	9	8

Source: Taylor H, Leitman R. *Corporate Health Plans: Past, Present, and Future.* Louis Harris and Associates: April 1989.

care cost containment policies than "litely" managed care options. Furthermore, as shown in Table 5-12, most large employers are not going so far as to actively require their employees to join HMOs.

In our view, the managed care approaches preferred by employers are just "holding tanks" on the way to more structured management of physician decision making, in order to contain costs. Figure 5-5 illustrates the way managed care is evolving. During the 1980s, companies moved from unfettered fee-for-service care to "litely" managed care. While a small percentage of the population has been in capitated HMOs since the 1970s, we expect many more to move in that direction during the 1990s. This is reflected in Table 5-13, which shows benefits managers' views on the evolution of corporate health benefits plans.

WHAT ABOUT CORPORATE CONCERN FOR QUALITY?

Ironically, the high price of health care services is also seen as an indicator of high quality (see Figure 5-6). When employers and major payers were asked

---

Table 5-12

Whether or Not Organizations Actively Encourage Employees To Join HMOs

Q.: Would you say that your organization actively encourages employees to join HMOs, or does it simply offer the HMO option without active encouragement?

	Corporate Managers	Corporate Benefits Managers
Base	50	52
Actively encourages	20%	21%
Simply offers without active encouragement	78	77
Not sure	2	2
No HMO (as option)	—	—

Source: Louis Harris and Associates, Elite Payers Survey, 1990.

Figure 5-5

The Evolution of Managed Care

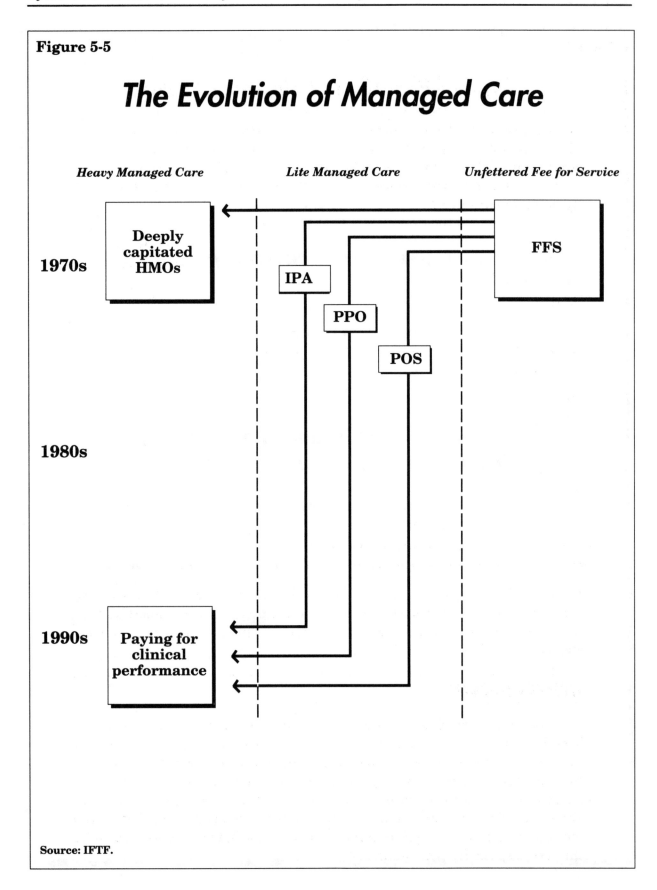

Source: IFTF.

Table 5-13

Type of Plan Likely To Increase Fastest

Q.: In the next three years, which one type of health plan is likely to see the greatest increase in enrollment among your employees? Will it be traditional fee-for-service indemnity plans, managed fee-for-service, HMOs, PPOs, or some other type of insurance?

	Corporate Benefits Officers
Base	52
Traditional fee-for-service indemnity plan	15%
Managed fee-for-service	38
HMOs	21
PPOs	15
Other	10
None of them	—
Not sure	—

Source: Louis Harris and Associates, Elite Payers Survey, 1990.

to identify how they assess quality, the importance of high price, the reputation of the providers, and feedback from employees were much more important than the seemingly more objective sources of information that often are given more weight in the health policy literature.[5]

CONCLUSION

Large U.S. employers are awakening to recognize health care costs and benefits as a strategic issue. Their concern for costs will begin to replace their concern for their employees. In the short run, employers are going to increase cost sharing with their employees and do their best to get discounts from appropriately qualified providers. In the long run, these interventions will simply further erode employees' satisfaction with the health care system and increase doctors' and hospitals' frustrations over the hassles of getting paid for the care they render their patients.

Figure 5-6

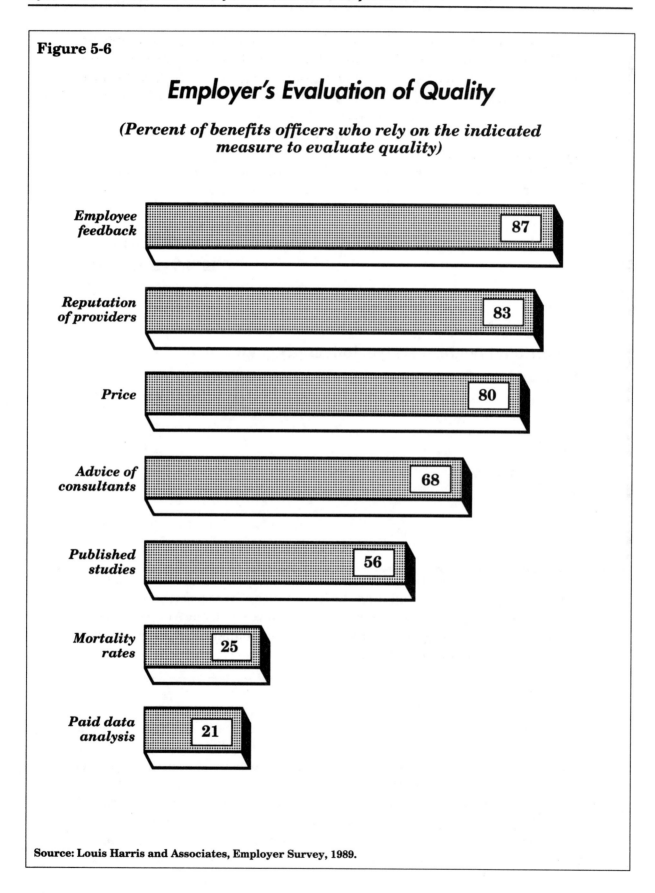

Employer's Evaluation of Quality

(Percent of benefits officers who rely on the indicated measure to evaluate quality)

Employee feedback	87
Reputation of providers	83
Price	80
Advice of consultants	68
Published studies	56
Mortality rates	25
Paid data analysis	21

Source: Louis Harris and Associates, Employer Survey, 1989.

Employer cost containment activities will evolve along the continuum we laid out, but we do not expect widespread use of single benefit plans and other more tightly managed programs. Employers are reluctant to interfere too much with their employees' care, and shortages in the labor force will make employers concerned about keeping the workplace attractive.

REFERENCES

1. Piacentini JS, Anzick MA. Employee Benefits in Total Compensation. *EBRI Issue Brief.* February 1991;111:1-25.

2. Levit KR, Cowan CA. The burden of health care costs: business, households, and governments. *Health Care Financing Review.* Winter 1990;12:127-137.

3. Institute for the Future projections, 1991.

4. U.S. Department of Labor, Bureau of Labor Statistics, *Employer Benefits in Medium and Large Firms, 1980, 1982, 1984, 1986, and 1988.* Government Printing Office. Washington, D.C.

5. Taylor H, Leitman R. *Corporate Health Plans: Past, Present, and Future.* Louis Harris and Associates: April 1989.

6. Taylor H, Leitman R. *Corporate Health Plans Survey.* Louis Harris and Associates, 1987.

7. Taylor H, Leitman R. *Elite Payers Survey.* Louis Harris and Associates: May 1990.

8. *Hay/Huggins Benefits Report.* Hay Management Consultants. Philadelphia; December 1990.

CHAPTER 6

Hospital Chief Executive Officers' Views of the Future

Ellen M. Morrison and J. Ian Morrison
Institute for the Future

INTRODUCTION

Hospital chief executive officers (CEOs) have a unique view of the U.S. health care system. Because their institutions are the focal point of most acute care delivery, hospital leaders are involved in close, interdependent relationships with all other key participants in health care — from public and private payers to providers of care, products, and services. Directors of hospitals also play significant community roles shaped by both historical and economic factors. For example, many community hospitals are part of the social, religious, or ethnic heritage of their communities, and are perceived to "belong" to the community as do public schools, churches, and parks. Philanthropy, volunteer support, and tax or bond financial support often link the hospital to the community by an economic obligation while, in return, hospitals serve as one of the largest employers in a community.

In addition, hospitals remain the backbone of our medical care delivery system. They account for more than 40 percent of expenditures for personal health care.[1] How they choose to respond to the growing, and often conflicting, consumer, cost containment, competitive, and regulatory pressures discussed earlier will shape our future health care system. Will they seek to join larger systems of care to achieve economies of scale and a broader service area? Will they increasingly contract with HMOs, PPOs, and managed care organizations? Are they likely to be more concerned with containing their internal costs or expanding their range of activities and services to improve their institutional revenues? The answers to these questions will give us a clearer picture of hospital care in the mid-1990s.

Our window on the issues comes from a random sample survey of 350 chief executive officers, conducted by Louis Harris and Associates in conjunction with the Institute for the Future.[2] The sample was stratified by hospital size and ownership type to represent the universe of beds in non-psychiatric hospitals in the United States. The margin of error is ±4 percent.

INDUSTRY CONSOLIDATION

As described in Chapter 1, we have not seen a significant downsizing of the hospital industry. What we have seen, instead, is a large number of mergers and formal affiliations between hospitals, though very different from the "Supermed" envisioned just five years ago.[3] Instead of national systems in ownership relationships with their members, the hospital systems that have emerged are more likely to be smaller, regional, and less formal in membership affiliation.

In the survey, we asked hospital CEOs about the likelihood that their institutions would merge with another or would become a member of a chain or alliance. According to their projections, "merger mania" has had its day, and either formal or informal consolidation into systems may also be slowing its pace. Joining a chain or alliance within the near future was perceived as somewhat more likely than merging with another institution. Most hospital directors, however, do not anticipate a great deal of consolidation in any form. The data indicate the organizations interested in consolidating have, for the most part, already done so. The survey finds fewer than 5 percent of managers of independent hospitals think it very likely they will affiliate with a chain, although more than one quarter think it very or somewhat likely. The managers of highly profitable independent hospitals are those most likely to believe their hospital will join an alliance or chain in the near future. Likewise, less than 5 percent of CEOs of all hospitals anticipate a merger. A poor financial picture makes a hospital most likely to merge, while hospitals that break even are *least* likely to merge. Church-affiliated hospitals are those most likely (over 80%) *already* to be a member of a chain or an alliance, and managers of those church-owned hospitals that remain independent say their hospitals are the most likely *both* to merge and to affiliate with a larger organization in the next few years (see Figure 6-1).

One factor that could encourage more mergers in the future would be an easing of federal anti-trust procedures. A 1991 survey of hospital CEOs found 92 percent favoring relaxed anti-trust laws, allowing hospitals in the same community to combine services more easily.[4] Survey results suggest, for those attempting major mergers, the possibility of a prolonged court challenge is deterring their willingness to undertake these activities.

Figure 6-1

Likelihood of Joining an Alliance by 1991 by Hospital Ownership Type

(Percent of independent respondents who report membership in an alliance or chain by 1991 as "not very likely" or "not likely at all")

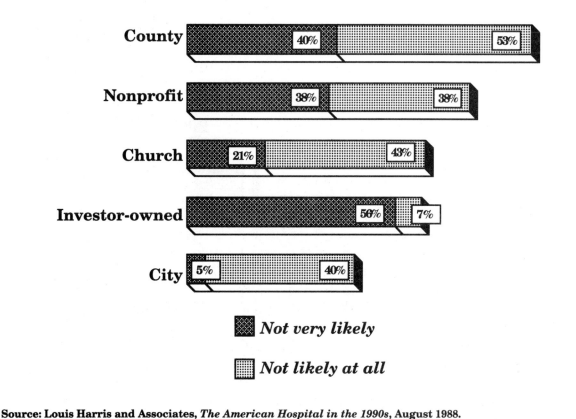

Source: Louis Harris and Associates, *The American Hospital in the 1990s,* **August 1988.**

MORE OUTPATIENT CARE AND DIVERSIFICATION?

The survey found that hospital CEOs will be more interested in outpatient services and diversification in the future. However, they are keenly aware that they have not yet achieved this goal. When asked to describe the sources of

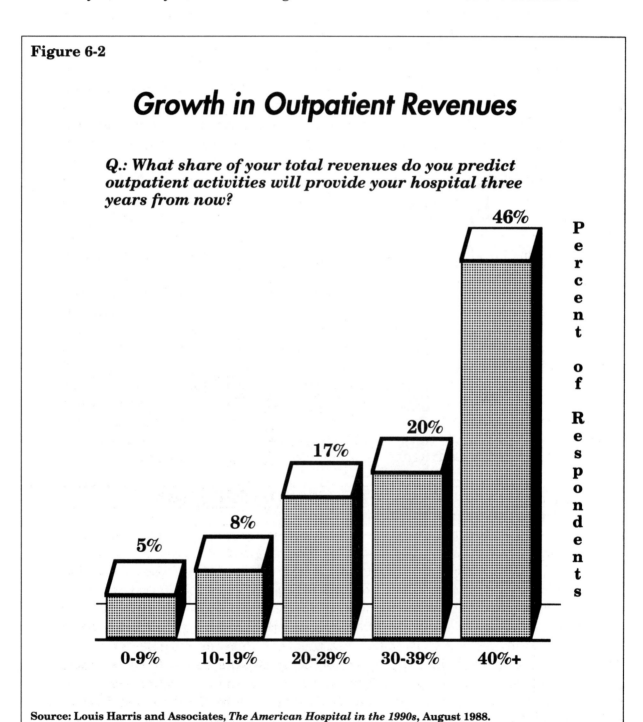

Figure 6-2

Growth in Outpatient Revenues

Q.: What share of your total revenues do you predict outpatient activities will provide your hospital three years from now?

Source: Louis Harris and Associates, *The American Hospital in the 1990s*, August 1988.

revenue they currently receive, CEOs indicate that 68 percent of revenues, on average, come from inpatient sources.[2] Because of their continuing reliance on inpatient resources in a more competitive environment, hospitals have developed a strong marketing focus for these services. CEOs report they emphasize the quality of their medical staff and the presence of specialized medical services at the hospital in order to attract new patients. Lowering costs is seen by only 5 percent of hospital CEOs as an important tool for increasing their hospital's occupancy.[2]

On the other hand, there has been a clear movement to the outpatient setting as hospitals continue to take advantage of new technologies, patient preferences, and reimbursement policies. Hospital CEOs from institutions of all sizes anticipate continued growth in their outpatient activity, with almost half of the respondents anticipating more than 40 percent of their revenues from outpatient services in 1991 (see Figure 6-2). Continuing the trend described in Chapter 1, hospital outpatient departments and clinics will grow the fastest. Given a range of outpatient care delivery models to choose from, 40 percent of surveyed hospital leaders projected hospital-based outpatient clinics would show the greatest growth between 1988 and 1991 (see Figure 6-3). The impact of this trend is reflected in a 1991 survey that shows 55 percent of hospital directors spending more than one-fifth of their time on issues pertaining to outpatient care.[5]

Alternative and non-traditional health care services are also on the rise. Over half (56 percent to 67 percent) of our respondents had added outpatient surgery, outpatient diagnostic facilities and wellness or health promotion programs within the past three years; more (4 percent to 7 percent) planned to add these services. A significant percentage (15 percent to 42 percent) of hospitals had added or planned to add women's medicine, outpatient psychiatric, and geriatric programs or housing (see Figure 6-4). Survey results suggest hospitals' investment in new types of services will grow even more quickly in the future. Forty-one percent of respondents projected that they would invest in new types of patient services over the next three years (see Figure 6-5).

FINANCIAL SECURITY AND COMPETITION

Even though the new age of competition has not swept small, less-well occupied hospitals from the landscape, size is a great advantage to a hospital's profitability. Among surveyed hospitals, having more than 100 beds and 10,000 inpatient days annually is associated with profitability; the largest group of profitable hospitals is among those with more than 100,000 inpatient days per year. When asked about their financial performance during the most recently completed fiscal year, city, county, and small hospitals were most likely to report large losses, while investor-owned and nonprofits were most likely to report large gains.[2] As for hospital ownership trends, most administrators were confident that nonprofit ownership would continue to be the dominant form of hospital organization, and their toughest competitors over the next three years.

Figure 6-3

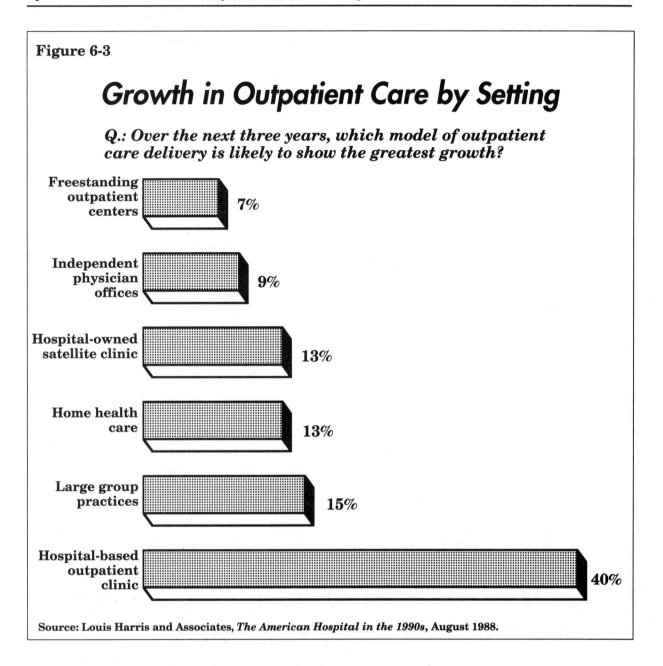

Growth in Outpatient Care by Setting

Q.: Over the next three years, which model of outpatient care delivery is likely to show the greatest growth?

Freestanding outpatient centers — **7%**

Independent physician offices — **9%**

Hospital-owned satellite clinic — **13%**

Home health care — **13%**

Large group practices — **15%**

Hospital-based outpatient clinic — **40%**

Source: Louis Harris and Associates, *The American Hospital in the 1990s*, August 1988.

MANAGED CARE AND HOSPITALS: WHERE ARE THEY HEADED?

The 1980s witnessed continued steady growth in managed care organizations and enrollments (see Figure 6-6). The greatest growth has been in the independent practice association (IPA) model HMO, which closely resembles a preferred provider organization (PPO). In an IPA, physicians continue to practice independently in their own offices, but offer a discounted price to an insurer. The insurer then presents a network of physicians to enrollees from which they can select a doctor. More than two-thirds of the hospital directors

Figure 6-4

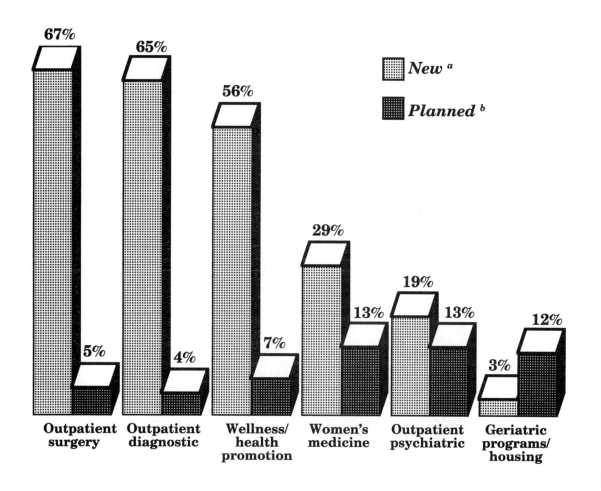

Diversification:
Top New and Planned Services

New [a]

Planned [b]

67% 65% 56% 29% 19% 12%

5% 4% 7% 13% 13% 3%

| Outpatient surgery | Outpatient diagnostic | Wellness/ health promotion | Women's medicine | Outpatient psychiatric | Geriatric programs/ housing |

a. New: Service developed within last three years
b. Planned: Service planned to be offered in the next three years

Note: Of twenty services surveyed, these services are the top three new and top three planned, respectively.

Source: Louis Harris and Associates, *The American Hospital in the 1990s,* **August 1988.**

surveyed believe that this model will continue to lead the growth in managed care plans over the next few years.[2]

Hospitals have often been caught between a rock and a hard place in the managed care world — either losing potential market share by refusing to contract or contracting for discounted charges for the hospital's existing patient population. As a result, hospital directors are skeptical about the advantages of managed care for their institutions. Only 20 percent of respondents believe managed care contracts improve a hospital's overall financial position, while 43 percent believe that such contracts decrease net revenues (see Figure 6-7).

Figure 6-5

Investment in New Types of Patient Services

Q.: *How much will you be investing in new types of patient services relative to traditional services over the next three years?*

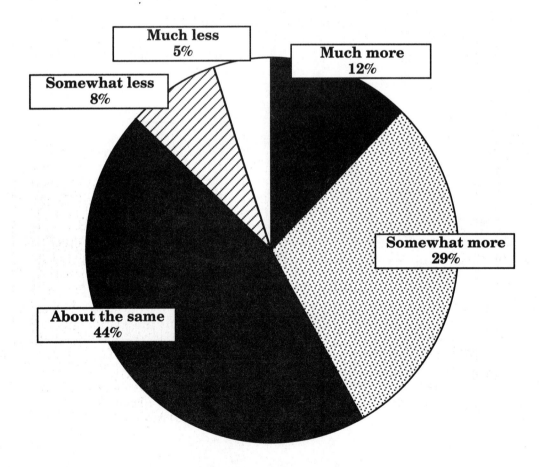

Much less 5%

Somewhat less 8%

Much more 12%

Somewhat more 29%

About the same 44%

Source: Louis Harris and Associates, *The American Hospital in the 1990s*, August 1988.

Figure 6-6

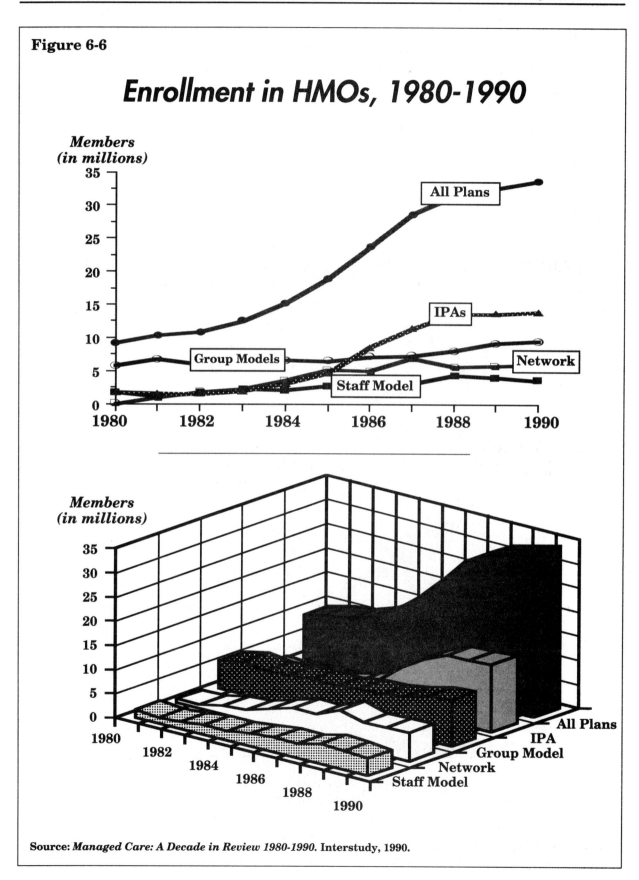

Enrollment in HMOs, 1980-1990

Source: *Managed Care: A Decade in Review 1980-1990.* Interstudy, 1990.

Figure 6-7

Profitability of Managed Care Contracts

Q.: Do you believe managed care contracts in general increase profits, decrease profits, or have little impact on profits?

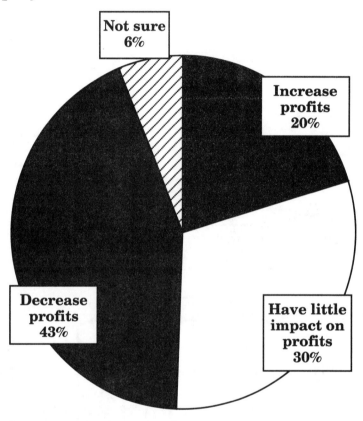

Not sure
6%

Increase
profits
20%

Decrease
profits
43%

Have little
impact on
profits
30%

Source: Louis Harris and Associates, *The American Hospital in the 1990s*, August 1988.

Reluctantly, hospital executives recognize that insurers and employers are basing their most important cost containment hopes on expanding this approach.

STILL A FRAGMENTED MARKET

The penetration of managed care activities varies dramatically. Many hospitals still have little experience while others are offered new contracts every week. Forty-five percent of CEOs report one percent or less of their total revenue comes from managed care, while almost a quarter of respondents report that 10 percent or more of their revenue comes from managed care (see Figure 6-8).

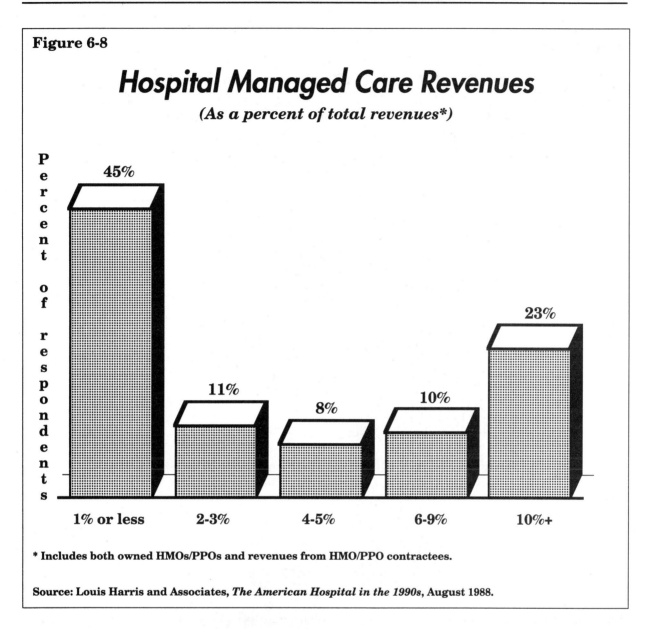

Figure 6-8

Hospital Managed Care Revenues

(As a percent of total revenues)*

* Includes both owned HMOs/PPOs and revenues from HMO/PPO contractees.

Source: Louis Harris and Associates, *The American Hospital in the 1990s*, August 1988.

Even though hospital directors are not convinced that managed care will help their financial health, they do foresee continued growth and sophistication in managed care methods. While only 15 percent currently contract directly with companies or employers for the hospitalization of employees, more than half of our respondents believe they would do so within the next few years (see Figure 6-9).

Hospital directors also foresee modest growth in the percentage of physicians who are directly employed by their hospital (see Figure 6-10). The use of salaried physicians, especially younger physicians, is on the rise. New graduates are far more likely to be salaried than physicians with several years of experience (see Figure 6-11).

Hospital CEOs also forecast a steady increase in DRG-based payments and the further decline of the use of full charges as the method of payment for hospital

Figure 6-9

Employer-Hospital Direct Contracting

Q.: Do you currently contract directly with companies/employers for hospitalization?

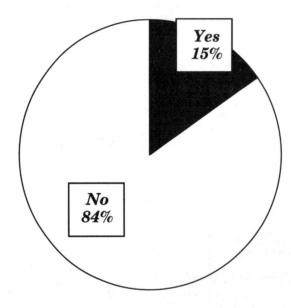

Q.: How likely is it that you will contract directly with companies/employers in the next three years?

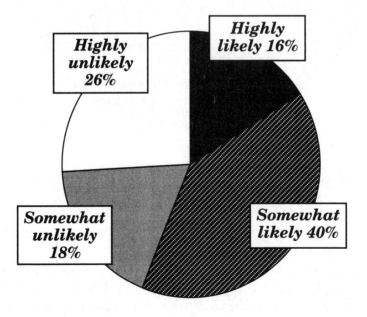

Source: Louis Harris and Associates, *The American Hospital in the 1990s,* **August 1988.**

Figure 6-10

Change in Use of Salaried Physicians

Q.: Over the next three years, do you expect the number of physicians you employ to increase substantially, increase somewhat, remain the same, or decrease?

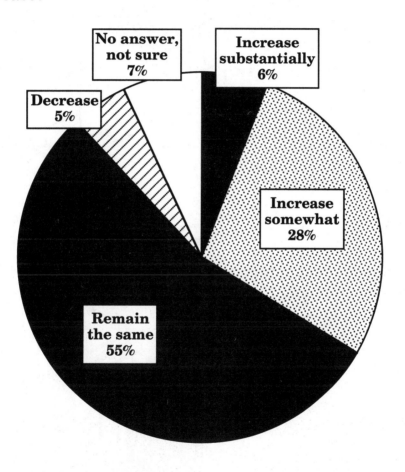

Source: Louis Harris and Associates, *The American Hospital in the 1990s*, August 1988.

care.[2] Table 6-1 displays hospital respondents' current and projected share of payments by payment method.

A surprising finding about managed care relationships is that, contrary to their original intent, they do not emphasize the quality of health care delivery. Our respondents do not perceive that private payers apply much pressure on hospitals for quality assurance. According to 56 percent of respondents, federal, state, and local governments are more likely to put pressure on hospitals for

Figure 6-11

Physicians as Employees

(Percent of physicians working as employees, 1983-1989, by years of experience)

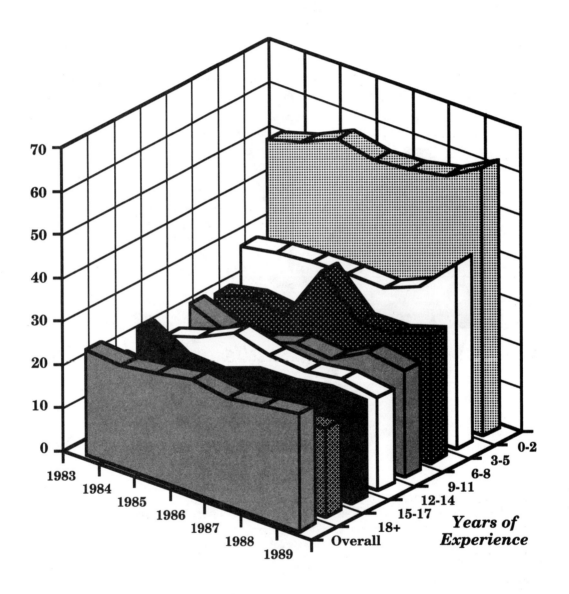

Source: 1983-1989 data: Gonzales ML and Emmons DW, (eds.) *Socioeconomic Characteristics of Medical Practice*: 1989. AMA. 1989:24. 1990 data: Gonzales ML (ed.) *Physician Marketplace Statistics: Fall 1990*. AMA. 1990:102. IFTF calculations.

quality assurance (see Figure 6-12). This finding supports anecdotal evidence from hospital executives that private payer, managed care contracts are largely seen as discount contracts, with little to no quality assurance required by the agreement.

CONTROLLING COSTS

The success of managed care, either in one individual plan or in the aggregate, requires reducing the rate of growth in health care costs. Managed care pins its hopes on a widely held belief that there is a large amount of over-utilization, unnecessary care and waste in the health care delivery system that can be reduced by appropriate management. Hospital costs, because they are the single largest item on any bill, have long been a target for cost management. As discussed in other chapters, payers and consumers believe controlling hospital outlays is the way to control costs for the system as a whole. A recently released report on hospital costs in Massachusetts closely links increases in services and procedures in Massachusetts hospitals with sharply rising health care costs between 1988 and 1989.[7]

The hospital executives we surveyed do not agree that hospitals can control these escalations. Only 26 percent of our respondents perceive that increased utilization is the single greatest contributor to hospital costs, while 46 percent

Table 6-1

Share of Paid Patient Days Accounted for by Various Payment Methods, 1988 and 1991

	1988	1991*
DRG	46.2%	50.6%
Full charges	23.8	20.5
Discounted charges	16.5	17.3
Per diem	12.1	8.8
Per capita	2.0	2.7
Other	0.3	0.2

* Projection

Source: Louis Harris and Associates, *The American Hospital in the 1990s*, August 1988.

Figure 6-12

Who Is the Greatest Source of Pressure for Quality Assurance?

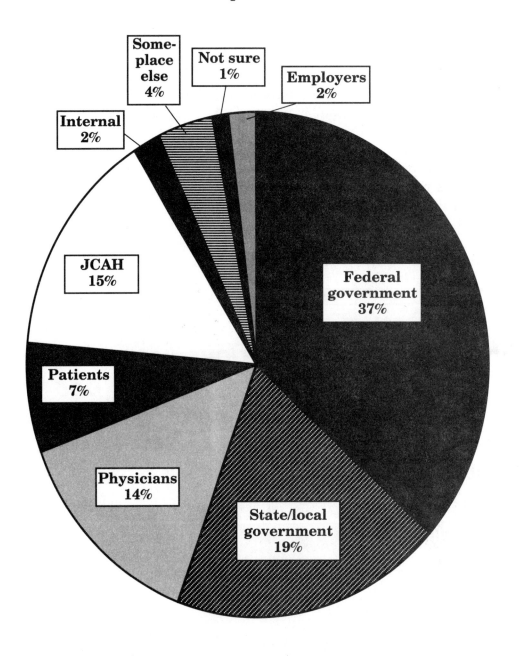

Source: Louis Harris and Associates, *The American Hospital in the 1990s***, August 1988.**

perceive that general inflation of medical costs is the primary culprit (see Figure 6-13). The discrepancy between the beliefs of third party payers and hospitals is significant. Hospitals' responses to cost control pressures will be to monitor and reduce utilization, even though their directors do not believe that greater utilization is what is driving up their costs. Cost controls, in this light, take on the quality of customer service (the customers being government and managed care companies) rather than operations improvement.

The most dramatic effect of cost containment pressures on hospitals has been in their reduction of hospital length of stay. Seventy-seven percent of our respondents report they have changed their policies, either somewhat or a great deal, regarding length of stay as a result of pressures to contain costs (see Figure

Figure 6-13

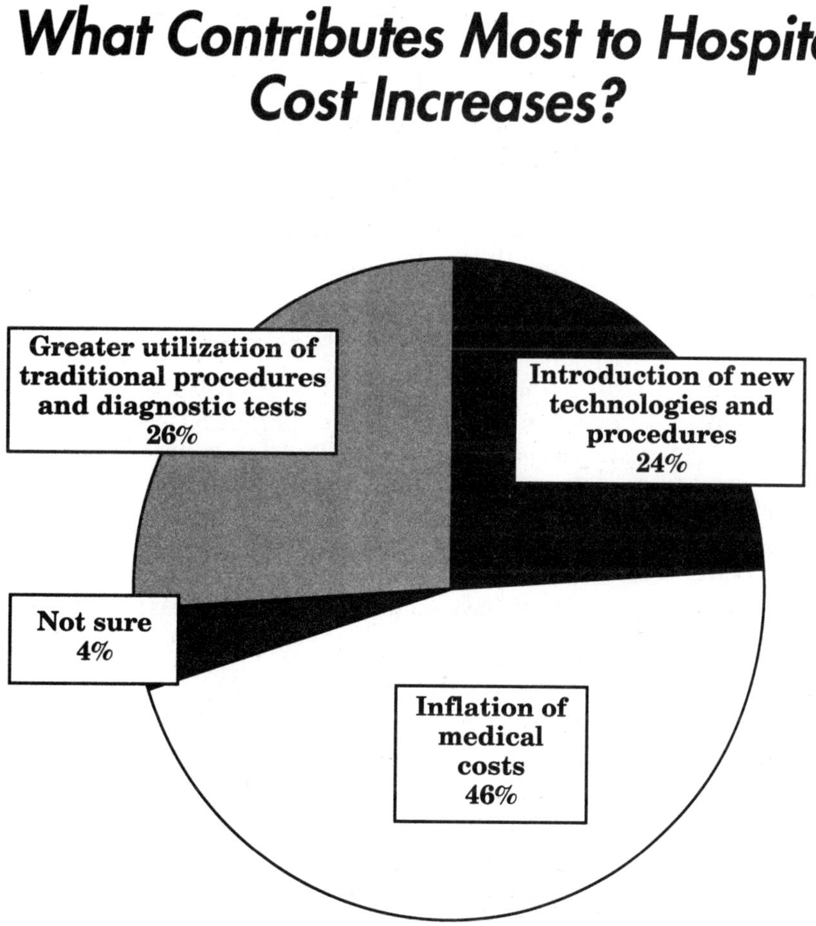

What Contributes Most to Hospital Cost Increases?

Greater utilization of traditional procedures and diagnostic tests
26%

Introduction of new technologies and procedures
24%

Not sure
4%

Inflation of medical costs
46%

Source: Louis Harris and Associates, *The American Hospital in the 1990s*, August 1988.

6-14). Usually changes are in the form of concurrent review procedures and utilization management. The more risk-bearing approaches of global budgets and physician risk pools have been used much more rarely (see Figure 6-15). Hospital investment in technologies and utilization of tests and drugs also have been affected. Until now, 41 percent of our respondents report that outpatient cost controls have been less stringent than inpatient controls, while only 3 percent think outpatient is more stringent. However, two-thirds of surveyed hospital CEOs forecast that outpatient cost controls will become more stringent in the coming years.[2]

Controlling inpatient drug costs has become more important since the implementation of the Prospective Payment System. Hospitals are now at risk for the cost of all services and products provided to Medicare patients, and drug therapy is commonly used by this population.[8] Of hospital leaders surveyed, 87 percent report they use pharmacy formularies to help contain drug costs. The most common cost control tool used in the formularies is generic substitution, employed strictly to moderately by 79 percent of our respondents. Coming a close second is therapeutic substitution, used strictly to moderately by 63 percent of responding hospitals (see Figure 6-16). Therapeutic substitution allows pharmacists to dispense a less costly, but similar drug instead of the one prescribed by the attending physician.

In the near future, hospital CEOs see themselves as being far more aggressive in containing costs. Figure 6-17 reveals that more than 70 percent of hospital directors surveyed see themselves exercising somewhat or much greater control over routine diagnostic tests, complex diagnostic procedures, the cost of supplies, and inventory. More than 60 percent will exercise greater controls over drug purchasing and inpatient physician prescribing practices.[2]

THE DISINTEGRATION OF BARGAINING POWER

When private health insurance was introduced, the payer entered into a health care relationship that was previously restricted to patients, doctors, and hospitals. The payer's role was a silent one until recently when the escalation of health care costs led to greater interest and eventually, intervention in the decisions made by patients and providers.[9] Hospital CEOs anticipate a loss of control over the management of their institutions as they lose bargaining strength to payers (including patients, insurers, HMOs, and employers). At the same time, hospitals are gaining more bargaining power relative to physicians, drug companies, and medical suppliers, as cost control mechanisms pervade the system and discounts replace billed charges (see Figure 6-18).

CONCLUSION

Through the 1980s, the hospital industry adapted to external changes at a slower pace than economics or logic would have predicted. The power of the third party payer became a driving force in the last few years. Hospital directors

Figure 6-14

Hospital Responses to Cost Containment Pressures

Q.: Certain recent developments such as DRGs or HMO contracts calling for capitated or per diem reimbursement place a high premium on hospital cost containment. How much have you changed your policies due to pressures to contain costs with regard to...

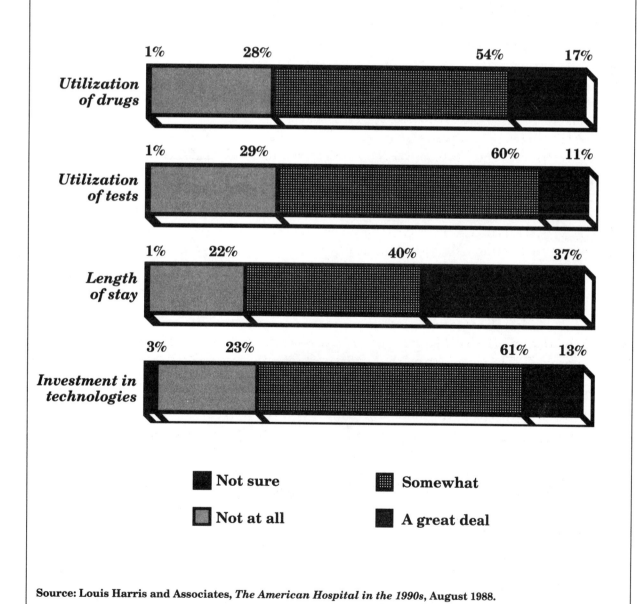

Source: Louis Harris and Associates, *The American Hospital in the 1990s*, August 1988.

Figure 6-15

Hospital Cost Containment Methods

Q.: What is the main way you contain the costs of ...

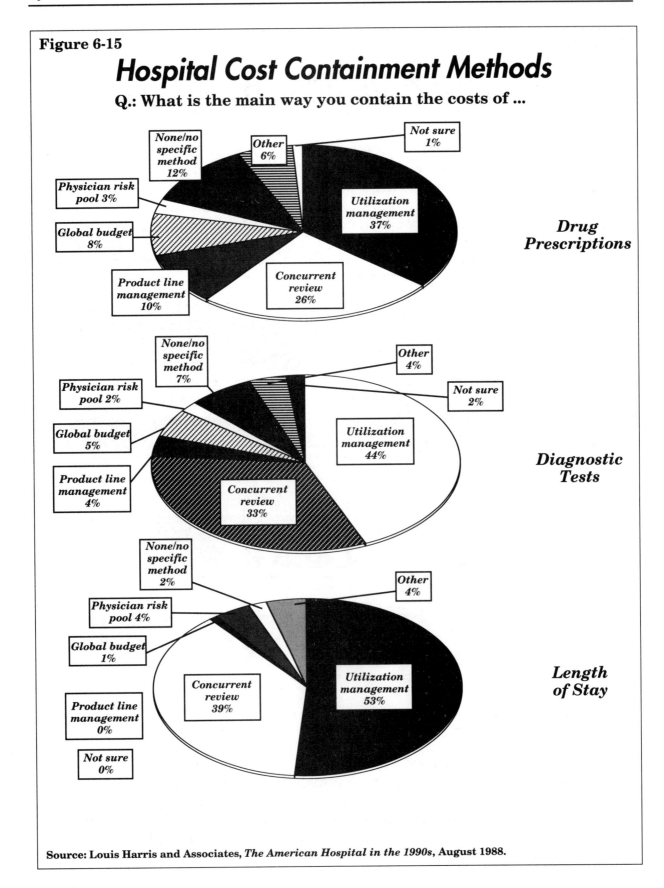

Drug Prescriptions

None/no specific method 12%
Other 6%
Not sure 1%
Physician risk pool 3%
Utilization management 37%
Global budget 8%
Product line management 10%
Concurrent review 26%

Diagnostic Tests

None/no specific method 7%
Other 4%
Not sure 2%
Physician risk pool 2%
Global budget 5%
Utilization management 44%
Product line management 4%
Concurrent review 33%

Length of Stay

None/no specific method 2%
Other 4%
Physician risk pool 4%
Global budget 1%
Utilization management 53%
Product line management 0%
Concurrent review 39%
Not sure 0%

Source: Louis Harris and Associates, *The American Hospital in the 1990s*, August 1988.

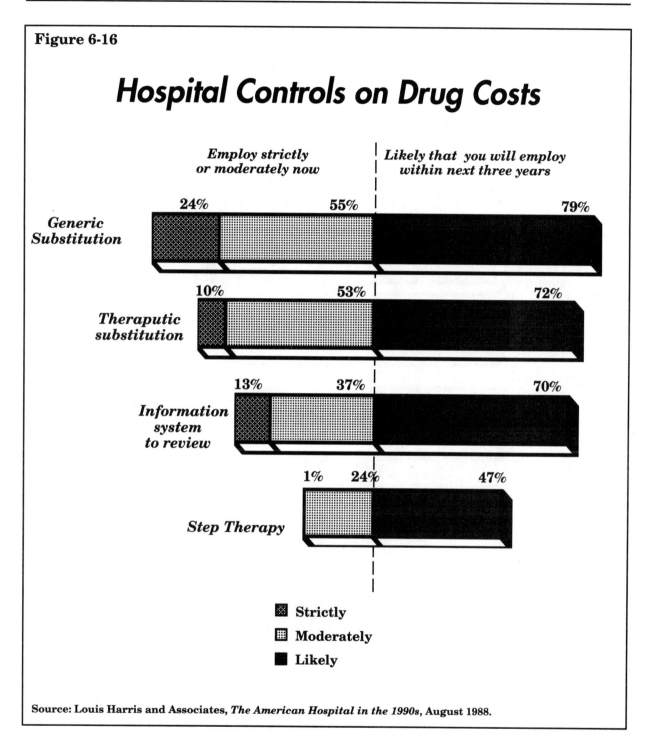

Figure 6-16

Hospital Controls on Drug Costs

Employ strictly or moderately now

Likely that you will employ within next three years

Generic Substitution — 24% · 55% · 79%

Theraputic substitution — 10% · 53% · 72%

Information system to review — 13% · 37% · 70%

Step Therapy — 1% · 24% · 47%

- ▦ Strictly
- ▤ Moderately
- ■ Likely

Source: Louis Harris and Associates, *The American Hospital in the 1990s*, August 1988.

foresee their institutions quickening the pace of expansion into outpatient and non-traditional patient services, investigating direct contract relationships with employers, strengthening their cost containment efforts, and adjusting to a softer voice at the bargaining table vis-à-vis payers. The next few years will be turbulent ones as hospitals seek to limit the regulation of hospital costs and utilization.

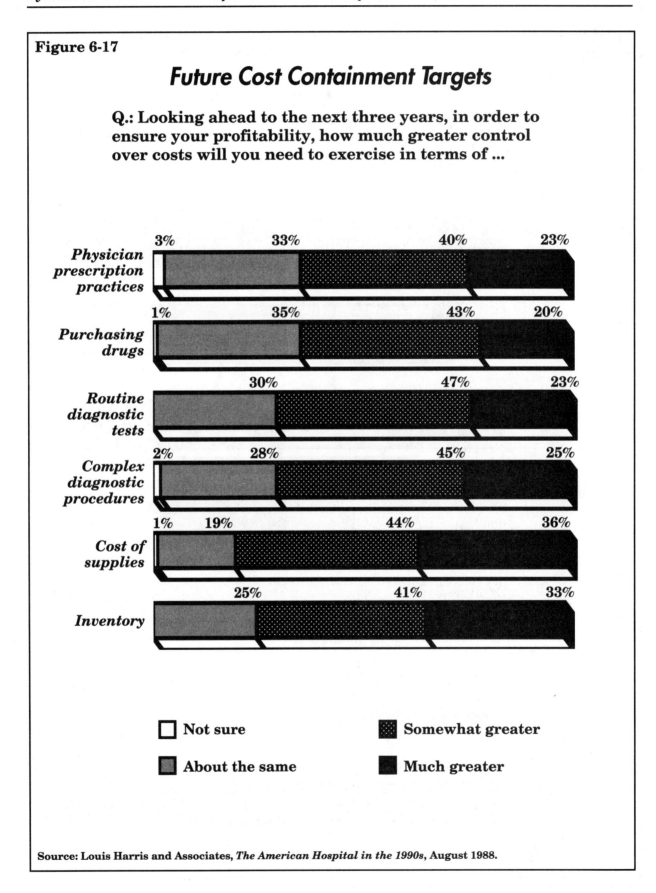

Figure 6-17

Future Cost Containment Targets

Q.: Looking ahead to the next three years, in order to ensure your profitability, how much greater control over costs will you need to exercise in terms of ...

	Not sure	About the same	Somewhat greater	Much greater
Physician prescription practices	3%	33%	40%	23%
Purchasing drugs	1%	35%	43%	20%
Routine diagnostic tests		30%	47%	23%
Complex diagnostic procedures	2%	28%	45%	25%
Cost of supplies	1%	19%	44%	36%
Inventory		25%	41%	33%

☐ **Not sure**   ▨ **Somewhat greater**

▨ **About the same**   ■ **Much greater**

Source: Louis Harris and Associates, *The American Hospital in the 1990s*, August 1988.

Figure 6-18

Hospitals' Perceived Clout

Q.: If you were to evaluate your clout or bargaining power with the following institutions or groups, who would you say has the upper hand?

(Question asked in sequence of institutions/groups for 1988 and 1991)

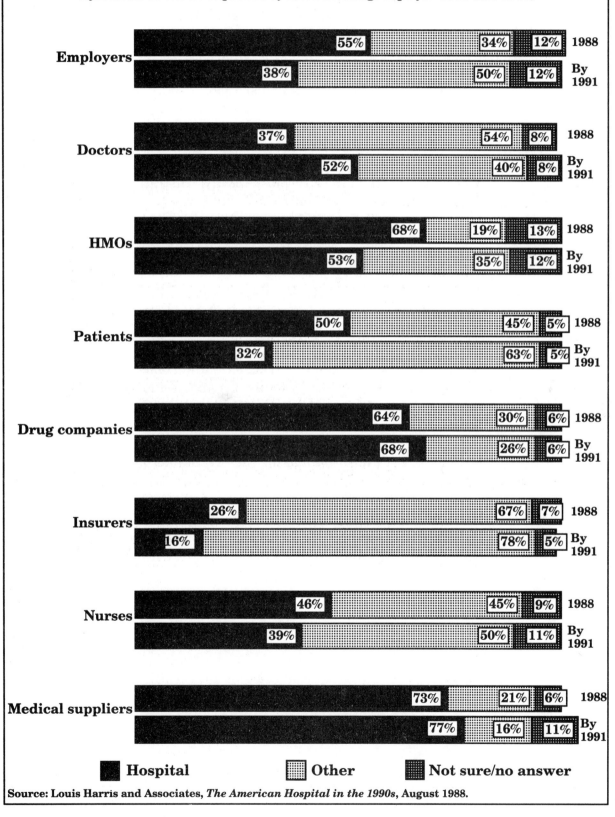

| | Hospital | Other | Not sure/no answer |

Source: Louis Harris and Associates, *The American Hospital in the 1990s*, August 1988.

147

REFERENCES

1. Lazenby HC, Letsch SW. National health expenditures, 1989. *Health Care Financing Review.* Winter 1990; 12:5.

2. Peele S. *The American Hospital in the 1990s.* New York, NY: Louis Harris and Associates; August 1988.

3. Ellwood says "Supermed" concept is gaining ground; expects up to 10 within the decade. *FAHS Review.* March/April 1986:69-70.

4. Johnsson J. Battling the FTC proves costly, frustrating. *Hospitals.* July 20, 1991;65:68.

5. Johnsson J. CEOs adapt style to cope with outpatient growth. *Hospitals.* August 5, 1991;65:60.

6. Gonzales ML, Emmons DW (eds.) *Socioeconomic Characteristics of Medical Practice: 1989.* American Medical Association; Chicago:1990.

7. Sager A, Docolar D, Hiam P. Paying for our mistakes: wrong incentives help boost 1989 hospital costs and use. A Report to the Access and Affordability Monitoring Project. Boston University School of Public Health; July 2, 1991.

8. Lipton HL, Lee PR. *Drugs and the Elderly.* Stanford, CA: Stanford University Press; 1988.

9. Morrison EM. *Interdependence Between HMOs and Health Care Providers: A Theoretical Model for the Growth of Managed Care.* Unpublished doctoral dissertation. Chicago, IL:University of Chicago;1987.

CHAPTER 7

Physicians' Responses to Their Changing Environment

Humphrey Taylor, Robert Leitman
Louis Harris and Associates
and
Jennifer N. Edwards
Harvard School of Public Health

INTRODUCTION

On an average day, 3.5 million people seek care from a doctor, and an additional 870,000 people are hospitalized under the care of one. Even though direct payments to physicians account for only 20 percent of total health care expenditures, physicians influence a much larger share of the spending, because they make the decisions to order tests, prescribe drugs, and admit patients to the hospital. These decisions continue to be a major force in shaping health care. Some have suggested doctors' decisions control as much as 80 percent of Americans' health care spending.[1] For this reason, awareness of changing trends in physician practice is critical to an understanding the of health care system.

In the past decade there have been efforts made by the Health Care Financing Administration, Congress, insurance companies, hospital administrators, and patients to limit some of doctors' control over patient care decisions in order to moderate the pace of health care spending and improve the quality of care. With the implementation of the resource-based relative value scale (RBRVS) in the next few years, doctors also are facing limits on their ability to set their own fees.

Physicians are becoming increasingly dissatisfied with the U.S. health care system. A growing proportion of doctors have joined the public, business executives, and union officials in the belief that fundamental reform is needed. In 1984, 48 percent of doctors thought that, on the whole, the current system works pretty well. Today, only 31 percent believe in its efficiency. Fifty-nine percent believe fundamental changes are needed, and 10 percent believe the health care system needs to be completely rebuilt.[2]

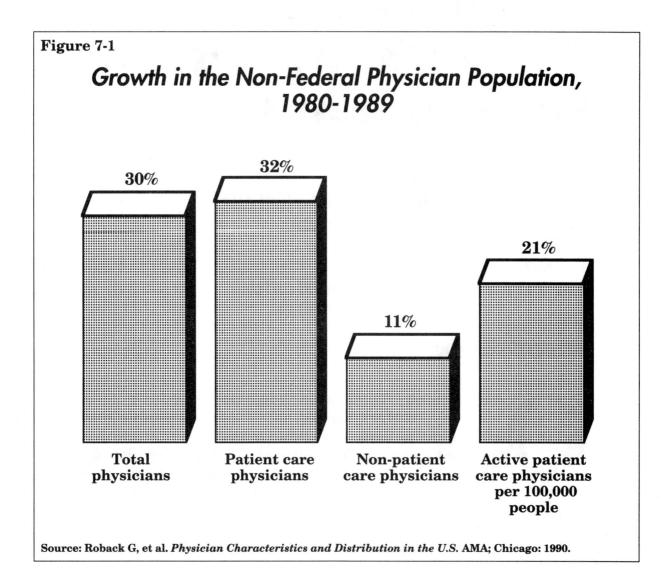

Figure 7-1

Growth in the Non-Federal Physician Population, 1980-1989

- Total physicians: 30%
- Patient care physicians: 32%
- Non-patient care physicians: 11%
- Active patient care physicians per 100,000 people: 21%

Source: Roback G, et al. *Physician Characteristics and Distribution in the U.S.* AMA; Chicago: 1990.

This chapter explores the reasons for this growing dissatisfaction, including the loss of autonomy by physicians; the changing shape of physicians' practices; and physicians' attitudes about medical practice in the 1990s. It describes how physicians are likely to respond to current and anticipated changes in the health insurance system, especially efforts to contain costs. These findings are based primarily on data collected by Louis Harris and Associates in a survey of 300 physicians in 1990.* Supplemental data from surveys conducted by the American Medical Association (AMA) also are cited.

PHYSICIAN SUPPLY AND INCOME

Most discussions of the future of medical practice start with an assessment of the supply of doctors. In the years ahead, will we have too many or too few doctors to meet the forecasted need for medical care? There are now more than 600,000 active physicians in the United States, a 30 percent increase since 1980. The number of patient-care physicians per 100,000 people has grown 21 percent between 1980 and 1989, from 202 to 240 per 100,000 population, meaning the number of doctors is growing three times faster than the general population (Figure 7-1).[3] The highest growth rate has been among women physicians, who now comprise about 17 percent of the total physician population, up from 8 percent in 1980. Despite the numerous national commissions and reports calling for the need for more family doctors and generalist physicians, growth in the number of specialists has been greater than the growth in the number of general physicians. Between 1980 and 1988, medical specialties experienced 30 percent growth, compared to general medicine and family practice, which grew 17 percent (see Figure 7-2).

DIMINISHING AUTONOMY

A series of simultaneous changes in the health care system has created a major change in medical practice by limiting physician autonomy and decreasing general satisfaction of physicians with medical practice. The desire of third party payers and insurers to control health care spending, increased competition among physicians for patients, demand by consumers for high technology medical care (and only successful outcomes), and increased government regulation all have contributed to the erosion of the physician's ability to make medical practice decisions independently without outside interference.

As shown in Table 7-1, 85 percent of doctors believe government planners and regulators have too much influence over the management of patient care, and 76 percent believe insurance companies wield inappropriate influence. Hospital and other non-medical administrators rank a close third in usurping physician autonomy.

---

*The survey was conducted of 300 office and hospital-based patient care physicians in the summer of 1990. The sampling error is ±6 percent.

Figure 7-2

Growth in Women, Foreign Medical Graduate, and Specialty Physicians, 1980-1988

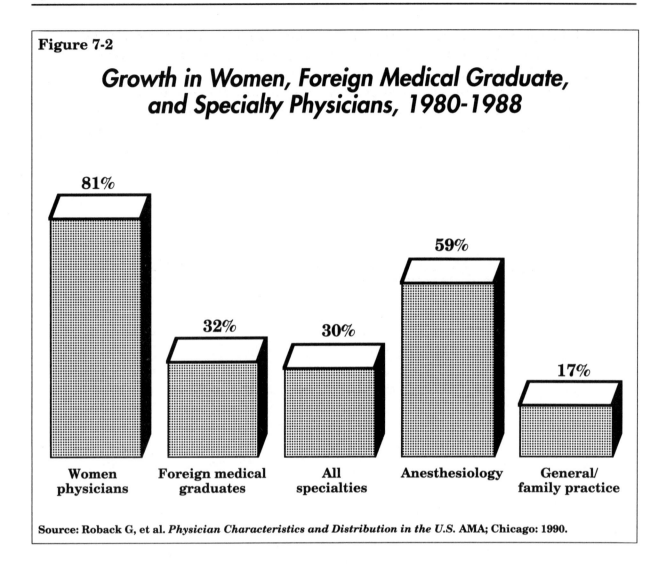

Source: Roback G, et al. *Physician Characteristics and Distribution in the U.S.* AMA; Chicago: 1990.

There is overwhelming agreement among physicians that insurers are a major source of frustration for them. Table 7-2 shows the problems physicians face in trying to interact with their patients' health insurance companies or government agencies. Between one-half and two-thirds of practicing physicians say that the administration of patient insurance creates *major* problems in their medical practice. Physicians' complaints are about paperwork and payment, including the amount of time spent completing required forms (65% say it's a major problem), partial or inadequate reimbursement (58%) and payments denied for services rendered (49%).[2] In fact, a recent survey found 89 percent of physician executives (*i.e.*, directors of medical societies) would accept a 10 percent reduction in net income in exchange for a substantial reduction in paperwork.[4]

Problems that directly affect patient care are less frequently considered of concern. For example, only 15 percent say restrictions on the choice of hospitals to which they can refer their patients is a major problem, and 19 percent cite limitations on the use of diagnostic facilities among their major problems.

Limitations set by third party payers on hospital admission and length of stay fall in the middle, with 38 and 37 percent of physicians respectively reporting them to be problems.[2]

Our survey finds that physician satisfaction with the current health care system and dissatisfaction with their insurance problems are interrelated. A doctor who perceives major problems with health insurance is the one more likely to believe the health care system needs to be completely rebuilt. Those physicians who have (1) had payments denied by health plans or have received

Table 7-1

Who Influences Physicians' Care?

Q.: Do you think each of the following has an appropriate amount of influence over the management of your patients' care, too much influence, or too little influence?

	Too Much Influence	Too Little Influence	Appropriate Influence
Base: 300			
Government planners and regulators	85%	2%	12%
Insurance companies	76	3	19
Other non-medical administrative personnel	46	5	40
Hospital administration	27	4	66
The patients	7	21	69
Members of practice groups	2	10	57

Source: Taylor H, Leitman R. *The American Physician: How Changes in the Health Care System Affect Their Behavior*. Louis Harris and Associates, 1990.

Table 7-2

Physicians' Perceptions of Insurance Problems

Q.: I will read a list of items that sometimes are problems with patients' health insurance. Please tell me if each item is a major problem, minor problem, or not a problem in your practice.

Base: 300	Major Problem	Minor Problem	Not a Problem	Not Sure
The amount of time spent completing required forms	65%	25%	9%	1%
Partial or inadequate reimbursement	58	32	8	2
Difficulty interpreting regulations	50	40	9	1
Payment denied by health plans for services rendered	49	39	10	1
Lack of understanding by administrators of physicians' practices	48	36	15	1
Delays in receiving payment	47	36	15	2
Limitations on when and if patients can be admitted to a hospital	38	41	17	4
The frequency of disputed insurance claims	37	47	13	3
Limitations on hospital length of stay	37	43	17	3
Limitations on use of diagnostic facilities	19	50	29	2
Limitations on the choice of institutions to which you can refer patients	15	44	38	3

Source: Taylor H, Leitman R. *The American Physician. How Changes in the Health Care System Affect Their Behavior.* Louis Harris and Associates, 1990.

inadequate reimbursement, (2) had frequent insurance claim disputes, and (3) faced limitations on when and where patients can be admitted are also the survey respondents who say the system needs change.[2]

Unlike the general public, doctors find it unacceptable for health plans to place limits on the treatments and procedures they prescribe. About one-third (35%) say it is not at all acceptable for insurers to limit a physician's ability to prescribe specific medications, and another third say it is not very acceptable. While 30 percent say is it acceptable, only three percent say it is very acceptable.[2] But, as we saw in Table 7-2, few doctors have actually faced limits in their own medical practices thus far. Their objections are more based on their general opposition to perceived threats to their autonomy and to their ability to make independent, professional judgments.

Further evidence that insurers do not frequently prevent physicians from doing what they think is necessary is shown in Table 7-3. When asked if doctors believe tests and procedures are used as needed, underused, or overused, fully 88 percent say that, within their specialty in their community, consultations and referrals are used either appropriately (75%) or overused (13%). Only 12 percent say that tests and procedures are underused. Even stronger evidence that physician practices are not yet being constrained by outside efforts is that 40 percent of doctors say that expensive tests and procedures are being overused, and only 6 percent say they are underused. Similarly, 36 percent say routine diagnostic tests are overused, while only 4 percent say they are underused.

The physician perception of the overutilization of tests and procedures and overall satisfaction with the health care system are related. Nearly two-thirds of those who think the system needs to be rebuilt think routine diagnostic tests are overused; and more than 55 percent of these dissatisfied doctors think expensive tests and procedures are overused.[2]

PRESSURES FROM PATIENTS

One of the reasons for overused tests and procedures is that physicians feel pressure from patients to prescribe and provide more care than they consider professionally appropriate. An AMA survey of 1,004 physicians in 1989 found 48 percent of physicians believe patients generally demand too many health care services, such as laboratory tests, x-rays, or drugs.[5] Doctors in our survey believe patients lack incentives to use care efficiently and, as a result, demand marginal, unnecessary, or inappropriate care.[2] In fact, physicians feel they are relinquishing control of some of their professional decisionmaking to their patients. Sixty-three percent of physicians report that their control over patient treatment decisions has declined in the last several years, a marked increase from 1988, when 51 percent felt they were losing control.[5] A partial explanation for patients' excessive demands may be their unrealistic expectations about the ability of doctors to treat or cure their illnesses. Fifty-three percent of doctors report their patients have unrealistic demands, compared to 41 percent who think their patients have realistic expectations.[5]

Table 7-3

Doctors' Views of the Use of Tests and Procedures

Q.: Thinking about physicians who practice in your medical specialty in your community, do you think each is used about the right amount, underused, or overused?

Base: 300	Right Amount	Underused	Overused	Not Sure
Expensive tests and procedures	52%	6%	40%	1%
Routine diagnostic tests	59	4	36	1
Consultations and referrals	75	12	13	—
Standard practice protocols	67	17	6	10

Source: Taylor H, Leitman R. *The American Physician: How Changes in the Health Care System Affect Their Behavior*. Louis Harris and Associates, 1990.

Another area where doctors fear they are losing autonomy is in regard to medical malpractice. As shown in Table 7-4, in the minds of doctors malpractice suits are the most significant factor that interferes with their clinical decisionmaking ability. The threat that their patients could sue them leads 75 percent of doctors to do more tests than they believe are medically necessary.[5] This is not an unfounded concern. Thirty-eight percent of physicians have incurred at least one liability claim in their career.[6]

A majority of physicians believe the professional liability situation in medicine has worsened in each of the last two years. As shown in Table 7-5, only 5 percent each year have found the situation to be improving. Although malpractice liability premiums are beginning to moderate, this issue continues to be a major concern for physicians.

Malpractice is not just an economic issue for doctors. The more critical issue is the psychological impact on a successful professional who is forced into a court of law and charged with negligence or incompetence. The result can be a cloud of doubt left in the minds of colleagues and patients about the doctor's professional abilities. Physicians may fear these less tangible consequences of a malpractice suit more than its ultimate economic repercussions. In fact, malpractice liability premiums involve only 10 percent of an average doctor's overall practice expense, up from 7 percent in 1982.[6]

PHYSICIAN COMPETITION

For some physicians, the increased supply of doctors has led to an increase in the number of physicians in their area with whom they must compete. Thirty-six percent of physicians believe economic competition in their community was too high in 1986 compared to just 20 percent who thought so in 1982.[7] In response, physicians have begun taking evening or weekend appointments, advertising in order to attract customers, or joining alternative delivery systems with a steady patient load. The percent of physicians offering evening and weekend office hours has risen from 39 percent in 1980 to 81 percent in 1987 with about one-fifth of these working more than 10 evening or weekend hours per week. The percent of physicians who have begun advertising reached 20 percent in 1987, up from just 9 percent in 1982. Not surprisingly, young physicians are more likely to feel the competitive pressures than older, more established physicians. The AMA reports the proportion of doctors working evening and weekend hours and the proportion who advertise decreases markedly with the doctor's age.[7]

Table 7-4

Factors That Most Interfere With Physician Clinical Decisionmaking, 1990-1991

Item	Percent of Physicians
Malpractice liability	31
Utilization review	21
Capitation and fee schedules	12
Medical practice guidelines	6
All other	9
None	21

Source: Slora EJ, Gonzalez ML. *Socioeconomic Characteristics of Medical Practice, 1990*; AMA; Chicago: 1991.

Table 7-5

Physicians' Views of the Professional Liability Situation

Q.: In the past year, do you believe the professional liability situation in medicine has gotten better, gotten worse, or stayed the same?

Physician Opinion	1988	1989
Gotten better	5%	5%
Gotten worse	67	61
Stayed the same	27	33
Not sure	1	1

Source: Harvey LK, Shubat SC. *Physician Opinion on Health Care Issues.* American Medical Association: Chicago; 1989: 25.

GOVERNMENT REGULATION

Physician payments made by the federal government have almost tripled in the last decade, rising from $376 per Medicare enrollee in 1980 to $1,042 per enrollee in 1989.[8] This has led to a major effort by the federal government to reduce these increases in the future. The recent restriction Congress placed on referrals to physician-owned diagnostic facilities is indicative of the sort of monitoring physicians can expect from Congress in the coming years.

The new Medicare physician payment system, based on Harvard's resource-based relative value scale (RBRVS) could have profound effects on medical practice, according to the physicians in our survey. The new payment scale would reduce physicians' fees for specific procedures, such as laboratory tests and surgery, and increase payments for time spent with patients and for the work involving diagnosis and treatment (*i.e.*, general medical care). The scale also is designed to control the future growth in expenditures and redistribute physician payments more equitably among various medical specialties. In general, surgeons receive less for each procedure and family doctors receive more than is currently paid by Medicare. It is still uncertain exactly how the RBRVS will affect the health care system as a whole. Its impact could be very limited, since it was developed for use by the Medicare program, which pays only 23 percent of physicians' total income, on average. It will be phased in gradually until 1996, when all Medicare payments will be based totally on the new fee schedule. It may result in only small cost savings, if there are increases in volume, as has been seen in Canada, where payment schedules are not controlled by volume performance standards. In Canada, it is reported that physicians encouraged more of their patients to come back for return visits when government limits were placed on their individual fee charges.[9]

RBRVS is not intended to change the way physicians practice medicine. However, it will alter two key financial aspects of medicine — the amount of money going to different specialties and the volume of patient care activity necessary to achieve a given income in different specialties. Therefore, once RBRVS is fully implemented in 1994, it will likely affect physicians' practices in two ways: (1) change the mix of physicians in each specialty and (2) change the volume of care delivered by some specialties.

Fifty-three percent of doctors believe RBRVS will have a major impact on the way they practice medicine, and an additional 32 percent believe it will have a minor impact. As shown in Table 7-6, the impact will be greater for higher income doctors and specialists whose fields are targeted for reductions — radiology, anesthesiology and pathology (74%), surgeons (65%), or expansions — family medicine (46%).[2] Most physicians say that if and when RBRVS is implemented in their specialty, they will set their fees for publicly insured patients at RBRVS levels. About one-fifth will set their fees for public patients above RBRVS scales (Table 7-7). Physicians will not do the same for other private payers. About one-third say they will set fees higher for Blue Cross (32%), fee-for-service (34%), and commercially insured patients (34%). About one-fourth say they will set their fees for their IPA, PPO, and HMO patients above RBRVS. Surgeons and higher-income physicians are the most likely to set their fees above RBRVS. If private insurers adopt the scale, doctors say they will still charge more, meaning there will be a large increase in billing to patients in excess of the amount paid by the insurer. The added paperwork involved in collecting from patients will undoubtedly be a source of even further dissatisfaction among doctors.

In the very long term, implementation of RBRVS may result in a change in the distribution of physicians and patterns of practice, as young physicians choose careers in traditionally lower-paid specialties. The biggest changes will occur in those specialties whose fees experience the tightest controls. Surgeons, for example, may see major changes in their field. At the same time Medicare is experiencing fee reductions, the growth in the number of new surgeons is outpacing the demand for surgery. While the number of surgeons grew from 58,000 in 1970 to 106,000 in 1985, the number of surgeries decreased from 16.2 million in 1979 to 16 million in 1985.[10] The technological and pharmaceutical advances that have alleviated the demand for surgery in recent years may flourish in the next several years as well. Over time, young physicians, discussed later in the chapter, will have even less incentive to specialize in surgery.

Table 7-6

Doctors' Expectations About the Impact of RBRVS on the Way They Will Practice Medicine

INCOME

	Total	$75,000 or less	$75,000-$100,000	$100,000-$125,000	$125,000-$200,000	More than $200,000
Base	300	76	64	50	61	37
Major impact	53%	49%	45%	52%	59%	68%
Minor impact	32	29	36	30	36	24
No impact at all	9	14	10	12	2	3
Not sure	7	8	9	6	3	5

SPECIALTY

	Family/ General Practice	Internal Medicine	RAP*	Pediatrics	Medical	Surgical
Base	57	34	38	25	58	72
Major impact	46%	53%	74%	64%	34%	65%
Minor impact	33	29	16	20	48	25
No impact at all	14	15	3	12	7	4
Not sure	7	3	8	4	10	6

*RAP= radiology, anesthesiology, and pathology.

Source: Taylor H, Leitman R. *The American Physician: How Changes in the Health Care System Affect Their Behavior*. Louis Harris and Associates, 1990.

OTHER CHANGES THAT WILL AFFECT THE PRACTICE OF MEDICINE

Many doctors agree that several other anticipated developments in health care will have some degree of impact on the way they practice medicine. As shown in Figure 7-3, providing coverage for the uninsured and implementing any of a number of managed care strategies would affect how they practice medicine. If efforts to evaluate the cost-effectiveness or the outcome of care were to become more prevalent, these factors could also have an impact on how doctors practice. Although few of these payment or administrative mechanisms are widely used at this time, they show us that payers may have tools available in the future that

Table 7-7

How RVS for Medicare Will Affect Fees for Other Payers

Q.: If and when the resource-based relative value scale is implemented by Medicare for your specialty, will you set your fees for your patients at RVS levels, or above RVS levels?

Payer	At RVS Levels	Above RVS Levels	Not Applicable	Below RVS Levels	Not Sure
Medicare	54%	23%	13%	*	10%
Medicaid	53	20	15	2	10
Blue Cross	48	32	8	1	11
Fee-for-service	47	34	7	—	12
HMO	43	26	20	*	10
PPO	42	28	19	*	10
Commercial	42	34	11	—	13
IPA	40	25	23	—	12

* Less than 0.5%

Source: Taylor H, Leitman R. *The American Physician: How Changes in the Health Care System Affect Their Behavior*. Louis Harris and Associates, 1990.

Figure 7-3

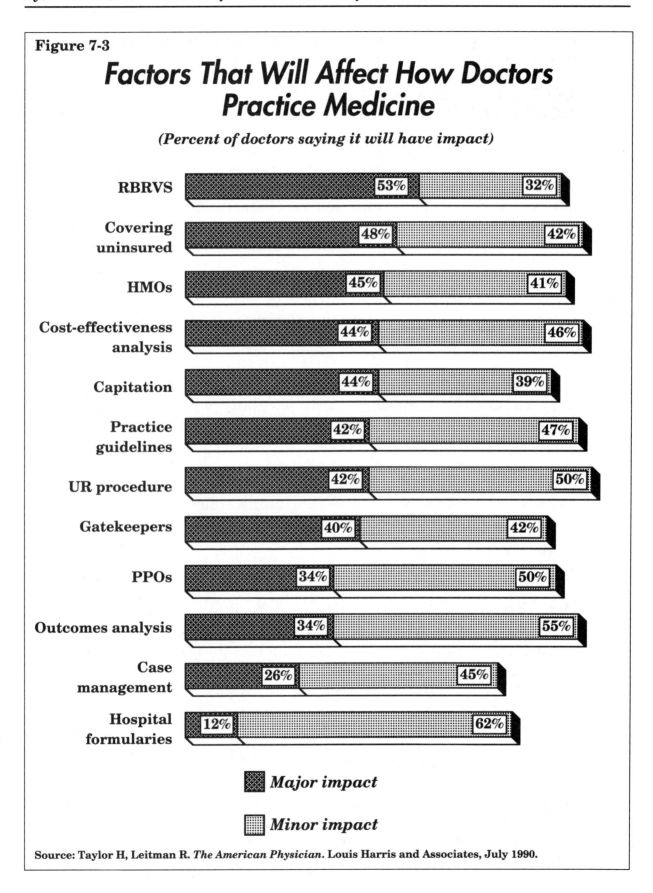

Factors That Will Affect How Doctors Practice Medicine

(Percent of doctors saying it will have impact)

	Major impact	Minor impact
RBRVS	53%	32%
Covering uninsured	48%	42%
HMOs	45%	41%
Cost-effectiveness analysis	44%	46%
Capitation	44%	39%
Practice guidelines	42%	47%
UR procedure	42%	50%
Gatekeepers	40%	42%
PPOs	34%	50%
Outcomes analysis	34%	55%
Case management	26%	45%
Hospital formularies	12%	62%

■ *Major impact*

▦ *Minor impact*

Source: Taylor H, Leitman R. *The American Physician*. Louis Harris and Associates, July 1990.

could have major impact on physician practice. The threat and uncertainty of such changes may affect physicians' attitudes about their career choice.

DOCTORS' VIEWS OF THE NEED TO CONTAIN COSTS

If we are ever to gain a consensus on approaches to containing costs, we need to reconcile the fact that doctors have views about the causes behind rising health care costs that are different than other groups we have surveyed. The two factors most doctors name as major causes of the inflation of health care costs nationally are malpractice insurance and defensive medicine (86%) and the increased availability and use of expensive, new medical technology (76%). Seven other factors are considered a major cause of health care inflation by fewer than half of all doctors (see Table 7-8). Nearly one-half of practicing physicians blame patient behavior for increasing health care costs — 48 percent say a major cause is the lack of incentives for patients to use their health care efficiently and 46 percent cite patients demanding unnecessary care as a major cause of health care inflation.

Twenty percent of the physicians in the survey say that patients receiving marginal, unnecessary, or inappropriate care are a major cause of cost inflation, while more than twice as many doctors (46%) say patients *demanding* care that might not be necessary is a major cause of inflation of health care costs. As shown earlier in this chapter, 40 percent say expensive tests and procedures are overused, 36 percent say routine diagnostic tests are overused, and 13 percent say consultations and referrals are overused. These inconsistencies are hard to reconcile. They may reflect doctors' unwillingness to acknowledge that they deliver unnecessary care themselves.

American physicians appear to exempt themselves from blame for health care inflation. In addition to blaming technology and patients (through the threat of malpractice and excessive demands), nearly half (45%) blame the freedom of drug companies to set prices. Half as many (23%) blame the freedom of doctors and hospitals to set prices independently. Similarly, slightly more than half as many physicians consider the lack of incentives for doctors (29%) and hospitals (28%) to deliver health care efficiently to be a major cause of inflation as think that the lack of patient incentives (48%) is a major cause. Only 14 percent blame the fee-for-service system of reimbursement for having a major impact on cost inflation.

Table 7-9 shows how American physicians think costs should be controlled. Fully 92 percent think reforming medical malpractice should be a high priority (86% think it is a major cause of inflation). About three-fourths (74%) think reducing expensive high-tech care at the end of life should be a high priority — similar to the 76 percent who think the increased availability and use of expensive medical technology is a major cause of increased costs. Nearly two-thirds (64%) agree regional plans to reduce duplication of high-tech hospital services and expensive equipment should be a high priority (74%).

Table 7-8

Doctors Name the Two Major Causes of Health Care Cost Inflation

Q.: Do you think that each item is a major cause, a minor cause, or not at all a cause of the inflation of health care costs nationally?

	Major Cause	Minor Cause	Not at All a Cause
Malpractice insurance and defensive medicine	86%	14%	0%
The increased availability and use of expensive new medical technology	76	23	1
The lack of incentive for patients to use their health care efficiently	48	45	7
Patients demanding care that might not be necessary	46	50	3
Patients receiving marginal, unnecessary, or inappropriate care	20	64	15
The freedom of drug companies to set prices	45	46	6
The freedom of doctors and hospitals to set prices	23	57	18
The lack of incentive for doctors to deliver health care efficiently	29	59	13
The lack of incentive for hospitals to deliver their health care efficiently	28	56	16

Source: Taylor H, Leitman R. *The American Physician: How Changes in the Health Care System Affect Their Behavior*. Louis Harris and Associates, 1990.

About half of the respondents think requiring consumers to pay more out-of-pocket for their care (54%) should be a higher priority, consistent with the proportion of doctors who think patient demands for care and lack of proper patient incentives are a major cause of inflation (although inconsistent with the smaller proportion of physicians who acknowledge that patients receive too much care). Likewise, 42 percent favor more price controls for prescription drugs, matching the 45 percent who think drug pricing causes health care inflation.

Physicians' lowest priorities are actions that could control or reduce their incomes — policies such as physician price controls, paying more doctors on a salaried or capitated basis, global budgets and expenditure caps, limiting what insurers will pay for, and reducing the specialist-to-primary-care-physician ratio. It is hard to read these results without some cynicism. Self-interest with regard to income appears to be a factor in these judgments.

THE FUTURE OF COST CONTAINMENT

A narrow majority of physicians agrees that "a major initiative by the federal government is needed to make improvements in the health care system" (Table 7-10). Fewer than a third of the doctors think that "managed health plans will eventually work to contain costs if we give them enough time," which explains the belief by the majority that government must intervene. Physicians are unique among major groups in the health care system in that more than one-half believe that reducing health care cost inflation will require a sacrifice of the quality of care available to patients. Of all those surveyed, doctors represent the lowest percentage of respondents who think that physicians must consider financial cutbacks to control health care costs.

INCOME

Despite the increased competition from other doctors in their community, doctors have been able to maintain their incomes, and most are still seeing increases. According to an annual survey of physician income conducted by *Medical Economics*, physicians' real earnings increased each year in the past decade.[11] Over the decade, physicians' real income has increased by 60 percent, compared to the national average income, which has increased one percent.[12] All specialties are not equally lucrative. Figure 7-4 shows that median net income ranges from $296,300 a year for cardiovascular surgeons to $86,860 for general practitioners.

An individual doctor's satisfaction with the operation of the health care system increases with his or her income. Physicians who report incomes of more than $125,000 are more likely to think the system works well than physicians making less than $125,000. The doctors most likely to say the system should be rebuilt are those making less than $75,000.[2]

Table 7-9

Priorities for Cost Containment

Q.: I will read a list of suggestions for controlling the cost of health care. Please say for each one if you think it should be a high priority, a low priority, or something that should not be done at all.

	<u>High Priority</u>
Reform medical malpractice	**92%**
Spend more on low-cost public health and preventive medicine	**80**
Reduce the amount of expensive high-tech care given to patients in the last weeks and months of their lives	**74**
Reduce unnecessary and inappropriate care	**68**
Have regional plans to reduce duplication of high-tech services and expensive equipment	**64**
Require consumers to pay a larger share of their health care costs out-of-pocket	**54**
Have more price controls for prescription drugs	**42**
Have more price controls for hospital charges	**33**
Reduce the ratio of specialists to primary care physicians	**28**
Set stricter limits on the services that health plans will and will not pay for	**20**
Have more price controls for doctor fees	**18**
Set global budgets or expenditure caps for hospital and doctor fees	**15**
Pay more doctors on a salaried or capitated basis and fewer on a fee-for-service basis	**14**

Source: Taylor H, Leitman R. *The American Physician: How Changes in the Health Care System Affect Their Behavior.* Louis Harris and Associates, 1990.

YOUNG PHYSICIANS

What will be the short term future of medical practice? Our best indicators are young physicians just beginning their practices and who will likely continue in practice for several decades. What we find is drawn from two recent surveys, both involving the American Medical Association, the latter study in conjunction with the Robert Wood Johnson Foundation.

First, based on factors already discussed, medicine as a career is financially less attractive for young physicians than in earlier years. However, in comparison to other career choices available today, medicine remains a very lucrative choice for college graduates. The slowdown in the general economy and the increasing numbers of baby-boomers now entering the college-educated and

Table 7-10

Doctors' Views on the Future of Cost Containment

Q.: Do you agree or disagree with the following statements?

	Agree	Disagree	Not Sure
A major initiative by the federal government is needed to make improvements in the health care system	53%	46%	—
Health care costs inflation in this country can't be significantly reduced without a sacrifice in quality	47	53	—
Managed care health plans will eventually work to contain costs if we give them enough time	32	64	3%
Until doctors are financially at risk for most aspects of health care, we won't get costs under control	15	82	3

Source: Taylor H, Leitman R. *The American Physician: How Changes in the Health Care System Affect Their Behavior*. Louis Harris and Associates, 1990.

Figure 7-4

How 15 Specialties Rank in Practice Income

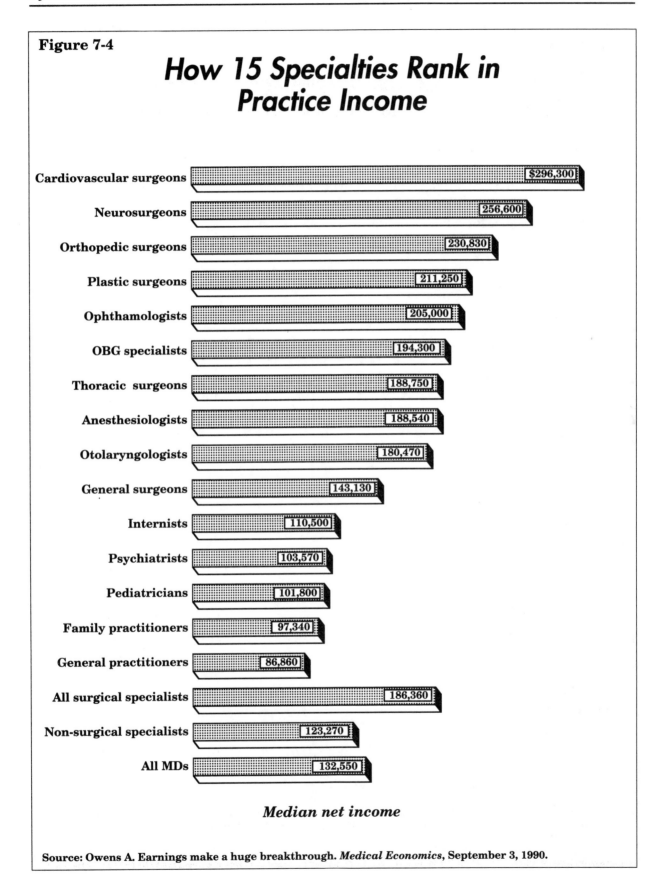

Cardiovascular surgeons	$296,300
Neurosurgeons	256,600
Orthopedic surgeons	230,830
Plastic surgeons	211,250
Ophthamologists	205,000
OBG specialists	194,300
Thoracic surgeons	188,750
Anesthesiologists	188,540
Otolaryngologists	180,470
General surgeons	143,130
Internists	110,500
Psychiatrists	103,570
Pediatricians	101,800
Family practitioners	97,340
General practitioners	86,860
All surgical specialists	186,360
Non-surgical specialists	123,270
All MDs	132,550

Median net income

Source: Owens A. Earnings make a huge breakthrough. *Medical Economics,* September 3, 1990.

Table 7-11

Physicians' Responses to Question, 'Given What You Know Now, Would You Go To Medical School?'

| | Percent Responding | | |
	Yes	No	Not Sure
All physicians	60.2%	31.0%	8.8%
Demographics			
White women	56.2	33.9	9.9
Black women	63.2	26.6	10.2
Hispanic women	68.2	29.5	2.2
Other women	62.6	33.0	4.3
White men	60.7	30.0	9.3
Black men	61.0	33.5	5.6
Hispanic men	63.3	30.8	5.9
Other men	61.9	33.2	4.9
Specialty			
Primary care	61.7	30.0	8.2
Nonprimary care	58.9	31.9	9.3
Employment			
Self-employed	58.3	33.3	8.4
Employee	62.4	28.3	9.3
Number of practices			
One	59.3	31.8	8.8
Two or more	65.2	26.1	8.7

Source: American Medical Association 1987 Young Physician Survey, cited in Cohen AB, et al. Young physicians and the future of the medical profession. *Health Affairs*. Winter 1990: 138-148.

professional labor force have made other fields both highly competitive and somewhat less financially rewarding than medicine for college graduates.

Second, though most young physicians are able to build their medical practice without feeling stress about conditions in health care, a significant minority (31%) report they are very disenchanted with medicine as a career to the extent, that given the choice, they would not enter medicine again. Of particular concern is the percentage of minorities and women who reflect this negative view of medical practice (see Table 7-11). These were the groups most sought after in the past to add diversity to the profession.

Also, we find a significant proportion are frustrated with the time con-

Figure 7-5

Ratio of Average Income of Physicians to Average Compensation of All Employees

(United States and selected countries, 1970-1987)

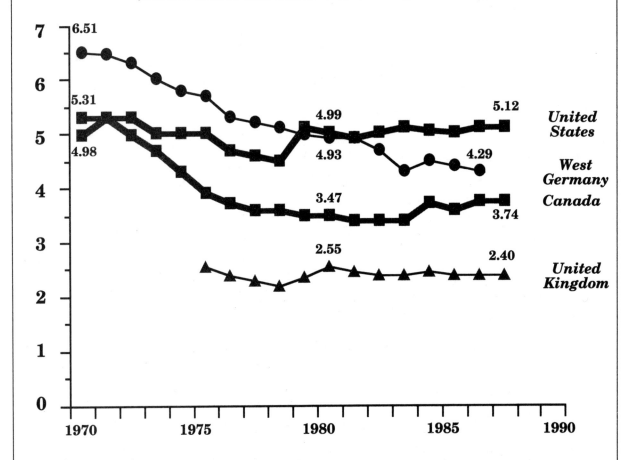

Source: Congressional Budget Office calculations based on data from the Organization for Economic Cooperation and Development, Health Data File, 1989.

straints and the location of their practices. Dissatisfied young physicians, compared to other young physicians, work longer hours, including nights and weekends; spend more time on administrative tasks; and see more patients per week. They report feeling that they do not have enough time to spend with patients or reviewing histories and test results, and they do not have control over their work schedules. As a result, many young doctors feel they underuse medical consultations and referrals.

CONCLUSION

What these findings imply for the future is that medicine is likely to remain an attractive career, especially in comparison to other fields. However, doctors will be more threatened by competition from other doctors and more burdened with outside intervention in their medical decisionmaking as third party payers expand efforts to manage their costs. The level of paperwork and administration involved in getting reimbursed for the care physicians provide will multiply, increasing their dissatisfaction with medical practice.

As the supply of doctors grows, doctors will face heightened efforts by both government and employers to narrow the gap between the average income of doctors and that of other workers in the labor force. As shown in Figure 7-5, the average income of physicians is five times greater than the average for all other occupations. In the United Kingdom, physicians' incomes are two-and-a-half times greater and in Canada four times as large. These differences will be targets for cost-cutters in the years ahead as thousands of new doctors open practices and seek the same kind of financial rewards as their predecessors.

REFERENCES

1. Eisenberg JM. *Doctors' Decisions and the Cost of Medical Care: the Reasons for Doctors' Practice Patterns and Ways to Change Them.* Health Administration Press Perspectives; Ann Arbor; 1986:4.

2. Taylor H, Leitman R. *The American Physician: How Changes in the Health Care System Affect Their Behavior.* Louis Harris and Associates, 1990.

3. Roback G, et al. *Physician Characteristics and Distribution in the U.S.* American Medical Association; Chicago:1990.

4. Taylor H, Leitman R. *Trade-offs and Choices. Health Policy Options for the 1990s.* Louis Harris and Associates; New York: 1991.

5. Harvey LK, Shubat SC. *Physician Opinion On Health Care Issues.* American Medical Association; Chicago: April, 1989.

6. Slora EJ, Gonzalez ML. Medical professional liability claims and premiums, 1985-1989. *Socioeconomic Characteristics of Medical Practice, 1990/1991.* American Medical Association; Chicago; 1991: 15-19.

7. Gonzalez ML, Emmons, DW. *Socioeconomic Characteristics of Medical Practice, 1987.* American Medical Association; Chicago: 1987.

8. Physician Payment Review Commission. *Annual Report to Congress, 1991.* Washington, D.C.

9. Evans RG. The dog in the night time: Medical practice variations and health policy. In Anderson TF and Mooney G (eds). *The Challenge of Medical Practice Variations.* London; Macmillan Press, 1989.

10. Rosenthal E. Innovations intensify glut of surgeons. *New York Times,* November 7, 1989: C1.

11. Owens A. Earnings make a huge breakthrough. *Medical Economics.* September 3, 1990.

12. Gonzalez ML, Emmons DW (eds.) *Socioeconomic Characteristics of Medical Practice, 1989.* American Medical Association; Chicago; 1989, in Committee on Ways and Means. *1991 Green Book. U.S.* House of Representatives; Washington, D.C.; 1991.

CHAPTER 8

The Public and the Future of U.S. Health Care System Reform

Robert J. Blendon and Karen Donelan
Harvard School of Public Health

INTRODUCTION

For the third time in the post World War II period, a major debate is taking place in America about whether there is a need for a national health program. The resurgence of that issue is evidenced by the increased interest of Congress, the scientific community, the media, and a number of national leadership groups, commissions, and task forces.[1-5] The public also is engaged in the discussion. Opinion polls indicate that support for a national health plan is at a 40-year high point,[6] and more than 10 national and statewide surveys conducted since 1989 indicate that between 60 and 72 percent of Americans are in favor of such a plan (see Table 8-1).[7-17] By some

Table 8-1

Surveys Measuring Public Support for a National Health Insurance Plan Financed Through Taxes

Date	Survey Organization	Percent Support
1989	NBC (national)	67
1989	Louisville Courier-Journal (Kentucky residents)	62
1990	Los Angeles Times (national)	72
1990	The Atlantic Financial Poll (West Virginia residents)	62
1990	CBS/New York Times (national)	64
1990	Gallup Organization for Blue Cross/ Blue Shield (national)	60
1990	Institute for Social Inquiry, University of Connecticut for The Hartford Courant (Connecticut residents)	60
1990	Roper Organization for HIAA (national)	69
1990	ICR Survey Research Group for Associated Press (national)	62
1991	CBS/New York Times (national)	60
1991	NBC/Wall Street Journal (national)	68

of these measures, the public's enthusiasm for the concept of a comprehensive program of national health insurance exceeds the level of support for Medicare in the year prior to its enactment.[18] In fact, a recent Roper Organization survey indicates that 69 percent of Americans surveyed would approve extending Medicare coverage to all citizens.[14]

Before discussing the issues that underlie this new wave of interest in a national health plan, it seems worthwhile to gain some insight into why the more than 50 national health insurance initiatives that have been introduced in the post World War II period have never been enacted. Many of these efforts were comprehensive in scope, included well-developed cost containment programs, and were sponsored by prominent public and private sector leaders and health organizations.[19-22] The reasons behind the rejection of those previous proposals clearly have implications for any future debate about this issue.

For many years, historians and policy analysts have suggested that the failure of earlier national health proposals was primarily the result of one factor: the continued and strident opposition of the medical profession to the implementation of such a plan.[22-24] Without diminishing the crucial role played by organized medicine in the failure of past initiatives, it is important to note that in our own nation, and others, there have been notable cases where sweeping health care reforms have been made over the objections of the medical community. In 1965, Medicare was enacted in the U.S., and a national health insurance program was introduced in Canada, both despite the widespread opposition of the medical profession in each country. In addition, the National Health Service was instituted in Great Britain at a time that the British Medical Association and, according to surveys conducted at the time, three-quarters of British physicians, opposed its establishment.[22,24-26]

It is clear that other factors also have played important roles in preventing the adoption of a universal health program in the United States. One of these factors is public opinion on this and related health issues. For example, at the time of the defeat of President Truman's national health insurance proposals in the late 1940s, not only did organized medicine oppose their enactment, so did nearly half of Americans surveyed. Conversely, at the time the British National Health Service was put in place, there was significant public support for the plan (61%).[27,28]

Americans' responses to a wide variety and long history of survey questions about national health insurance, attitudes toward government and taxation, and priorities for spending begin to reveal why a people who claim to see health care as a right have been less forceful than people of other countries in their support for universal health care. This chapter will focus on the forces of public opinion that have shaped both the national interest in a federal program of health insurance for all Americans and our nation's failure to achieve a public consensus on any form of such a plan. Finally, based on lessons learned from the realities of public opinion of these issues, we offer some guiding principles for designing a national approach to universal health coverage, which, if adhered to, might help in reaching an agreement on this issue.

WHY IS THE PUBLIC DISSATISFIED WITH THE U.S. HEALTH CARE SYSTEM?

It is widely recognized by leadership and policy groups and by the public that major changes must be made in the current U.S. health care system. Although the United States spends more per person for health care than any other industrialized country ($2,051 in the U.S. versus $1,483 in Canada, $1,093 in West Germany, $915 in Japan, and $758 in the United Kingdom, for example),[29] our nation fails to provide access to health care insurance to all our citizens, and our system is viewed more negatively by its populace than are the systems of several other industrialized nations. The results of a series of comparative international surveys conducted between 1988 and 1990 indicated very low levels of support for their health care system among Americans compared with residents of Canada, the United Kingdom, and West Germany, although Americans were more satisfied with health services used by their family members than were Britons or Germans (see Table 8-2).[30,31]

Table 8-2

Public Satisfaction in Four Nations With Their Health Care System and Their Personal Medical Care

	Satisfied With Current Health Care System*	Very Satisfied With Personal Medical Care
United States	10%	55%
Canada	56	60
Great Britain	27	39
(West) Germany	41	45

*Believe nation's health system "works pretty well and only minor changes are needed."

Source: Louis Harris and Associates, 1990.

Public dissatisfaction with the U.S. health care system appears to be driven by two concerns: dramatic increases in health care costs, and fear about losing all or part of their health benefits in our largely employment-based system of health insurance.

The magnitude of the impact of increasing health care costs is reflected in the fact that per capita costs in the U.S. rose from $1,016 in 1980 to a projected $2,425 in 1990, and at current rates of increase are doubling every seven years.[32] Large corporations say that the cost of providing health insurance benefits is hindering their ability to compete in international markets, small businesses claim that proposed government requirements for employers to provide insurance coverage would put them out of business. Disputes over health benefit premiums were the second leading cause of labor strikes in 1989.[33] As shown in Figure 8-1, employers surveyed by *Business and Health* magazine indicated that increasing premiums, deductibles, and copayments were the options they would most likely use to cut their health care costs in the future.[34]

The public shares the business community's concerns about costs, but worries that the solution to this problem has increasingly been to shift the burden of paying those costs away from employers to their employees. Eighty-four percent of respondents to a 1990 Conference Board survey said the cost of medical care was a very serious or serious problem, greater than crime, pollution, AIDS, homelessness, poverty, unemployment, and 14 other items. Only drug abuse ranked equally with medical care costs (see Figure 8-2).[35] Americans are far more likely than Canadians or Germans to say that their nation spends too much money on both hospital and physician care (see Figure 8-3).[31]

The American public and many leading economists hold diametrically opposed views about whether Americans are over- or under-insured against the high cost of health care services. Many economists feel that today's insurance policies (for those who have them) are so comprehensive that they shelter individuals from any concern about high health care costs, often to the extent that they are induced to use more services than they need. The public perceives this issue differently. On average, Americans pay 26 percent of their health costs themselves, and nearly 20 percent report that they pay more than 40 percent directly.[32] These figures compare, for example, with approximately 10 percent of bills paid out of pocket by citizens of Scandinavian countries.[36] As a result, there is a great deal of public anxiety about the ability to cope with these costs in the future — although 68 percent of Americans are confident that they could cover their health costs if they had a serious illness today, 60 percent are worried that they will not be able to handle the costs in the future.[37] Fear of being left without adequate insurance appears to be a major factor underlying the sharp rise in public interest in national health insurance.

Data about the dynamics of insurance coverage in the U.S. suggest that Americans have legitimate cause for concern. Today, nearly 34 million people in the U.S. are without health insurance coverage, a figure that has grown by 25 percent since 1980.[38] Because of its largely employment-based structure, the U.S. health insurance system provides little guarantee of continuing health

Figure 8-1

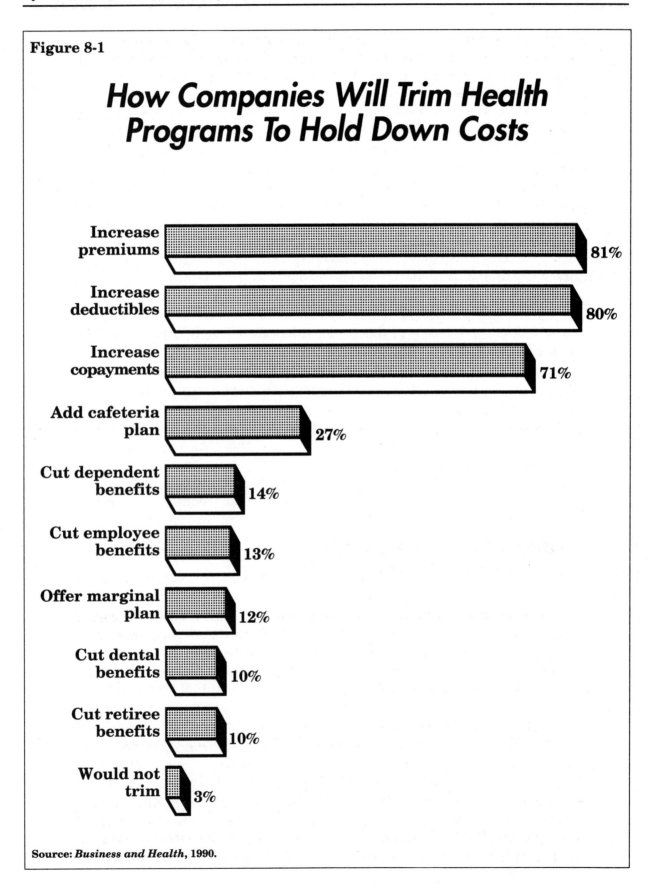

How Companies Will Trim Health Programs To Hold Down Costs

Increase premiums — 81%
Increase deductibles — 80%
Increase copayments — 71%
Add cafeteria plan — 27%
Cut dependent benefits — 14%
Cut employee benefits — 13%
Offer marginal plan — 12%
Cut dental benefits — 10%
Cut retiree benefits — 10%
Would not trim — 3%

Source: *Business and Health*, 1990.

insurance coverage to almost any individual and the threat of losing the coverage they have is quite worrisome to many Americans. While being without insurance is not a personal problem for more than 15 percent of Americans at any point in time, a Census Bureau survey released in 1989 underscores the instability of insurance coverage. More than one in four Americans (28%) reported having been without insurance in the 28-month period prior to the survey.[38] In 1989, a majority of insured persons were afraid they would lose their coverage if they changed jobs, or had a health problem or a work schedule that would disqualify them from obtaining employer-sponsored insurance coverage.[7] A 1990 *Los Angeles Times* survey found one in six adults (18%) reporting that their insurance benefits had been reduced over a two-year period,[9] and since 1983 the percentage of employers who pay the total cost of health premiums for their employees has declined from 67 percent to 51 percent, leaving employees with increased deductions from their paychecks.[39] Coupled with these historical trends is evidence from several new surveys of employers that more cuts in benefits or coverage are planned for the years ahead.

Policymakers are, as they have been in the past, left with a two-pronged problem — providing universal access to coverage and controlling health care costs. To many, the two goals are mutually exclusive, because to provide guaranteed insurance coverage for the whole population will entail spending more, not less, money.

How do we resolve this dilemma? Public opinion surveys can provide us with some clear preferences on the part of Americans, but also with some ambiguities. In this discussion, we will look first at support for different cost-containment strategies, and then at the public's views on shaping a national health plan.

PUBLIC SUPPORT FOR STRATEGIES TO CONTROL HEALTH CARE COSTS

As previously noted, there is extensive public concern about the cost of health care services. Not surprisingly, therefore, Americans hold some very strong views about the future direction of the nation's cost-containment strategy. There are a number of approaches to cost control that are acceptable to the public, and others that are not popular.

Will Americans be willing to limit spending on health? Americans' concerns about the cost of health services should not be interpreted to mean that they want fewer total dollars spent on the health care system. For nearly 20 years the General Social Survey conducted by the National Opinion Research Center has shown that the majority of the public believe that the U.S. spends too little, not too much, on health. In these surveys only 3 to 4 percent say too much is spent on health care.[40] What appears to bother Americans is the rapidly escalating inflation of individual service charges and fees. They feel that the continuing increases in hospital charges and physicians' bills are not warranted by improvements in overall quality.[41] Americans are not, however, troubled by new expenditures which lead to more or better health services being provided.

Do Americans want to ration health care? In the effort to reduce health care costs, health policy analysts often look to ways of limiting the amount of medical care provided to and used by Americans. These proposals take different forms, from encouraging various managed care strategies to denying access to certain kinds of treatment for certain kinds of patients. In recent years, proponents of this approach have dared to use the word "rationing," usually reminding the public that in many ways the U.S. already rations care by denying access to insurance and health services to many Americans. The challenge, we are told, is to find a more rational approach to doing what we already do. Indeed, the most noted effort in this regard came in 1990 when Oregon introduced a plan to rank spending priorities for medical care used by Medicaid recipients in that state, a plan that has generated considerable debate.[42]

What does the public think about rationing services, and for whom, and in what contexts, do they support such efforts? The data are somewhat limited, but do address a few fundamental issues that are being debated in the health policy arena.

Limiting services for the elderly. In the 1990 gubernatorial election campaign in Massachusetts, one candidate noted the amount of money spent on health care for the elderly and indicated that rationing might be acceptable for this group, saying "when you've had a long life and you're ripe, then it's time to go."[43] Public opinion quite forcibly rejects this approach to reducing the cost of health care.

A recent survey sponsored by the Northwest National Life Insurance Company framed two different questions about limiting health care for the elderly. Sixty-nine percent of Americans surveyed disagreed with the concept that "as patients grow older, their age should be considered when determining whether or not expensive treatments should be allowed." A similar proportion (65%) disagreed with the statement that "less money should be spent on health care for the elderly and more on health care services for children."[37]

Following the general trend supporting more spending on health, a majority of Americans supports increased rather than decreased spending on health programs for the elderly, including Medicare. There is also considerable support for proposals for the government to expand its role by providing the elderly with access to long term and catastrophic insurance coverage. Despite the recent repeal of the Medicare Catastrophic Act, surveys indicate that the public's, especially the elderly's, rejection of the plan was tied to certain elements of the financing and structure of the plan and not to its final objectives, which were quite popular.[41,44]

Figure 8-2

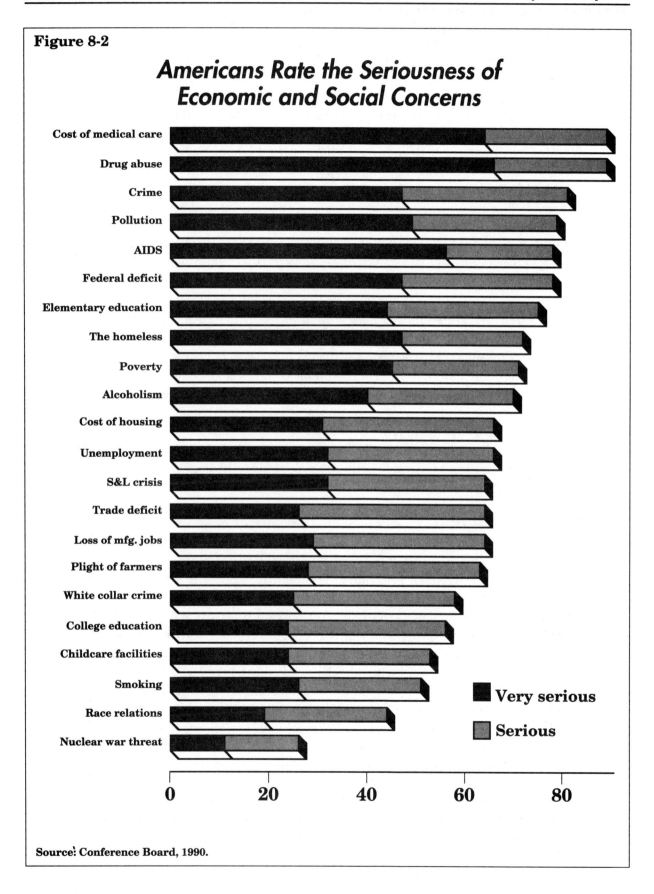

Americans Rate the Seriousness of Economic and Social Concerns

Source: Conference Board, 1990.

Limiting sevices for the terminally ill. There is a strong consensus among Americans that individuals suffering from terminal illness should have the option of requesting that certain medical care interventions be stopped at their, or their families', request. Recent surveys show that 70 to 81 percent (depending on whether the request is from patient or family member and patient is conscious or not) are in favor of withdrawing life-sustaining treatment from a terminally ill patient.[45] Responses to the General Social Survey indicate that, since 1982 an only slightly smaller proportion, between 60 and 66 percent, have supported the concept of allowing doctors to end the life of a patient with an incurable disease by some painless means if the patient and his family request it.[40] The public does not view these as potential cost-savings measures, but as quality of life considerations. These perceptions are underscored by their belief that such personal decisions should be made by patients, families, and physicians (80%), not by legislators (2%) or courts (7%).[45]

Limiting services for the poor and disadvantaged. Americans are deeply ambivalent about supporting government programs that are intended to provide medical care assistance to the poor and disadvantaged in our society. On one hand, an overwhelming majority (94%) of the public believes that health care should be available to everyone, even if they cannot afford it. In addition, only 16 percent agree with the statement that denying or limiting access to certain treatments should only apply to people whose health care is paid for through public funds.[37]

In practice, garnering public support for such programs is a difficult task. Medicaid, our nation's largest health care program for the poor, today covers only about half of Americans living in poverty (below 125 percent of the federal poverty standard). In some states, three out of four persons below this level of poverty are ineligible to receive benefits through this program.[46]

Public opinion polls suggest that Medicaid, which is financed and administered through welfare systems, is caught between the public's conflicting views about health and welfare programs. The health aspects of the program are popular, and a slight majority (51%) endorse the concept of increased government spending to ensure that all people below the poverty line can get access to medical care. However, only 31 percent want to provide the substantial increases in Medicaid spending that would be required for such a plan.[47,48]

The relative unpopularity of welfare spending is reflected in the General Social Survey. Since 1973, only 25 to 30 percent of Americans have said they think the U.S. spends too little on welfare, making it the lowest ranked item on a scale that includes health, the environment, education, mass transport, and parks and recreation.[40] Medicaid's ties to the welfare system leave it enmeshed in a strong set of public beliefs reflected in a 1988 survey in which large proportions of Americans said that welfare encourages poor young women to have babies (48%), fathers to desert their families (61%), healthy adults not to work (92%), and the poor to cheat to obtain eligibility (89%). In the public's mind, the true answer to the problem of poverty lies in creating jobs for the poor — related job training programs are supported by more than 70 percent.[49]

Figure 8-3

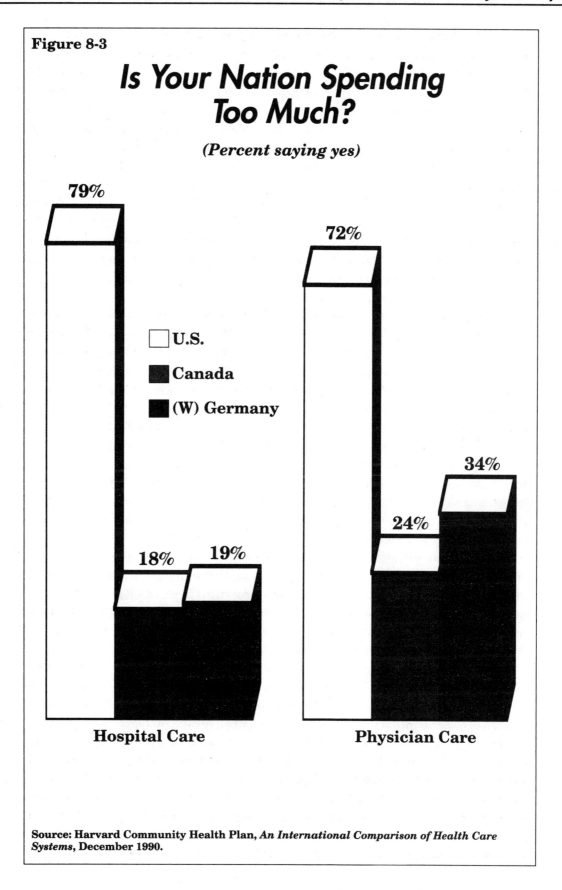

Is Your Nation Spending Too Much?

(Percent saying yes)

79%

72%

☐ U.S.

■ Canada

■ (W) Germany

34%

24%

18%   19%

Hospital Care

Physician Care

Source: Harvard Community Health Plan, *An International Comparison of Health Care Systems*, December 1990.

In addition to these perceptions, there is another major factor that underlies the public's tacit, if not openly acknowledged, willingness to limit health care services to certain poor and disadvantaged groups in our society. Racial, ethnic, and other social prejudices have clearly affected attitudes toward paying for the health care needed by low income groups. Today, government spending to improve the conditions of black Americans is considered to be too little by only about 30 percent of Americans. On the other hand, nearly 70 percent feel our current level of spending is about right or too much (see Figure 8-4).[40] Similarly, in a 1990 study, on a scale of 1 to 7, with 1=tend to be self-supporting and 7=prefer to live off welfare, only one percent of Americans ranked whites as a 6 or 7, and 32 percent ranked blacks in one of these categories. At the other end of the scale, 45 percent ranked whites 1 or 2 and only 5 percent said blacks are generally likely to be self-supporting. These latent attitudes make it difficult to extend Medicaid to socially disadvantaged individuals who, research has shown, have the most serious health problems.[50]

Other examples of our national prejudices have been seen in the United States' response to the AIDS epidemic. Surveys conducted in the earlier years of the epidemic indicated that more than half of Americans felt that government funding to fight the disease would have been more forthcoming if homosexual men were not disproportionately affected. One in 12 persons nationally said they were protecting themselves against the spread of the disease by avoiding interaction with homosexuals.[51] More recent surveys show that compassion toward persons suffering from the disease change depending on how it was contracted — only 2 percent disagreed with the statement that persons who contracted AIDS from a blood transfusion should be treated with compassion, but more than 25 percent of Americans felt that way toward persons who contracted the disease through a homosexual act, intravenous drug use, or sexual relations with a drug user.[52]

Collectively, these data point to a need to consider the attitudes that Americans hold toward the poor, minorities, and other disadvantaged groups in our society as we shape policy. Government programs focused primarily on these needy populations will face considerable resistance in terms of public support for any proposed expansion. We will need to decide as a society if these are acceptable standards by which to decide to limit access to care for our most vulnerable citizens.

Will Americans accept limitations on their choice of doctors or hospitals? A crucial factor in understanding the public mood is to be aware of the dichotomy between Americans' views of the U.S. health care system versus their satisfaction with their personal medical care arrangements. Surveys show that only 10 to 30 percent of Americans are satisfied with the health care system. In fact, as noted before, in an international comparative study, the U.S. tied for last among the industrialized countries on this satisfaction measure.[30] There is clear evidence that when Americans express their dissatisfaction with our health system they are referring to very specific issues — high health care costs,

Figure 8-4

The Public's View of Spending To Improve the Conditions of Black Americans

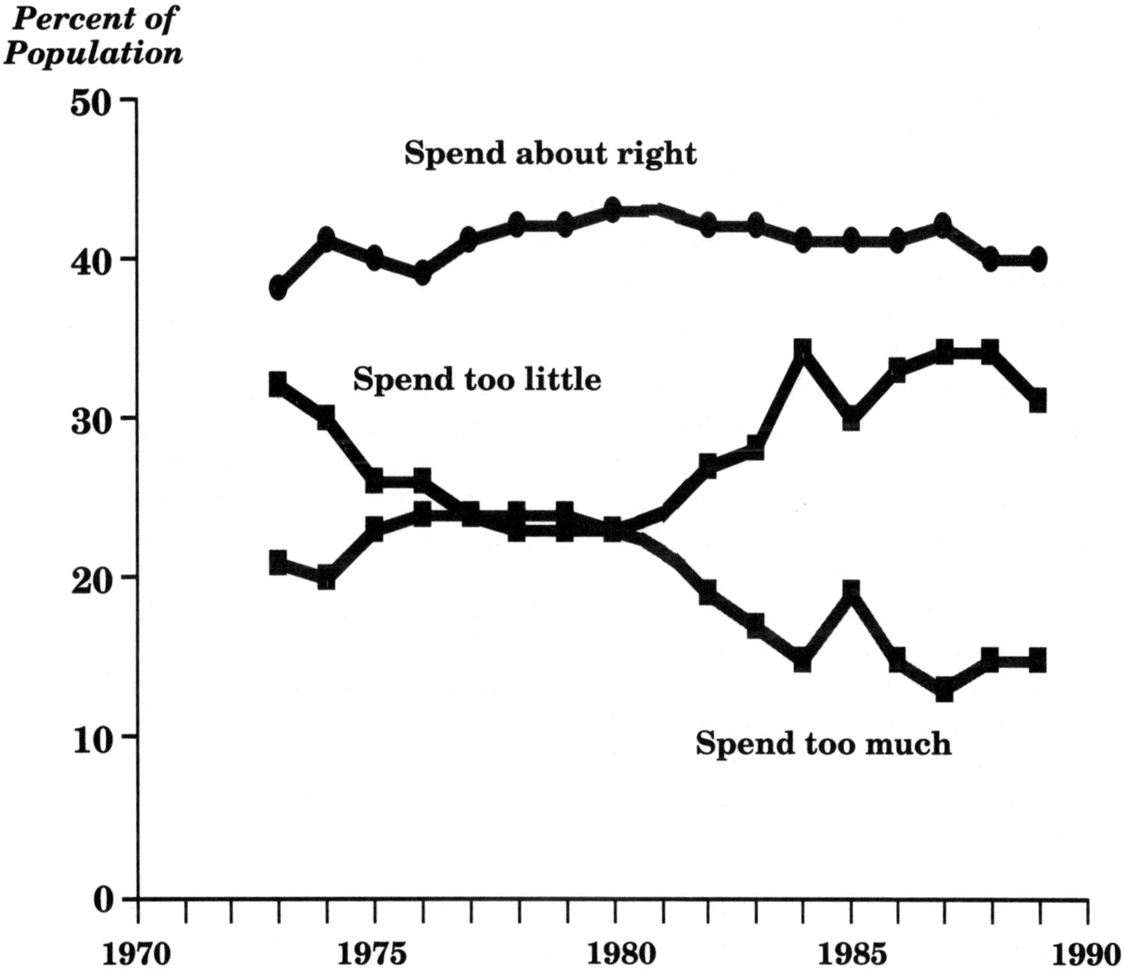

Percent of Population

Source: National Opinion Research Center, General Social Survey 1972-1989.

lack of universal insurance coverage, and the absence of a guarantee that their health benefits can not be arbitrarily reduced.

However, this high level of negative public attitudes toward the health care system and the accompanying pressures for change are not accompanied by dissatisfaction with personal health care services. In fact, the vast majority of Americans who use the health care system are generally very happy with the care they receive. In a 1990 Gallup survey for the American Medical Association, 85 percent say they were very or somewhat satisfied with their most recent physician visit;[53] in another survey conducted by the Roper Organization, 88 percent were satisfied with the quality of their physician care and 76 percent with the quality of their hospital care.[14]

What do these data mean when viewed in light of the public's dissatisfaction with the system as a whole? The public wants change in the structure of their health care system, but not in their personal health care arrangements. For example, the majority (60%) say they are not inclined to participate in insurance plans, such as health maintenance organizations, that would limit their choice of health care providers.[54] Similarly, a 1989 NBC News survey demonstrated that support for a national health insurance system dropped from 67 percent to 36 percent when the public was asked if they would still favor such a plan if they were not able to choose their own physician.[7]

Will the public support government efforts to regulate provider fees?
Responses to surveys by the American Medical Association since 1983 indicate that less than one third of Americans believe that physician fees are reasonable,[53] and in a 1990 poll by the *Los Angeles Times* physician fees and hospital charges were cited as two of the top three reasons health care is so expensive in the U.S. It is, therefore, not surprising that more than 60 percent of Americans find government controls on physician and hospital fees to be an acceptable way of containing costs.[9] The new provider payment systems under Medicare — Diagnosis Related Groups (DRGs) for hospitals and a Resource Based Relative Value Scale (RBRVS) for physicians — correspond to the public's views that government established price controls should be a major focus for cost containment activities. Extending those into the private sector is seen as a logical next step by most Americans.

How do Americans view measures to reduce inefficiencies in the provision of health services? In past studies, Americans have expressed fears about being hospitalized, having surgery, or being admitted to a nursing home. For the average individual, these are traumatic events. Thus, Americans see the reduction in the number of unnecessary tests, surgical procedures, and hospitalizations as a positive objective, not only for cost containment reasons.[41] Requiring or encouraging the use of outpatient treatment rather than hospitalization is supported by nearly three quarters of those surveyed, and requiring or encouraging patients to obtain a second opinion before surgery is favored by 85 percent of respondents.[54] Similar measures such as utilization review would appear to hold popular support.

However, once in a hospital, Americans want the best technology available to them, almost without restriction. Although Americans want access to new and often expensive medical technologies, they are willing to travel further to obtain such services. Seventy-four percent support regionalizing the use of expensive equipment as a cost-savings measure.[54]

It is clear that the public believes that elimination of this kind of inefficiency can be accomplished without jeopardizing the quality of care available to them. Nearly seven in ten (69%) of Americans think we can substantially reduce medical costs in this country without affecting the quality of health care.[9] As with the pre-Gulf military, the public senses a good deal of administrative waste in the system and does not see the need for draconian cost control measures that reduce services, at least at this time, as might be found in other health care systems.

PUBLIC SUPPORT FOR NATIONAL HEALTH INSURANCE

As noted earlier, in addition to their concerns about the cost of medical care, Americans are also profoundly concerned about the lack of financial security provided by our current health insurance system. Their uncertainties about finding secure and stable insurance coverage are driven by a great flux in employment patterns and a decreased enthusiasm on the part of employers for absorbing the increasing costs of care. In this part of the discussion we look at the American public's preferences for reforming the health care system and at other perceptions underlying these opinions that will shape the emerging debate about a national program of health insurance.

Public opinion about the government's responsibility to provide health care. For more than four decades, public opinion surveys have shown that the American public believes that all people have a right to adequate health care. As far back as 1942, three out of four Americans said that, after World War II ended, the federal government should be responsible for providing the resources necessary to see that medical care was available for everyone who needed it.[55] International comparative studies have shown, however, that although Americans hold these beliefs, they do not feel as strongly about them as do citizens of some other nations. For example, whereas nearly eight out of ten Italians and Britons see their government as having an essential responsibility to provide universal access to medical care, only four out ten Americans feel this way.[56]

Other survey results suggest that although Americans believe universal access to health care is desirable, they do not view our nation's failure to enact a program of national health insurance as a deep concern compared with other issues on the national agenda. The public's priorities can be explained in part by two factors. First, more than eight out of ten Americans already have insurance and may not see themselves as benefitting directly from such a plan, even in the atmosphere of anxiety about reductions in benefits. Second, as noted earlier, those who would benefit are subject to some rather negative stereotypes on the part of a small but significant segment of our populace.

Public support for different options for health care reform. Despite the fact that a number of polling organizations have surveyed Americans on these issues using a wide array of questions and concepts, there is remarkable consistency in the public's response to the two central national policy options that have been suggested in the U.S. One such model is a national health insurance scheme that would cover all Americans and be financed through taxation or Social Security. The model for this system that is most frequently cited is that in place in Canada, though given the lack of familiarity with this system in the United States, it might be more commonly understood as Medicare for the entire U.S. population. In surveys conducted by Louis Harris, NBC, Gallup, the American Association for Retired Persons, the Roper Organization, the *Los Angeles Times*, and state polling units in Connecticut and Kentucky, approximately 60-70 percent of Americans support this type of approach (see Table 8-1), even given variations in question wording.

The second approach to health reform that has been put forth, both by Richard Nixon in 1970 and in another form by the federal bipartisan Pepper Commission in 1990, is a plan that would require all employers to provide private health insurance for their employees and create public insurance programs for the unemployed and poor. This type of program would address the fact that two-thirds of the uninsured in the U.S. are employed or are family members of someone who works. In several studies, this type of plan has garnered a similar or marginally greater measure of public support than an entirely government financed insurance system. In surveys conducted by a number of different organizations, 68-82 percent of Americans supported this type of proposal in 1989, 1990, and 1991.

The controversy over a public versus private financing scheme. One problem with many of the surveys conducted on the preferred restructuring of the system is that pollsters do not often phrase questions to include both major options — a national system or an expansion of the current private-public system — in order to see which is preferable to the public. As a result, survey results show a large degree of support for each option, but do not indicate whether people are willing to make a choice between the two, a controversial decision that is at the heart of making policy on this issue. Polls conducted during the national health insurance debate in the 1970s showed that the public, when offered both options, was split over the choice between creating a new public system or modifying our current private-public system to expand insurance through employer requirements.[57,58] Louis Harris and Associates asked a different version of this question in 1990 and found that there had been a slight shift in which option was supported by the plurality, but there was still no majority consensus for any one plan.[59] If supporters of change are divided about what form the change should take, the will of the minority that wants nothing done could prevail.

The public's willingness to pay for health care reform. Three surveys undertaken between 1988 and 1990 show that the level of public support for the adoption of a national health insurance plan declines in proportion to the increase in taxes proposed to fund it.[7,9,59] Americans will express support for this program if it entails a modest increase in their tax burden. The *Los Angeles Times* reported in 1990 that 72 percent would support a national plan even if it entailed a tax increase. However, only 22 percent would be willing to pay more than $200/ year to see this happen, and 33 percent remain undecided. Harris surveys have demonstrated that the most popular source of revenues to fund a universal health program are, in descending order, increases in taxes on cigarettes and liquor; required employer contributions; Social Security taxes paid by employers for each employee; insurance premiums paid by the individual; and income taxes. Other surveys suggest support for an earmarked health-related sales tax.

CONCLUSION

Policy makers now face a window of opportunity for achieving the enactment of a universal health care program. However, to accomplish this end will require a level of pragmatism and *realpolitik* not seen in earlier periods of national concern about this issue. Today, there is no firm consensus on what form a national health plan should take, or on what measures should be undertaken to resolve the health care cost problems we face.

In this uncertain environment, the only plan that could achieve widespread public support is one that does not seek to resolve all of this country's health care system problems in one piece of legislation. In fact, it will be a proposal that puts off making difficult choices about cost containment and major structural reforms to another time. At present, Americans will not support a program that will dramatically raise individual taxes or in any way lead to deterioration in the availability and quality of the medical care they now receive.

Absent a consensus on the specifics of major health care reform, the compromise legislation would have to contain elements of the following: (1) a mixed private-public insurance program involving expanded coverage through employers for those who are working; (2) a plan to phase in the program over a period of years, with taxes gradually increasing as more groups are included; (3) taxes should be earmarked for the program, should involve a fixed employer contribution, and should rely as little as possible on the direct use of the federal income tax as a financing mechanism; (4) the development of an alternative program to Medicaid that is administered outside of the welfare system (like, for example, the popular Headstart education program); (5) cost-containment efforts that focus on limiting hospital and doctor charges, as well as curtailing the inappropriate use of medical, hospital, and other services; and (6) health benefits, like the minimum wage, should be expanded gradually, but there should be no explicit policy to ration any types of care. Services initially excluded from coverage under the program should be those where there is a wide consensus that few people would suffer irreversible harm without them.

In the final analysis, we must acknowledge that there are limits to the conclusions that can be drawn from opinion surveys on any public policy issue, including health care reform. Responses to polls can indicate in what direction the wind is blowing, but it takes strong leadership to turn the force of public opinion into government action. Without such an effort either by the President, or some other national group or political figure, America's renewed interest in health care reform will once again falter. The successful enactment of any national plan will require attention to forging a consensus among many diverse interests in an effort similar to that which the President applied in holding the diverse coalition of nations together in the Gulf. The likelihood of such an action is discussed in Chapter 10. Although President Bush has not demonstrated any interest to date in playing this role in the health care reform debate, a number of prominent leaders and national groups have emerged which, in the right moment, could come together to achieve this end.

AUTHORS' NOTE:

Substantial portions of this chapter are drawn from articles published previously in The New England Journal of Medicine and the Stanford Law and Policy Review. Grateful acknowledgement is given to John Benson at the Roper Center for Public Opinion Research for providing data essential to this discussion, and to the Esther A. and Joseph Klingenstein Fund, Inc. for partial funding of the research presented here.

REFERENCES

1.   Kosterlitz J. The year of commissions. *National Journal.* October 28, 1989;2634-2637.

2.   Enthoven A, Kronick R. A consumer choice health plan for the 1990s. *New England Journal of Medicine.* 1989;320:29-37, 94-101.

3.   Himmelstein DU, Woolhandler S. A national health program for the United States. *New England Journal of Medicine.* 1989;320: 102-108.

4.   U.S. Bipartisan Commission on Comprehensive Health Care. *A Call for Action.* Washington, DC: The Pepper Commission on Comprehensive Health Care;1990.

5.   Lundberg GD, Blendon RJ, eds. Caring for the Uninsured and Underinsured (special issue). *Journal of the American Medical Association.* 1991;265:2491-2567.

6.   Blendon RJ, Donelan K. The public and the emerging debate over national health insurance. *New England Journal of Medicine.* 1990;323:208-212.

7.   NBC News. February, 1989. Storrs CT: Roper Center for Public Opinion Research.

8.   Hershberg BZ. Poll charts changing face of health insurance. *Louisville Courier Journal.* February 18, 1990; E1.

9.   Los Angeles Times Poll. Health Care in the United States, January, 1990. Storrs CT: Roper Center for Public Opinion Research.

10.   The Atlantic Financial Poll. April 1990. Storrs CT: Roper Center for Public Opinion Research.

11.   CBS/New York Times Poll. October 1990. Storrs CT: Roper Center for Public Opinion Research.

12.   Gallup Organization for Blue Cross and Blue Shield. January 1990. Storrs CT: Roper Center for Public Opinion Research.

13.   Hartford Courant/Institute for Social Inquiry. Connecticut Poll #101. April 1990. Storrs CT: Roper Center for Public Opinion Research.

14.   Jajich-Toth C, Roper BW. Americans' views on health care. *Health Affairs.* Winter 1990; 9:149-157.

15.   ICR Survey Research Group/Associated Press. December 1990. Storrs CT: Roper Center for Public Opinion Research.

16.   CBS/New York Times. May 1991. Storrs CT: Roper Center for Public Opinion Research.

17.   NBC News/Wall Street Journal. June 1991. Storrs, CT:Roper Center for Public Opinion Research.

18.   Erskine H. The polls: health insurance. *Public Opinion Quarterly*.
       1975;39:128-143.

19.   Waldman S. *National Health Insurance Proposals*. SSA 74-11920.
       Washington D.C.: Social Security Administration; 1974, pp. 21-44.

20.   The Urban Institute. *National Health Insurance: Conflicting Goals
       and Policy Choices*. Feder J, Holahan J, Marmor T, eds.
       Washington D.C.: The Urban Institute; 1980.

21.   Leonard Davis Institute of Health Economics. *National Health
       Insurance*. Eclers RD and Moyerman SS, eds. Homewood IL:
       Richard D Irwin; 1971.

22.   Starr P. *The Social Transformation of American Medicine*. New
       York: Basic Books; 1982, pp. 266-419.

23.   Burrow JG. *AMA: Voice of American Medicine*. Baltimore MD: The
       Johns Hopkins Press; 1963, pp. 281-394.

24.   Rayack E. *Professional Power and American Medicine: the
       Economics of the American Medical Association*. Cleveland OH:
       The World Publishing Company; 1967, pp. 135-201, 273-290.

25.   Taylor MG. The Canadian health care system: after Medicare. in
       Coburn O et al, eds. *Health and Canadian Society*. Markham
       Ontario: Fitshenny & Whiteside; 1987, pp. 73-100.

26.   *The Economist* 1989; 310:61.

27.   Gallup Organization. November 4, 1949. U.S.A.I.P.O. 49-449.
       Storrs, CT: Roper Center for Public Opinion Research.

28.   Gallup GH, ed. *The Gallup International Opinion Polls: Great
       Britain 1937-1975*. New York: Random House; 1976.

29.   Schieber GJ and Poullier JP. International health spending:
       issues and trends. *Health Affairs*. Spring 1991;10:106-116.

30.   Blendon RJ, Leitman R, Morrison I, Donelan K. Satisfaction with
       health systems in ten nations. *Health Affairs*. Summer 1990;9:185-192.

31.   *An International Comparison of Health-Care Systems*. Harvard
       Community Health Plan Annual Report 1990. Brookline
       MA: Harvard Community Health Plan; December, 1990.

32. Lazenby HC, Letsch SW. National health expenditures, 1989. *Health Care Financing Review*. Winter 1990; 12:1-26.

33. *Los Angeles Times*. February 20, 1990; p.D5.

34. *Business and Health*. April 1990; 8:24-38.

35. Linden F. What are people worried about these days? *Across the Board*. September 1990, p.13.

36. Organization for Economic Cooperation and Development. *Health Care Systems in Transition: The Search for Efficiency*. Paris: OECD; 1990.

37. *Americans Speak Out on Health Care Rationing*. Minneapolis MN: Northwestern National Life Insurance Company, November 1990.

38. Nelson C, Short K. Health Insurance Coverage 1986-1988. Bureau of Census. *Current Population Reports*, Series P-70(17), 1990; pp.1-3.

39. U.S. Department of Labor, Bureau of Labor Statistics. *Employee Benefits in Medium and Large Firms, 1983 and 1989*. Washington DC: U.S. Government Printing Office; June 1989.

40. National Opinion Research Center. *General Social Survey Trends, 1972-1990*. Chicago, Illinois. Distributed by Roper Center for Public Opinion Research, Storrs, CT.

41. Blendon RJ. The public's view of the future of health care. *Journal of the American Medical Association*. 1988; 259:3587-3593.

42. Iglehart J, ed. Rationing: Oregon's plan (special section). *Health Affairs*. Summer 1991;10:5-51, 78-95.

43. Knox R, *The Boston Globe*. July 18, 1990; p.1.

44. Straw M. Polling on the Medicare Catastrophic Coverage Act: Findings and Lessons Learned. Washington DC: American Association for Retired Persons; 1990.

45. Yankelovich, Clancy, Shulman for *Time* and Cable News Network. February, 1990. Storrs CT: Roper Center for Public Opinion Research.

46.   Congressional Research Service. *Medicaid Source Book: Background Data and Analysis.* Washington DC: U.S. Government Printing Office; 1988.

47.   Harvey LK, Shubat SC. *Physician and Public Attitudes on Health Care Issues, 1988 edition.* Chicago IL: American Medical Association; 1989.

48.   ABC News/Washington Post. August 1989. Storrs CT: Roper Center for Public Opinion Research.

49.   Melville K, Doble J. *The Public's Perspective on Social Welfare Reform.* New York: Public Agenda Foundation; 1988.

50.   National Opinion Research Center. General Social Survey, February 1990. Roper Center for Public Opinion Research, Storrs, CT.

51.   Blendon RJ and Donelan K. Discrimination against people with AIDS: the public's perspective. *New England Journal of Medicine.* 1988;319:1022-1026.

52.   KRC Communications for *The Boston Globe*, May 1990. Storrs CT: Roper Center for Public Opinion Research.

53.   Harvey LK, Shubat SC. *Public Opinion on Health Care Issues, 1991 edition.* Chicago IL: American Medical Association; 1991.

54.   Cambridge Reports, *Trends and Forecasts*, February, 1989; p.7.

55.   Fortune Magazine survey, July 1942, cited in Cantril H. ed., *Public Opinion 1935-1946.* Westport CT: Greenwood Press, 1978.

56.   Smith TW. The welfare state in cross-national perspective. *Public Opinion Quarterly* 1987; 51:404-421.

57.   Watts W, Free LA. *State of the Nation.* New York: Universe; 1973, p. 288.

58.   Opinion Research Corporation. Public opinion index, December 31, 1976. Storrs CT: Roper Center for Public Opinion Research.

59.   Louis Harris and Associates. March 1990. Storrs CT: Roper Center for Public Opinion Research.

CHAPTER 9

The Special Role of the Elderly in Health Care Policy

Robert Leitman
Louis Harris and Associates
and
Jennifer N. Edwards
Harvard School of Public Health

INTRODUCTION

A discussion of Americans' attitudes toward health care reform would not be complete without a consideration of the preferences of the elderly, the group that our surveys show carries the most clout in health care politics. They are one of the best organized groups of people in the country, and their opinions are often sought by policymakers before changes are made that would affect their well-being.

This chapter describes the health care interests of elderly people to the extent they are different than those of younger people. It is based on results of seven national surveys of the elderly conducted in the last few years. The findings have important implications for containing costs and providing health services in the next few years.

THE POLITICAL POWER OF THE ELDERLY

What most people do not realize about the elderly is that, aside from being increasingly numerous and heavy users of care, they also have cultivated a great deal of political power. With a strong organization representing their views in Washington and an impressive record of participation in elections, the elderly have become a key group shaping U.S. health care policy. In a 1988 Harris survey

Table 9-1

Political Power of the Elderly

(Percent of respondents ranking each group first in political power)

	House of Representatives	Senate	Federal Officials
The elderly	78%	63%	46%
Doctors	8	13	22
Hospitals	3	13	7
Employers	3	10	5
Health insurers	3	3	5
Drug/medical equipment manufacturers	—	—	12
Some other group	2	—	—
Minorities and the underprivileged	—	—	—
Not sure	3	—	2

Source: Louis Harris and Associates. *Survey of Legislators and Regulators, 1988.*

Figure 9-1

Proportion of Population That Voted by Age, Race, and Income, 1988

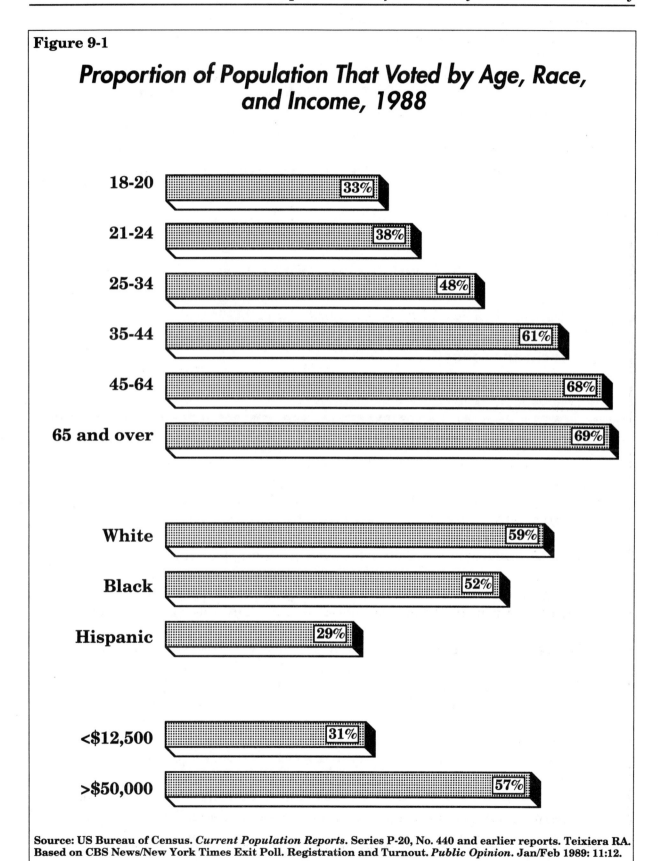

18-20	33%
21-24	38%
25-34	48%
35-44	61%
45-64	68%
65 and over	69%
White	59%
Black	52%
Hispanic	29%
<$12,500	31%
>$50,000	57%

Source: US Bureau of Census. *Current Population Reports.* **Series P-20, No. 440 and earlier reports. Teixiera RA. Based on CBS News/New York Times Exit Poll. Registration and Turnout.** *Public Opinion.* **Jan/Feb 1989: 11:12.**

Table 9-2

Satisfaction With Health Care Services

	Percent Very Satisfied	
	<u>Age 65 and Over</u>	<u>Age 18-64</u>
Ability to see a doctor whenever needed	59%	44%
Access to high quality medical technology	36	35
Cost of health care	26	14
Health insurance benefits	31	28

Source: Louis Harris and Associates. *Consumer Survey*, **1990.**

of federal legislators and government policymakers, the elderly were ranked first in terms of political influence by 69 percent of legislators and policymakers.[1] As shown in Table 9-1, they have more political power in influencing health care policy than doctors, hospitals, or employers. Elected officials report being sensitive to the clout of the elderly more often than non-elected government officials.

The political power of the elderly can also be explained, in part, by their voting habits. Approximately 50 percent of registered voters are over age 45, and voters between the ages of 55 and 74 are most likely to vote. Figure 9-1 shows that people aged 45 to 64 and over age 65 voted more than other age voters did in 1988.[2]

Much of the political activity of the elderly can be attributed to the American Association of Retired Persons (AARP), a nonprofit, nonpartisan organization with almost 30 million members that lobbies both the federal and state governments regarding issues of concern to elderly Americans. It is the nation's largest and oldest organization of Americans over 50 years old, retired or not, and has enrolled about half the eligible population. By enrolling people over 50 years old, AARP straddles the two fastest growing age cohorts in the 1990s — people in their early 50s and those over 75 years of age.

Health care is at the heart of elderly people's agenda. The elderly would rather the government spend more on health care and Social Security than on other national concerns such as education, defense, or housing.[3] The elderly are afraid about their future health. When asked what things they fear most, the elderly cite a fear of failing health first (mentioned by 23% of all elderly), followed by fear of losing independence (15%), and fear of being institutionalized (7%).[4] We would expect, then, that the elderly might put a lot of their influence behind health care issues.

ATTITUDES TOWARD HEALTH CARE AND THE HEALTH CARE SYSTEM

Given the concern of the elderly about health care and their political clout, we believe it is important for policymakers and institutional leaders to learn how the elderly view their health care system and what changes they believe are necessary in the next few years. Like other Americans, the elderly generally are happy with the care they get, but would like to see a number of changes enacted to improve the health care system as a whole.

Although people generally have the perception that the elderly are getting lower quality health care than the rest of the population and have a harder time getting it,[5] the elderly tend to be slightly more satisfied with their health care services than people under age 65, though there is still much room for improvement.[6] Almost 80 percent of the elderly were satisfied, overall, with the services

---

Table 9-3

The Need for Health Care System Reform

	Age 65 and over	Age 18-64
On the whole, the health care system works pretty well and only minor changes are needed	15%	16%
There are good things in our health care system, but fundamental changes are needed	53	60
The American health care system has so much wrong with it that we need to completely rebuild it	28	23
Not sure	4	<1

Source: Louis Harris and Associates. *Consumer Survey*, 1990.

Table 9-4

What Type of Health Care System Do the Elderly Prefer?

	Percent <u>Preferring</u>
Present system	27%
Present system plus employer mandates and the government covering the uninsured	18
Comprehensive national health insurance	47
Not sure	6

Source: Louis Harris and Associates. *Consumer Survey*, 1990.

they used in the last few years, the same proportion as below age 65. As shown in Table 9-2, 59 percent are very satisfied with their ability to see a doctor whenever needed, compared to 44 percent of people ages 18-64. The same proportion of each age group is very satisfied with access to high quality medical technology (35% and 36%), and health insurance benefits (31% and 28%). The elderly are somewhat more satisfied with the cost of health care than younger people are: 26 percent of the elderly are very satisfied with their costs, compared to 14 percent of the nonelderly.[6]

On the other hand, many elderly would support changes to the system. Twenty-eight percent believe that so much is wrong with the health care system that is needs to be completely rebuilt, 53 percent believe fundamental changes are needed, and only 15 percent would keep the current system with only minor changes (see Table 9-3). When offered a choice of two types of improvements to the health care system currently under consideration, 47 percent favor a comprehensive national health insurance system, 18 percent favor employer mandates with the government covering the uninsured, and 27 percent favor the present system over the other two choices (Table 9-4). A significant source of their dissatisfaction is their insecurity about being able to afford care in the future. More than half of the elderly report that they worry that their future health care costs will not be taken care of.[7]

OTHER PRIORITIES FOR THE ELDERLY

Like most Americans, the elderly would like more complete coverage for their health care needs. They are not willing to let the discussion of long term care and prescription drug benefits die with the repeal of the Medicare Catastrophic Care Act of 1989. Many favored its demise in 1990 because when they understood the nature of the program, the majority of the elderly did not think the benefits were worth the taxes. Apart from the financing question, they still want some of the benefits it would have provided as well as new ones. As shown in Table 9-5, 88 percent of the elderly want Medicare to cover nursing home and home health care costs (52 percent support it very strongly). Eighty-eight percent of the elderly also support adding prescription drug coverage under Medicare, with 63 percent supporting it very strongly.[6] With attention on the federal budget deficit and some lingering sensitivities on Capitol Hill from the Medicare Catastrophic Act repeal, interest will likely be focused on the less expensive option — expanding prescription drugs rather than long term care, at least in the short run.

When given a choice of how they would like expanded benefits to be structured, AARP members showed an overwhelming preference for adding to the Medicare program. Sixty-five percent of members prefer a social insurance approach, compared to only 8 percent who would prefer a solution from the private sector.[8] Were this to come to fruition, private long term care policies would not be in great demand in the future, and the large investment of resources

---

Table 9-5

Support Among the Elderly for Expanded Medicare Benefits

	Medicare Coverage of Nursing Home and Home Health <u>Costs</u>	Medicare Coverage of Prescription <u>Drugs</u>
Support very strongly	52%	63%
Support somewhat strongly	36	25
Support not very strongly	7	5
Oppose	3	6
Not sure/It depends	2	1

Source: Louis Harris and Associates. *Consumer Survey,* 1990.

Table 9-6

Elderly Support for Increased Cost Sharing

	Very Acceptable	Moderately Acceptable	Not Very Acceptable	Not at All Acceptable
Increase individual's premium contribution by $200/year	6%	19%	29%	45%
Increase annual deductible by $200	8	21	20	47
Increase doctor visit copayments by $10	7	26	25	40

Source: Louis Harris and Associates. *Consumer Survey,* 1990.

necessary to enter that market could be a bad decision. However, a comprehensive government program is uncertain, and, at minimum, private long term care policies could have the same, limited role as Medigap policies now have.

If there is a debate over the expansion of Medicare benefits, it will raise questions about how expansions will be financed and how the cost of new benefits will be kept under control. Undoubtedly, Congress will consider regulating prescription drug prices, a move the public will encourage. About half of elderly consumers do not think prescription drug prices are reasonable, and more than half (56%) do not believe the price they are charged is related to the cost to the manufacturer of producing the drug.[6]

Additional savings could be achieved by more widespread use of mail order drugs and generic substitutes. While only 17 percent of the elderly now use mail order drugs, 63 percent say they would be interested in using them.[6] (The question included the information that they would cost 25 percent less than at the local pharmacy.) The use of generic drugs is already fairly common. Most people know what generics are, and 44 percent of the elderly asked for them last time they had a prescription filled. Both of these approaches could have a role if new legislation is considered.

CONTROLLING COSTS IN THE HEALTH CARE SYSTEM

Assuming that expanded benefits cannot be enacted in our current fiscal environment without some cost containment, we looked for signs from the elderly of what type of cost containment would be acceptable to them. In an earlier survey we found the elderly approved of price controls for doctors and hospitals. Two constraints that have since been adopted in limited form are DRGs and the relative value scale for physician payment. What else would they find acceptable?

Table 9-6 shows the response when we put this question to the elderly in 1990. The elderly dislike strategies that control costs by increasing cost sharing. About half of the elderly report it would not be at all acceptable to them if their premium contribution or annual deductible was raised $200 per year; and 40 percent would not find increased copayments for doctors' visits at all acceptable.[6]

A second approach to containing costs has been suggested in several national proposals — controlling health care spending through the increased use of managed care, especially prepaid, capitated health plans. Despite the apparent advantages for policymakers, capitated plans have not been very popular with the majority of people over age 65. According to the Health Care Financing Administration, only 6 percent of Medicare beneficiaries were enrolled in HMOs last year.[9] Our survey found that 66 percent of the elderly reported that they were not interested in joining an HMO. Their dislike of HMOs is based on the restrictions placed on their choice of physician. As shown in Table 9-7, 72 percent of the elderly would find it unacceptable to be in a plan that restricted their choice

---

Table 9-7

Elderly Support for Managed Care

	Very Acceptable	Moderately Acceptable	Not Very Acceptable	Not at All Acceptable
Restrict choice of general practitioner	2%	21%	22%	50%
Restrict choice of specialist	2	16	23	57
Require consultation with case manager when expenses exceed $200	7	25	28	36
Require pre-admission certification	7	35	18	36
Require seeing family doctor before seeing specialist	25	38	16	20

Source: **Louis Harris and Associates.** *Consumer Survey,* **1990.**

---

of general practitioner, and 80 percent of the elderly would not want their choice of a specialist restricted. Likewise, case management was unacceptable to a majority of elderly people. Sixty-four percent would not want to have to consult with a case manager before using services costing more than $2,000 in a year. The elderly were not totally inflexible, however. Sixty-three percent reported being willing to seek authorization from the health plan before seeing a specialist.[6]

Table 9-8

Acceptability of Rationing to the Elderly

Rationing Concept	Percent of Elderly Who:		
	Agree	**Disagree**	**Don't know**
Treatments or procedures that are rationed or denied should be denied to everyone, even to people who could afford to pay for them out of their own pocket	51%	39%	10%
Where health care is provided at public expense, only treatments or operations with a certain chance of being successful should be allowed	43	49	8
As patients grow older, their age should be considered when determining whether or not expensive treatments should be allowed	40	55	5
Smokers who rely on public funds for health care should be denied treatment for illness caused by smoking	34	61	5
Less money should be spent on health care for the elderly and more on health care services for children	26	60	14
Denying or limiting certain treatments should only apply to people whose health care is paid for by public funds	9	85	6

Source: *Americans Speak Out on Health Care Rationing.* **Northwestern National Life Insurance Company, 1990.**

A third approach to containing costs is to place limits on services available to patients — rationing. The basis for these limits could be who the payer is, who the patient is, or the potential outcome of the treatment. A majority of the elderly do not find any of these approaches acceptable.[7] Fully 90 percent believe that if health care is rationed, the same rules should apply to all types of insurance policies, not just public insurance. However, people who are able to pay out of their pocket should still be allowed to buy rationed services, according to 39 percent of elderly. The elderly, like the nonelderly, do not think age is a good criteria for rationing. Sixty percent disagree with the statement that less should be spent on health care for the elderly and more on children. The elderly are split on whether treatments and operations provided at public expense that may not be highly successful should be limited. Forty-nine percent think there should not be limits, while 43 percent think there should be. Nor are people ready to ration care to "health abusers." Sixty-one percent oppose denying treatment to smokers who rely on public funds for health care. The elderly were more inclined toward restrictions placed on doctors' professional choices. Almost half (45%) believe it is acceptable to restrict doctors' freedom in prescribing, opening up the possibility of practice guideline implementation and limits on tests and drugs. These attitudes, and those summarized on Table 9-8, indicate that the elderly oppose rationing as a means of saving money.[7]

Table 9-9

Attitudes of the Elderly Toward Advance Directives and Life-Sustaining Treatment

	Yes	No	Not Sure
Do you think doctors should be required to honor advance directives?	76%	18%	6%
Do you think the family of a terminally ill patient should have the right to demand life-sustaining treatment?	25	65	10

Source: **Louis Harris and Associates.** *Consumer Survey,* 1990.

THE RIGHT TO USE/REFUSE MEDICAL TREATMENT

On issues related to death and the restriction of medical treatment it is especially relevant to know the views of the elderly as often it is their medical care that is questioned. Three-fourths of the elderly, and slightly more of the nonelderly, believe the law should allow doctors to honor the written instructions of their patients who are very ill, even if it means allowing them to die. Seventeen percent say the law should not allow doctors to follow the will of the patient, and a surprisingly small number, just 4 percent, are unsure.

Opinion is more divided on what decisions the family should be allowed to make. Twenty-five percent of the elderly, and 39 percent of the nonelderly, think the patient's family should have the right to demand a very ill family member be kept alive by very expensive life-support, even when the doctor says there is no hope of recovery. Sixty-five percent of the elderly believe the family should not be allowed to insist on life support, and 10 percent are unsure (Table 9-9).

While limiting care delivery to patients who have little chance of survival is acceptable to many, limiting care based exclusively on age is not. Sixty-nine percent of people surveyed think that age should not be a consideration when determining whether or not expensive treatment should be allowed. The elderly, though, find rationing by age slightly more acceptable. Fifty-five percent say rationing by age is not all right, but 40 percent believe age can be a criterion.[7]

Responses to these questions indicate the elderly, and the nonelderly to a lesser degree, are willing to curtail the use of life saving treatment for people who have no hope of recovery. The legal issues of how this preference can be carried out will undoubtedly play out in the court system in the next few years. A popular resolution will include mechanisms for maximizing the impact of the wishes of patients, or in the absence of the expressed wishes, their families' preferences. A large minority of people are also willing to limit care based on the age of the patient — a policy that would be onerous to implement equitably.

CONCLUSIONS

With the high levels of support among the elderly for expansion of Medicare benefits, it it likely this expansion will, at least, be debated by Congress. A central focus of the debates will be the financing of new benefits. The elderly favor adding new benefits to the Medicare Social Security system rather than creating new tax incentives for the private purchase of long term care, but new developments related to the Medicare Trust Fund may dampen that prospect.

In policy discussions about containing health care costs, the elderly will favor more price controls over hospitals and doctors rather than managed care. We can expect, then, to see some lively debates between the elderly and the provider community who, as we will see in Chapter 10, are prepared to fight over fee controls.

REFERENCES

1. Louis Harris and Associates. *Survey of Legislators and Regulators.* 1988.

2. U.S. Bureau of the Census, CBS News/New York Times Exit Poll, 1988.

3. Louis Harris and Associates. *Attitudes to, Satisfaction with, and Access to Health Care Services in Canada, the United States, and Britain.* November 1988.

4. ICR Survey Research Group. *The Atlanta Journal and Constitution.* June 23, 1990.

5. Harvey LK. *Survey of Public Opinion on Health Care.* American Medical Association; Chicago: March 1991.

6. Louis Harris and Associates. *Consumer Survey.* 1990.

7. *Americans Speak Out on Health Care Rationing.* Northwestern National Life Insurance Company. 1990.

8. Prisuta RH. *AARP Member and Volunteer Views on Legislative Priorities for 1991.* January 1991.

9. Health Care Financing Administration, Office of Prepaid Health Plans, unpublished data, January 1991.

CHAPTER 10

Key Interest Groups and the Future of Health Care Reform

Humphrey Taylor and Robert Leitman
Louis Harris and Associates

INTRODUCTION

Although public interest in a universal health plan may be extraordinarily high, national action is not inevitable. Public opinion is but one of many factors that affect public policy. The views of key interest groups, such as employers, insurers, unions, doctors and hospitals, as well as the preferences and priorities of elected and appointed policymakers also will play a major role.

Having looked for the possibility of a public consensus in Chapter 8, in this chapter, we look at the views of key interest groups and their perspectives on the future of health care system reform.

A broad consensus among these groups is a necessary but not sufficient condition for reform. There also must be agreement on the specifics of a reform plan. During the health care reform debate in the early part of the 1970s, a similar level of concern about our health care system existed. Public anxiety over the state of our health care system was high; many key interest groups had taken positions, favoring national health care reform and more than a dozen initiatives for universal health care coverage were introduced in Congress, including one by a Republican President. However, leaders of key groups and the public were unable to reach agreement on any of the specific approaches to reform, and the issue drifted from the nation's agenda as other pressing problems emerged.

In this chapter, we examine the trade-offs and choices facing these interest group leaders as they consider the possibility of major health care changes. Our perspective is based on a survey conducted by Louis Harris and Associates* and sponsored by the Metropolitan Life Insurance Company.[1] The survey focused on four over-arching questions that are at the heart of today's debate over health care reform:

1. Does each group see the need for reform?

2. If they do, what type of a universal health insurance system do they favor?

3. Similarly, what types of specific major cost containment measures do they find acceptable?

4. Do they favor a one time, comprehensive reform or do they prefer incremental changes spread over many years?

The answers to these key questions are presented in the format of 22 specific findings. Together, they point to areas of consensus and contention among the groups. They also help define the avenues along which agreement is most likely to be reached in the years ahead. The findings are:

1. **There is a broad consensus among the groups surveyed that all is not well with the nation's health care system and that fundamental changes are necessary.** As reflected in Table 10-1, no more than 14 percent of any of the groups surveyed, apart from 31 percent of physician leaders, believe that "on the whole, the health care system works pretty well, and only minor changes are necessary to make it work better." Physician leaders are the survey

---

*The survey interviewed 2,048 respondents selected as representative samples of nine groups who play an influential role as payers, regulators, administrators, or providers in the American health care system. A total of 1,175 corporate executives were interviewed, including 200 from companies with 10,000 or more employees, 200 with 1,000 to 9,999 employees, 250 with 100-999 employees, 250 with 26-99 employees, and 275 with 6-25 employees. From the federal government, 260 legislators, 25 key committee staff, and 15 regulators were interviewed, as were 50 state health care officials. Also interviewed were 251 hospital CEOs, 201 physicians executives of medical societies, 50 union leaders, and 21 major health insurers.

Table 10-1

Attitudes Toward the Health Care System

Which of the following statements comes closest to expressing your overall view of this country's health care system ?

	Total Sample	Corporate Executive	Federal Legisl.	Key Committee Staff	Federal Regulator
Base	2,048	1,175	260	25	15
On the whole, the health care system works pretty well, and only minor changes are necessary to make it work better	13%	12%	4%	8%	—
There are some good things in our health care system, but fundamental changes are needed to make it work better	67	63	80	72	100%
The health care system has so much wrong with it that we need to completely rebuild it.	20	25	16	12	—
Not sure	*	*	*	8	—

	Union Leaders	Physician Leaders	Hospital CEOs	Major Insurers	State Officials
Base	50	201	251	21	50
On the whole, the health care system works pretty well, and only minor changes are necessary to make it work better	—	31%	14%	10%	14%
There are some good things in our health care system, but fundamental changes are needed to make it work better	30%	64	80	76	70
The health care system has so much wrong with it that we need to completely rebuild it.	70	4	6	10	16
Not sure	—	—	*	5	—

* Less than 0.5%.

group most satisfied with the health care system and the least likely to want radical change, while the union leaders are the most critical and the most likely to press for the complete rebuilding of the system.

2. **Most of those who want to see fundamental changes in the health care system or who believe that we need to completely rebuild it believe that we should try to introduce change in an incremental way.** Large majorities of almost all the groups take this view and greatly outnumber those who favor a more rapid and comprehensive reform (Table 10-2). The one clear exception is among union leaders who in balance, if not overwhelmingly, favor comprehensive reform.

Table 10-2

Incremental or Comprehensive Changes

Do you think we should try to introduce change in an incremental way or do you think we should make changes comprehensively in a short period of time?*

	Total Sample	Corporate Executive	Federal Legisl.	Key Committee Staff	Federal Regulator
Base	1,779	1,031	249	21	15
Incrementally	65%	63%	57%	57%	87%
Comprehensively	33	35	39	38	13
Not sure/refused	2	2	4	5	—

	Union Leaders	Physician Leaders	Hospital CEOs	Major Insurers	State Officials
Base	50	138	214	18	43
Incrementally	44%	80%	76%	72%	70%
Comprehensively	52	19	23	22	28
Not sure/refused	4	1	1	6	2

* Asked of those who replied that change is needed.

Table 10-3

Support for Universal Coverage

Do you agree strongly, agree somewhat, or disagree strongly with the following statement?

Everyone should have health insurance, even if this means an increase in taxes.

	Total Sample	Corporate Executive	Federal Legisl.	Key Committee Staff	Federal Regulator
Base	2,048	1,175	260	25	15
Agree strongly	38%	34%	42%	52%	47%
Agree somewhat	34	33	31	24	33
Disagree somewhat	15	17	14	20	13
Disagree strongly	11	15	10	—	7
Not sure/refused	1	1	2	4	—
—All agree	72	67	73	76	80
—All disagree	27	32	24	20	20

	Union Leaders	Physician Leaders	Hospital CEOs	Major Insurers	State Officials
Base	50	201	251	21	50
Agree strongly	64%	49%	41%	33%	40%
Agree somewhat	28	33	40	57	48
Disagree somewhat	4	12	14	10	8
Disagree strongly	4	6	5	—	—
Not sure/refused	—	—	*	—	4
—All agree	92	82	80	90	88
—All disagree	8	18	19	10	8

* Less than 0.5%

Table 10-4

First Priority for Additional Spending—Access, Catastrophic Coverage, or Quality

Assume you are running the health care system and have finite resources to spend to improve the system. Which one of the following would you prefer to spend the largest amount of additional money on?

	Total Sample	Corporate Executive	Federal Legisl.	Key Committee Staff	Federal Regulator
Base	2,048	1,175	260	25	15
Making sure that everyone can afford access to physician services and health care	40%	29%	64%	48%	40%
Making sure nobody suffers catastrophic financial loss because of the cost of health care	43	51	21	32	33
Improving the quality of health care services	16	18	11	4	13
None	1	*	*	4	—
All equal	1	1	2	4	13
Not sure	*	*	2	8	—

	Union Leaders	Physician Leaders	Hospital CEOs	Major Insurers	State Officials
Base	50	201	251	21	50
Making sure that everyone can afford access to physician services and health care	58%	53%	47%	29%	64%
Making sure nobody suffers catastrophic financial loss because of the cost of health care	22	38	37	57	18
Improving the quality of health care services	16	6	15	14	18
None	2	1	—	—	—
All equal	2	*	1	—	—
Not sure	—	—	—	—	—

* Less than 0.5%.

3. **There is widespread support for the concept of health insurance coverage for all Americans, despite the current aversion to increased taxation.** Large majorities of all the groups sampled, varying from 92 percent of the union leaders to 67 percent of the corporate executives, believe that

Table 10-5

Government as Manager or Rulemaker

Do you think the appropriate role for the federal government in the future of the health care system should be more as a manager and an administrator of health insurance as it is for Medicare, or more as a rulemaker setting the rules for the private sector to manage and administer health care ?

	Total Sample	Corporate Executive	Federal Legisl.	Key Committee Staff	Federal Regulator
Base	2,048	1,175	260	25	15
Manager and administrator	30%	31%	30%	36%	13%
Rulemaker	63	64	63	56	87
Neither	6	4	5	8	—
Not sure/refused	1	1	2	—	—

	Union Leaders	Physician Leaders	Hospital CEOs	Major Insurers	State Officials
Base	50	201	251	21	50
Manager and administrator	48%	23%	26%	—	32%
Rulemaker	50	61	63	90	58
Neither	2	15	11	10	8
Not sure/refused	—	1	—	—	2

Table 10-6

Attitudes Toward Three Alternative Systems

A number of plans have been proposed as ways to improve the health care system in this country. Which one of the following three systems would you like the best ?

	Total Sample	Corporate Executive	Federal Legisl.	Key Committee Staff	Federal Regulator
Base	2,048	1,175	260	25	15
The present system, based on private health insurance, mostly through employers, plus Medicare and Medicaid	32%	35%	37%	32%	13%
The present system with two changes: A law requiring employers to provide health insurance to all their employees, and the government to provide health insurance to everyone who is not employed	43	35	35	44	60
A comprehensive government health insurance program, covering all medical and hospital expenses, paid for by taxes. Under such a program, the government would control hospital costs, physician fees, and other charges	21	27	18	16	20
None	3	2	8	8	7
Not sure	1	*	2	—	—

*Less than 0.5%.   (Continued)

Table 10-6 (Continued)

Attitudes Toward Three Alternative Systems

A number of plans have been proposed as ways to improve the health care system in this country. Which one of the following three systems would you like the best ?

	Union Leaders	Physician Leaders	Hospital CEOs	Major Insurers	State Officials
Base	50	201	251	21	50
The present system, based on private health insurance, mostly through employers, plus Medicare and Medicaid	10%	33%	21%	33%	20%
The present system with two changes: A law requiring employers to provide health insurance to all their employees, and the government to provide health insurance to everyone who is not employed	28	61	72	67	54
A comprehensive government health insurance program, covering all medical and hospital expenses, paid for by taxes. Under such a program, the government would control hospital costs, physician fees, and other charges	58	3	6	—	26
None	2	2	2	—	—
Not sure	2	*	—	—	—

*Less than 0.5%.

"everyone should have health insurance, even if this means an increase in taxes." Furthermore, majorities of all of the different groups believe that at some time in the future, everyone will have some kind of health insurance. A majority of all of the groups surveyed except for state officials (and 50% of them) would favor, in principle, reallocating $50 billion currently spent on other goods and services to provide some kind of health insurance for those who are currently uninsured. Union leaders, physician leaders, and hospital CEOs are the most strongly in favor of this reallocation of resources, while state officials, managers of major insurance companies, federal legislators, and corporate executives are the least enthusiastic about this proposal (Table 10-3).

4. **Consensus does not exist among the nine groups surveyed about the most important priority for change.** Given a choice between spending additional monies to improve access, provide catastrophic coverage or improve quality, only very small numbers in any group think that improving the quality of health care services is the most important priority, as shown in Table 10-4. Majorities of federal legislators, union leaders, physician leaders, and state officials think that providing universal access to health care services is the most important priority. Majorities of corporate executives and major insurers think that protecting people from catastrophic financial loss is the top priority.

When given a choice of three other potential priorities, a clear consensus does emerge. Large majorities of all nine groups agree that access to important preventive medical services is more important than providing long term care insurance or keeping the United States at the cutting edge of new medical technology developments.

5. **While the leadership groups surveyed (except for union leaders) express serious reservations about the federal government's ability to manage the health care system, large majorities of all groups believe that major government initiatives will be necessary to solve the problems facing the health care system.** By sizable majorities all groups except for union leaders believe that the appropriate role for the federal government in the health care system should be (at most) that of a rulemaker, setting the rules for the private sector, rather than as a manager and administrator. This opinion is shared not only by corporate executives, hospital CEOs, physician leaders, and major insurers but also by most federal legislators and regulators, and key committee staff members as shown in Table 10-5.

6. **This tension, between the desire to limit the role of government on the one hand and the belief that government intervention is needed on the other, is reflected in the overwhelming consensus among all the groups surveyed (90% or more) who believe that the health care system of the future should continue to involve both the public and private sectors.** Further, with the exception of union leaders, who are split 50-50, all

Table 10-7

Attitudes of Corporate Executives Toward Three Alternative Systems

A number of plans have been proposed as ways to improve the health care system in this country. Which one of the following three systems would you like the best?

CORPORATE EXECUTIVES

| | Total Cor- porate Sample | Number of Employees | | | | | Region | | | |
		1,000 or More	1,000- 9,999	100- 999	26- 99	6- 25	East	Mid- west	South	West
Base	1,175	200	200	250	250	275	308	311	334	222
The present system, based on private health insurance, mostly through employers, plus Medicare and Medicaid	35%	32%	41%	37%	33%	32%	27%	39%	40%	32%
The present system with two changes: A law requiring employers to provide health insurance to all their employees, and the government to provide health insurance to everyone who is not employed	35	47	40	34	31	28	40	34	28	41
A comprehensive government health insurance program, covering all medical and hospital expenses, paid for by taxes. Under such a program, the government would control hospital costs, physician fees, and other charges	27	19	19	26	32	36	31	24	28	25
None	2	2	1	2	3	3	1	2	3	3
Not sure	*	—	—	*	*	1	1	*	*	—

* Less than 0.5%.

Table 10-8

Expected System in Year 2000

Looking ahead to the year 2000, which one of these three systems do you think the United States is likely to have?

	Total Sample	Corporate Executive	Federal Legisl.	Key Committee Staff	Federal Regulator
Base	2,048	1,175	260	25	15
The present system, based on private health insurance, mostly through employers, plus Medicare and Medicaid	21%	22%	33%	20%	7%
The present system with two changes: A law requiring employers to provide health insurance to all their employees, and the government to provide health insurance to everyone who is not employed	50	42	53	72	87
A comprehensive government health insurance program, covering all medical and hospital expenses, paid for by taxes. Under such a program, the government would control hospital costs, physician fees, and other charges	28	35	12	4	7
None	1	1	2	4	—
Not sure	*	1	—	—	—

* Less than 0.5%   (Continued)

Table 10-8 (Continued)

Expected System in Year 2000

Looking ahead to the year 2000, which one of these three systems do you think the United States is likely to have?

	Union Leaders	Physician Leaders	Hospital CEOs	Major Insurers	State Officials
Base	50	201	251	21	50
The present system, based on private health insurance, mostly through employers, plus Medicare and Medicaid	10%	16%	9%	38%	14%
The present system with two changes: A law requiring employers to provide health insurance to all their employees, and the government to provide health insurance to everyone who is not employed	48	64	64	52	70
A comprehensive government health insurance program, covering all medical and hospital expenses, paid for by taxes. Under such a program, the government would control hospital costs, physician fees, and other charges	38	18	26	10	14
None	2	1	—	—	—
Not sure	2	—	1	—	2

Table 10-9

Preferences for Many Plans, Limited Number, or Only One Benefit Plan

Which of the following do you think would be better?

	Total Sample	Corporate Executive	Federal Legisl.	Key Committee Staff	Federal Regulator
Base	2,048	1,175	260	25	15
A system with a variety of health plans, with many different levels of benefits and costs	40%	39%	47%	36%	27%
A system with a limited number of plans, levels of benefits and costs	40	36	41	56	53
A system with one plan for everyone with the same benefits and costs	19	24	10	8	13
None of these	*	*	1	—	7
Not sure	*	*	1	—	—

	Union Leaders	Physician Leaders	Hospital CEOs	Major Insurers	State Officials
Base	50	201	251	21	50
A system with a variety of health plans, with many different levels of benefits and costs	20%	49%	33%	67%	44%
A system with a limited number of plans, levels of benefits and costs	30	43	55	29	34
A system with one plan for everyone with the same benefits and costs	46	7	11	5	20
None of these	4	—	—	—	—
Not sure	—	—	—	—	2

* Less than 0.5%.

other leadership groups surveyed believe our insurance system should continue to operate largely through employment-based plans.

      7. **Most respondents believe government involvement will be required to make health benefits affordable for small businesses.** Large majorities of all groups, with one exception, believe that making health insurance affordable for small business will not be done by the private sector alone and that government involvement will be necessary. The one exception is the sample of major insurers who, by 52 percent to 38 percent, believe that this problem can be solved by the private sector.

Table 10-10

Attitudes Toward Rationing

Do you believe that in order to provide health insurance for everyone and control costs, it will be necessary to limit, or ration, the availability of expensive high-tech medical services?

	Total Sample	Corporate Executive	Federal Legisl.	Key Committee Staff	Federal Regulator
Base	2,048	1,175	260	25	15
Yes, it will be necessary	63%	56%	61%	64%	73%
No, it will not be necessary	34	42	36	32	27
Not sure/refused	3	2	3	4	—

	Union Leaders	Physician Leaders	Hospital CEOs	Major Insurers	State Officials
Base	50	201	251	21	50
Yes, it will be necessary	50%	77%	82%	95%	74%
No, it will not be necessary	50	15	16	5	22
Not sure/refused	—	7	1	—	4

Table 10-11

Acceptability of Taxing Insurance Premiums

How acceptable would it be to you if paying income tax on health care paid by employers were part of a program where each group would make some concessions in order to reach a consensus — totally acceptable, somewhat acceptable, or totally unacceptable?

	Total Sample	Corporate Executive	Federal Legisl.	Key Committee Staff	Federal Regulator
Base	2,048	1,175	260	25	15
Totally acceptable	7%	7%	8%	28%	13%
Somewhat acceptable	38	34	41	32	53
Somewhat unacceptable	27	26	33	36	27
Totally unacceptable	27	33	16	4	7
Not sure/refused	1	1	2	—	—
—All acceptable	45	40	49	60	67
—All unacceptable	54	59	49	40	33

	Union Leaders	Physician Leaders	Hospital CEOs	Major Insurers	State Officials
Base	50	201	251	21	50
Totally acceptable	6%	5%	7%	10%	12%
Somewhat acceptable	20	57	40	48	46
Somewhat unacceptable	24	24	28	24	32
Totally unacceptable	50	13	25	19	8
Not sure/refused	—	—	—	—	2
—All acceptable	26	63	47	57	58
—All unacceptable	74	37	53	43	40

8. **There is, as yet, no consensus on what the health care system of the future should be.** Most of the many proposals that have been aired for reforming the health care system over the longer term fall into one of three categories. Some propose the continuation of the present system based on private health insurance plus Medicare and Medicaid. A second set of proposals would essentially continue the present system but make two major additions, mandating employers to provide insurance and adding some government mechanism to provide health insurance for those who are unemployed. A third set of proposals calls for a comprehensive government health insurance program managed by the government, funded primarily with tax dollars. There is no consensus among the nine groups surveyed as to which of these three alternatives is preferable. This dilemma is reflected in Table 10-6.

As shown in Table 10-7, the preferences of larger and smaller employers differ quite sharply. While there is not a majority favoring either of the three alternatives, a preference for a comprehensive government-run tax-funded program ranges from only 19 percent in the largest companies to 36 percent in the smallest companies.

In addition, as shown in Table 10-8, when asked not which of these three alternatives they would prefer but which they think is most likely to be in place in the year 2000, majorities of most groups pick the second option; that is, the present system with the addition of mandatory employer-provided coverage and government insurance of the uninsured. Federal committee staff members, federal regulators, and state officials are the most likely to believe that this will happen. Among two groups, corporate executives and union leaders, there is no majority agreement as to what will happen, but pluralities in both groups agree that the second option is the most likely.

9. **The most popular option overall, supported by majorities of federal regulators, physician leaders, hospital CEOs, large insurers, and state officials, is the second option, an extension of the present system to provide universal coverage through both mandated benefits and government coverage of the uninsured.**

One reason for the relative popularity of this option is the belief that it would increase access (and overall costs) while improving the quality of care. In contrast, a comprehensive government insurance program is generally perceived as increasing access and costs while making the quality of care worse (union leaders, however, disagree).

10. **In the event that the government were to mandate that all employers must provide health insurance for employees and dependents, it would be acceptable to all nine groups if this mandate covered only basic hospital and doctors' services.** However, large majorities of all groups, except for union leaders, would not favor a uniform system with only one plan for everyone, with the same benefits and costs (46 percent of union leaders would prefer this option). As shown in Table 10-9, a 67 percent majority of

Table 10-12

Acceptability of Prior Approval of Primary Care Physicians for Specialty Care

How acceptable would it be to you if having to obtain prior approval of a primary care doctor in order to see a specialist for non-emergency care were part of a program where each group would make some concessions in order to reach a consensus—totally acceptable, somewhat acceptable, or totally unacceptable?

	Total Sample	Corporate Executive	Federal Legisl.	Key Committee Staff	Federal Regulator
Base	2,048	1,175	260	25	15
Totally acceptable	40%	45%	31%	36%	40%
Somewhat accept.	40	39	47	40	47
Somewhat unaccept.	12	9	18	12	7
Totally unacceptable	8	7	4	12	7
Not sure/refused	*	*	*	—	—
—All acceptable	81	84	78	76	87
—All unacceptable	19	16	22	24	13

	Union Leaders	Physician Leaders	Hospital CEOs	Major Insurers	State Officials
Base	50	201	251	21	50
Totally acceptable	30%	25%	39%	76%	52%
Somewhat accept.	42	39	41	19	42
Somewhat unaccept.	18	17	13	—	4
Totally unacceptable	10	18	6	5	2
Not sure/refused	—	—	*	—	—
—All acceptable	72	65	81	95	94
—All unacceptable	28	35	19	5	6

* Less than 0.5%

insurers and pluralities of corporate executives, federal legislators, physician leaders, and state officials prefer a system with a wide variety of many different plans. A majority of key federal committee staff members, federal regulators, and hospital CEOs would prefer a system with a limited number of plans, levels of benefits, and costs.

11. **Notwithstanding the generally pejorative connotation of the word "rationing," majorities of all groups except union leaders, who are equally split, believe that it will be necessary to ration expensive high-tech medical services in order to provide health insurance for everyone and control costs.** As can be seen in Table 10-10, fully 95 percent of the large insurers, 82 percent of hospital CEOs, and 77 percent of physician executives from medical societies perceive that some kind of rationing of care will be necessary in the future.

In addition, the survey found that substantial majorities of those who believe that some kind of rationing of expensive high-tech medical services will be necessary (the questions were only asked of these people) believe that several criteria are appropriate in making decisions about when patients would or should not get expensive care. These criteria are:

◆ How much treatment is likely to improve the patient's quality of life,

◆ How many years or months the treatment is likely to add to the patient's life,

◆ Whether the treatment is likely to permit the patient to be productive, and

◆ The patient's age.

Majorities of all groups who were asked this question, except for the union leaders, also think that the cost of treatment is a relevant factor.

There is widespread agreement that it would be undesirable to ration care differently for patients who have private or government paid health insurance.

12. **Among a number of other mechanisms to pay for the additional costs of an improved health care system, the two most acceptable mechanisms are "sin taxes" and higher premiums for people with unhealthy lifestyles.** Higher income taxes are seen as acceptable by smaller numbers of each group.

Spreading the increased costs uniformly through substantially higher health insurance premiums is much less acceptable to those surveyed. Similarly, as presented in Table 10-11, there is no agreement on the acceptability of paying income tax on the health care premiums paid by employers. Majorities, but not

Table 10-13

Acceptability of Plans Limited to Cost-Effective Providers

How acceptable would it be to you if being a member of a health plan that limits members to the most cost-effective providers and excludes those who are not cost-effective were part of a program where each group would make some concessions in order to reach a consensus—totally acceptable, somewhat acceptable, totally unacceptable?

	Total Sample	Corporate Executive	Federal Legisl.	Key Committee Staff	Federal Regulator
Base	2,048	1,175	260	25	15
Totally acceptable	27%	29%	27%	36%	47%
Somewhat acceptable	42	40	43	36	33
Somewhat unaccept.	19	17	22	20	7
Totally unacceptable	11	13	8	8	13
Not sure/refused	*	*	—	—	—
—All acceptable	70	70	70	72	80
—All unacceptable	30	30	30	28	20

	Union Leaders	Physician Leaders	Hospital CEOs	Major Insurers	State Officials
Base	50	201	251	21	50
Totally acceptable	26%	10%	27%	57%	28%
Somewhat acceptable	48	46	45	38	46
Somewhat unaccept.	18	34	18	5	16
Totally unacceptable	6	10	10	—	10
Not sure/refused	2	—	—	—	—
—All acceptable	74	56	73	95	74
—All unacceptable	24	44	27	5	26

* Less than 0.5%.

overwhelming majorities, of key committee staff members, federal regulators, physician leaders, major insurers, and state officials felt that this would be at least somewhat acceptable. On the other hand, majorities of corporate executives, union leaders, and hospital CEOs felt that this was unacceptable as a policy choice.

13. **Some aspects of cost containment programs and managed care are generally viewed as acceptable elements of a changed health care system, while others are more controversial.** Majorities, varying from 56 percent to 86 percent, of most of the groups surveyed feel that it would be acceptable for consumers to pay substantially higher out-of-pocket costs for health care services used. However, federal legislators are equally divided (49%-50%) on this, and most union leaders find this increased cost-sharing unacceptable. Majorities of all groups feel it would be acceptable to have to join a managed care plan such as an HMO. Eighty percent or more of union leaders, major insurers, and state officials feel this would be acceptable.

As shown in Table 10-12, the use of primary care doctors as "gatekeepers" is one of the most acceptable proposals on this list. Very large majorities of all of the groups surveyed say that it would be acceptable to have to obtain the prior approval of a primary care doctor before seeing a specialist for nonemergency care.

Belonging to a health plan that limits members to the most cost-effective providers and excludes those who are not cost-effective is acceptable to large majorities of all groups except physician leaders, for whom it is acceptable to a 56 percent majority. This high level of support is reflected in Table 10-13.

Changes to the system that involve longer waits for nonemergency elective services and non-coverage of expensive procedures and treatments do not have support. On the other hand, accepting limits on the right to sue for medical malpractice is one of the most popular alternatives, with large majorities of all groups finding it acceptable, a promising finding for future reform.

This survey is unique in that it goes beyond the questions of general policy concerns and probes key institutional leaders about the kinds of trade-offs and choices they may have to make to resolve some of the problems of the American health care system. The results suggest the following.

TRADE-OFFS FOR HOSPITALS

14. **Of eight proposals presented in the context of a total plan in which everyone made some concessions, five are at least somewhat acceptable to majorities of hospital CEOs. Three are acceptable to 64 percent or more of them:**

◆ Closing more under-used hospitals,

◆ Having tougher constraints on capital expenditures, and

Table 10-14

Acceptability of Six Proposals to Corporate Executives

How acceptable would each of the following be to you, as a part of a total plan in which everyone made some concessions—totally acceptable, somewhat acceptable, somewhat unacceptable, or totally unacceptable ?

	Totally Accept.	Somewhat Accept.	Somewhat Unaccept.	Totally Unaccept.	Not Sure
Be required by law to provide a basic health insurance benefit for all full-time employees and dependents	33%	40%	13%	15%	*
If required to provide coverage, be limited by law to providing only a standard health plan which would be the same for every employer and every employee	18	51	17	14	*
Pay health insurance premiums based on a community rate—rather than the experience of your own group	18	43	21	17	1%
Be required to provide health insurance benefits to retirees not eligible for Medicare	16	45	21	17	1
Be required by law to provide a basic health insurance benefit for all part-time employees who work at least 20 hours a week and for their dependents	9	35	25	31	*
Pay a payroll tax to support the cost on insuring the unemployed and their dependents	5	32	30	34	*

* Less than 0.5%.

◆ Being required to accept and treat all patients even if reimbursement is below cost.

Two proposals are at least somewhat acceptable to slender 53 percent majorities of hospital CEOs but are opposed by very substantial minorities:

◆ Having to operate within predetermined global budgets, and

◆ Operating under a uniform one-payer system with prospective payment fees for all health plans, public and private.

Three proposals — all of which affect long term financing — are overwhelmingly unacceptable even in the context of a plan in which everyone else was making concessions. These are:

◆ The loss of tax-exempt status,

◆ The loss of the ability to float tax-free bonds, and

◆ The loss of separate Medicare reimbursement of capital expenses.

Many hospital CEOs may be willing to sacrifice potential growth for long term stability. A sizable (62%-37%) majority would accept stricter limits on capital spending on new capacity, and stricter limits on spending on expensive new technologies if they could realistically expect a generally high level of occupancy of their beds and more predictable reimbursement.

Much smaller majorities (53% and 51% respectively) would also accept a significant reduction in the number of beds in their hospitals or a significant reduction in the revenues per bed day.

The great majority of hospital CEOs (77%) report it would be acceptable to reduce the number of hospitals in areas with low occupancy rates if this resulted in a significant increase in occupancy in the remaining area hospitals.

TRADE-OFFS FOR BUSINESS

15. **Corporate America appears willing to accept several requirements as its part of an overall plan to improve the health care system. Employers of different sizes respond somewhat differently.** A substantial majority of all employers (72%) say that it would be acceptable if, as part of a total plan, they were required by law to provide a basic health insurance benefit for all full-time employees and dependents. This concept is somewhat more acceptable to large employers than to small employers.

Most employers (69%-30%) say that in the event that they were required by law to provide coverage, it would be acceptable if they were limited by law to providing only a standard health plan that would be the same for every employer and every employee. However, this concept of a uniform mandated benefit plan is somewhat less acceptable to the larger employers than it is to smaller employers.

Premiums based on community ratings and paying for benefits for retirees not eligible for Medicare are acceptable to smaller but still substantial majorities of employers. Community rating would be acceptable not only to many small employers, but also to half of the large employers surveyed.

Table 10-15

Acceptability of 10 Proposals to Physician Executives

How acceptable would each of the following be to you, as part of a total plan in which everyone made some concessions—totally acceptable, somewhat acceptable, somewhat unacceptable, or totally unacceptable?

	Totally Accept.	Somewhat Accept.	Somewhat Unaccept	Totally Unaccept.	Not Sure
Have somewhat lower incomes for specialists	17%	42%	21%	19%	*
Be compensated on a fee-for-service basis— but entirely from a fixed budget with an expenditure cap	6	49	29	15	—
Be required to generally follow practice guidelines on how to treat different conditions	12	55	18	14	—
Require patients to obtain the prior approval of a primary care doctor in order to see specialists for non-emergency care	14	49	27	9	—
Be placed at financial risk for part of the cost of care doctors provide	3	38	39	19	1

* Less than 0.5%.

(Continued)

232

As reflected in Table 10-14, the data also reveal several less acceptable options. Paying health benefits for part-time employees and paying a payroll tax to support the uninsured are acceptable to only a minority of employers.

16. **The strength of the corporate executives' opposition to the whole idea of a national health insurance system is clearly illustrated in their replies to two questions about it.** By three to one they say that if it was the only

Table 10-15 (Continued)

Acceptability of 10 Proposals to Physician Executives

How acceptable would each of the following be to you, as part of a total plan in which everyone made some concessions—totally acceptable, somewhat acceptable, somewhat unacceptable, or totally unacceptable?

	Totally Accept.	Somewhat Accept.	Somewhat Unaccept	Totally Unaccept.	Not Sure
Be prohibited from ownership of a laboratory, pharmacy, or rehabilitation center	9%	32%	43%	16%	*
Be compensated partly on some measure of patient satisfaction	5	36	29	29	—
Have a uniform national fee schedule for specific services for all health plans, public and private, with no balance billing	7	30	22	41	—
Be compensated only on a capitated (fee per patient/member) basis	4	29	39	27	*
Be compensated on a purely salaried basis	5	16	21	58	—

* Less than 0.5%.

Table 10-16

Acceptability of Nine Proposals to Largest Group Health Insurers

How acceptable would each of the following be to you, as part of a total plan in which everyone made some concessions—totally acceptable, somewhat acceptable, somewhat unacceptable, or totally unacceptable ?

	Totally Accept.	Somewhat Accept.	Somewhat Unaccept.	Totally Unaccept.	Not Sure
Be required to participate in a reinsurance mechanism to spread excess health costs for small employers	47%	47%	5%	—	—
Be required to renew health insurance for all small groups regardless of claims experience if there is a reinsurance mechanism	42	47	11	—	—
Be required to issue health insurance to all individuals requesting it regardless of health status if there is a reinsurance mechanism	32	53	16	—	—
Operate on some form of community rating for all health insurance risks in the small cash market	16	58	11	16%	—
Give up current underwriting practices (such as pre-existing conditions exclusions) for small groups if there is a reinsurance mechanism	26	37	32	5	—
Accept somewhat lower long-range earnings on health insurance business	5	37	32	26	—
Be subject to federal regulation for health insurance	5	37	47	11	—
Function solely as an administrator of a federally sponsored health plan	—	26	11	63	—
Be subject to government rate regulation of group health insurance for small employers	—	21	21	58	—

Table 10-17

Principal Responsibility for Ensuring Access

In the future, who do you think should have the principal responsibility for making sure that everyone has reasonable access to care?

	Total Sample	Corporate Executive	Federal Legisl.	Key Committee Staff	Federal Regulator
Base	2,048	1,175	260	25	15
Employers	10%	13%	8%	8%	—
Federal government	53	51	61	64	67%
State government	12	12	11	—	—
Doctors' organizations	5	4	2	—	13
Hospital industry	4	5	1	—	—
Health insurance industry	7	7	6	12	—
Someone else	6	5	6	12	—
Nobody	1	1	1	—	7
Not sure/refused	2	2	4	4	13

	Union Leaders	Physician Leaders	Hospital CEOs	Major Insurers	State Officials
Base	50	201	251	21	50
Employers	6%	5%	5%	19%	4%
Federal government	82	37	60	57	62
State government	4	16	12	—	18
Doctors' organizations	—	18	4	—	4
Hospital industry	—	*	9	—	—
Health insurance industry	—	8	5	14	—
Someone else	2	9	3	10	4
Nobody	2	2	*	—	4
Not sure/refused	4	3	1	—	4

* Less than 0.5%.

way to prevent the introduction of a national health insurance system, they would be willing to have a much more aggressively managed health care plan with less freedom of choice and much higher cost-sharing for their employees.

Even when corporate executives are asked, if, in a few years' time, it is clear that private sector managed care plans are not sufficiently containing health care costs, only a slender 53 percent majority of the corporate employers surveyed say they would be willing to accept a government mandated and controlled national health insurance system.

TRADE-OFFS FOR UNIONS

17. **Union leaders, while generally better disposed to a broader governmental role than others surveyed, have many areas where their views are consonant with those of employers and report a willingness to work with employers to improve the health care system.** As part of an overall plan in which everyone makes concessions, most union leaders say they would accept:

◆ Being limited by law to a standard health plan that would be the same for every employer and every employee, and

◆ Being required to belong to managed care plans such as HMOs or other health plans using limited panels of doctors, hospitals, and other providers.

They would not accept:

◆ Being required to pay higher deductibles and co-payments, and

◆ A cap on employer-provided health care benefits that are tax-free to their members.

Further, the great majority of union leaders surveyed say they would be willing to enter into cooperative ventures with management to contain health care costs through tightly managed care plans if the savings would be used for wage increases; to improve the competitiveness of the company in order to save jobs; or if the savings were shared equally between wage increases and job saving. On the other hand, health benefits are so important to union leaders that 72 percent say they would be willing to strike in order to prevent changes in their health plans that would substantially reduce their members' benefits.

TRADE-OFFS FOR PHYSICIANS

18. **On the whole, physician leaders appear to be the group surveyed that is most reluctant to make concessions. Even as part of a total**

Table 10-18

Principal Responsibility for Cost Containment

In the future, who do you think should have the principal responsibility for health care cost containment?

	Total Sample	Corporate Executive	Federal Legisl.	Key Committee Staff	Federal Regulator
Base	2,048	1,175	260	25	15
Employers	10%	14%	3%	4%	—
Federal government	37	37	53	36	60%
State government	9	8	8	4	—
Doctors' organizations	10	9	4	20	13
Hospital industry	10	7	7	8	—
Health insurance industry	13	15	12	12	20
Someone else	4	4	5	8	—
Nobody	2	1	2	4	—
Not sure/refused	3	2	5	4	7

	Union Leaders	Physician Leaders	Hospital CEOs	Major Insurers	State Official
Base	50	201	251	21	50
Employers	10%	4%	5%	19%	4%
Federal government	68	19	26	33	44
State government	4	7	10	—	24
Doctors' organizations	6	33	4	—	6
Hospital industry	—	3	38	—	—
Health insurance industry	4	12	5	33	2
Someone else	—	8	4	10	2
Nobody	2	9	2	—	6
Not sure/refused	4	3	3	5	12

Table 10-19

The Toughest Barrier to Reform

Which of the following do you think will be the toughest barrier?

	Total Sample	Corporate Executive	Federal Legisl.	Key Committee Staff	Federal Regulator
Base	2,048	1,175	260	25	15
Doctors	35%	39%	31%	12%	53%
Hospitals	8	12	2	8	7
Consumers	6	5	7	12	20
Taxpayers	12	11	12	4	13
Employers	6	4	10	4	—
Insurers	15	12	25	36	—
Labor unions	15	16	10	24	7
None	1	*	1	—	—
Not sure/refused	1	1	3	—	—

	Union Leaders	Physician Leaders	Hospital CEOs	Major Insurers	State Officials
Base	50	201	251	21	50
Doctors	48%	9%	38%	62%	32%
Hospitals	2	5	1	5	10
Consumers	—	7	10	19	6
Taxpayers	2	27	14	—	10
Employers	14	12	5	—	8
Insurers	32	15	15	—	22
Labor unions	2	20	16	14	6
None	—	2	—	—	2
Not sure/refused	—	1	*	—	4

* Less than 0.5%

plan in which everyone made concessions, no more than 67 percent of physician leaders find any one of 10 proposals acceptable. As shown in Table 10-15, four proposals are acceptable to majorities of 55 percent or more. These are:

◆ Having somewhat lower incomes for specialists (as will happen under the resource-based relative value scales for Medicare),

◆ Being compensated on a fee-for-service basis but entirely from a fixed budget with an expenditure cap,

◆ Being required to follow practice guidelines on how to treat different conditions, and

◆ Requiring patients to obtain the prior approval of a primary care physician in order to see specialists for nonemergency care.

Six of the proposals are unacceptable to majorities of physician leaders. The most unacceptable proposal (totally unacceptable to 58 percent and somewhat unacceptable to 21 percent) is to be compensated on a purely salaried basis.

19. Physician leaders are far more receptive to specific trade-offs that would reduce their income in exchange for fewer complications and less "outside interference" in their practices. Specifically, very large majorities of physician leaders would be willing to trade a 10 percent reduction in physician fees in return for any one of the following:

◆ A very substantial reduction in paperwork,

◆ Malpractice reform with limits on punitive damages and damages for pain and suffering, and

◆ Substantially increased physician autonomy with less utilization review and less regulation.

As with other groups, physician executives of medical societies report strong hostility to the concept of national health insurance. Fully 63 percent of most physician leaders say they would not be willing to accept a national health insurance system that required them to negotiate with the government for any changes in their income and fees *even* if it guaranteed payment of their fees, substantially reduced utilization review, reduced malpractice insurance premiums, and cut their paperwork.

TRADE-OFFS FOR INSURERS

20. **On the whole, large insurers appear willing to participate in a health insurance system that would cover everyone if a reinsurance mechanism were in place. They draw the line at functioning solely as administrators of a federally sponsored plan and at government rate regulation.** As portrayed in Table 10-16, fully 94 percent also would be willing to accept a requirement that they participate in a reinsurance mechanism to spread excess health costs for small employers (47 percent find this totally acceptable); 89 percent would be willing to accept the requirement to renew small group coverage regardless of claims experienced if there is a reinsurance mechanism. A sizable if smaller majority (63%) would be willing to accept giving up their current underwriting practices (such as pre-existing conditions exclusions) for small groups if there is a reinsurance mechanism. Three-quarters of insurers (74%) would be willing to accept some form of community rating for all health insurance risks in the small case market.

21. **Improving the health care system is widely perceived as a process in which many groups and interests should be involved.** Majorities of most of the nine groups surveyed think that employers, the federal government, state governments, doctors' organizations, the hospital industry, and the health insurance industry should play a major role in improving the system.

A large majority of each group surveyed believes its own group should play a major role in improving the health care system. Similarly, a majority of all groups surveyed except for physician leaders (and a plurality of them) believe that the federal government should have the principal responsibility for ensuring that everyone has reasonable access to care. A plurality of all groups except for physician leaders and hospital CEOs and a majority of federal legislators, federal regulators, and union leaders think that the federal government also should have the principal responsibility for health care cost containment. These findings are reflected in Tables 10-17 and 10-18. However, there is a total absence of consensus as to who should have responsibility for quality assurance. The federal government and doctors' organizations are mentioned more than any other parties.

22. **Very large majorities of corporate executives, union leaders, physician leaders, hospital CEOs, and insurers all believe that their own industries or organizations should be willing to compromise in order to achieve viable reforms.** However, amongst every group, except physician leaders, doctors are more likely than any other interest group to be thought of as a major barrier. This consensus is reflected in Table 10-19.

Although the issue was not addressed in this survey, it is widely believed that doctors, and organized medicine, have lost some of their clout over the last decade, with both government and third party payers being much more willing to take them on than they used to be. However, all of the other groups represented in this survey believe that doctors still have a lot of power and influence over the course of health care policy.

The fact that so many people surveyed single out doctors as a major stumbling block to reform also may reflect fundamentally changed attitudes toward health care politics. There was a time when it was thought to be wholly appropriate that almost all health care policy issues should be substantially determined by physicians. That is no longer the case. Doctors may realize they have the most to lose, and therefore may be likely to put up the greatest resistance to change.

CONCLUSION

In summary, this study finds that, although all nine groups are dissatisfied with the functioning of our current health care system, there is not a widespread agreement on what major health care reforms should be adopted. Rather what we see is a consensus around numerous incremental changes that are likely to make up the reform agenda of the next few years. More sweeping national health care reforms await a broader set of agreement among these groups over the direction these reforms should take and the role that should be played by government in achieving them.

REFERENCES

1. Taylor H, Leitman R. *Trade-offs and Choices: Health Policy Options for the 1990s.* Louis Harris and Associates, New York;1991.

CHAPTER 11

AIDS in the Mid-1990s

Joanna E. Siegel, Robert J. Blendon, and Karen Donelan
Harvard School of Public Health

INTRODUCTION

The AIDS epidemic is entering its second decade. Many of the predictions which seemed incomprehensible during the early years of the epidemic have materialized over the 1980s. From an unusual syndrome identified among several homosexual males,[1] AIDS has evolved into one of the major killers of young adults in the United States, both male and female.[2] As of July 1991, 182,834 people had been diagnosed with AIDS, and 114,338 had died.[3] These numbers are expected to more than double by the end of 1993.[4] As foreseen by many, the epidemic also has changed course. At first largely a disease affecting gay white males, AIDS is steadily spreading to other segments of the population.

In this chapter, we describe the current direction of the AIDS epidemic and some of the issues that will be of increasing importance during the 1990s. Many of the points we discuss reflect the very concentrated effect AIDS has had. Although HIV infection has entered other risk groups, most AIDS patients in the U.S. are either homosexual men or intravenous drug users living in large coastal cities. Despite AIDS' terrible toll on gay communities and high rates of infection in inner-city populations, 4 out of 5 Americans still report they have never known anyone HIV-infected or with AIDS.[5] While AIDS threatens to overwhelm health care providers and strains social service systems in hard-hit areas, it remains a distant problem in most of the country. This dynamic has shaped the national response to AIDS, raising many practical as well as ethical conflicts.

We focus in this chapter on the impact AIDS has had nationally, as well as on problems emerging in the most affected areas. We consider trends in AIDS and the current climate of public and professional opinion in examining a range of issues facing public health agencies and health care providers. We begin by describing current assessments of the size and near-term growth of the epidemic.

MAGNITUDE

Despite initial overestimates and continuing uncertainty about the total number of people infected with HIV, there is little doubt about the magnitude of the AIDS epidemic in the near future. Most people infected with the virus have not yet developed AIDS. The number of cases and deaths will more than double between 1991 and 1993 and continue to grow into the 1990s.

Forecasts of the spread of HIV infection in the United States have evolved since the beginning of the epidemic and have generated considerable controversy. Initially, gay activists charged that the Reagan administration, reluctant to deal with a "homosexual" illness, deliberately understated estimates of the extent of infection. Later, overestimates of HIV infection were said to be politically motivated, part of a strategy to justify overspending on AIDS.[6,7,8] To an important degree, however, the inconsistency among estimates has been due to the difficulty of tracking a disease that remains hidden for two to ten years after a person is infected.

The initial estimates of 1 to 1.5 million HIV-infected persons in 1986 are now recognized to be too high. These estimates were based on very limited information about the number of people engaging in risky behaviors (male-to-male sex, intravenous drug use). The extent of HIV infection within these risk groups was also poorly documented, as the ELISA screening test had only recently become available. While forecasting the epidemic remains an inexact science, much progress has been made. Although many obstacles to obtaining population-level data remain, surveys have now documented seroprevalence in drug users (in and out of treatment), homosexuals, military recruits, Job Corps applicants, and newborns.[4]

Current estimates also use more sophisticated forecasting methods.[9] Mathematical models are used to simulate transmission within and among risk groups. For example, these models can predict epidemic spread from drug users to the non-drug-using heterosexual population, or account for variation in frequency of sexual contact. Another approach, backcalculation, is used to reconstruct past HIV prevalence based on the number of AIDS cases diagnosed subsequently. Researchers also have addressed sources of error in models, including reporting delays, changes in survival, and saturation of high-risk groups. Still, because current rates of infection are difficult to monitor, predictions of cases can only be approximate.

Revised estimates of HIV prevalence as of 1986 are half of the original estimates, in the range of 500,000 to 750,000 nationwide. Estimates of infection in 1988 vary; the official Public Health Service estimate is 1 million, with 390,000 to 480,000 persons expected to develop AIDS by 1993.[4] Many of the projected AIDS cases may be delayed if zidovudine (AZT) and other drugs extend the latency period of HIV in asymptomatic patients. Current planning also must consider the implications of increased survival of AIDS patients. Patients can now be treated prophylactically for many opportunistic infections, surviving long enough to acquire other infections, lymphomas, and dementia. Costs, treatments, and maintenance needs of future patients will differ dramatically from those of earlier cohorts as HIV infection assumes the character of a chronic disease.

CONCENTRATION

The epidemic remains concentrated in six states. In most states, the impact on the health care system — and resulting political interest in AIDS — will be limited.

Almost two-thirds of all reported cases have occurred in six states, half in the three states of New York, California, and Florida (Table 11-1). On a per capita basis, the highest rates of reported AIDS cases are in New York, Puerto Rico, and New Jersey (Table 11-2) — all states (or a territory, in one instance) in which the impact of drug use is responsible for the majority of cases. The District of Columbia, although not truly comparable to states, has even higher per capita rates and tops the Centers for Disease Control (CDC) lists of affected "states." The already heavy burden of AIDS cases will continue to worsen in these areas, as evidenced by the high per capita incidence of new cases.

In contrast, other states remain virtually untouched by AIDS. While every state had at least five cases diagnosed during the past year, 15 states in the Northeast and West still have fewer than five cases per 100,000 population.

Within states, AIDS is also concentrated in specific cities. New York City has by far the largest number of AIDS cases, some 34,490 as of July 1991. This

Table 11-1

Total AIDS Cases by State

State	New Cases	Total Cases	Percent of U.S. Cases	Cum. Percent
NY	7,799	38,536	21.1	21.1
CA	7,407	34,282	15.7	39.8
FL	4,945	16,914	9.3	49.1
TX	3,108	12,773	7.0	56.1
NJ	2,442	11,575	6.3	62.4
PR*	1,799	5,819	3.2	65.6

* Territory of Puerto Rico.

Source: CDC, July 1991.

represents 87 percent of the cases in New York state and more than one fifth of all reported cases nationally. Los Angeles and San Francisco have the next largest numbers (Table 11-3). More than 5,000 cases have been diagnosed in the cities of Houston, Miami, and Washington D.C. — a relatively large number, but fewer than were diagnosed in New York during the past year.

The cities with the greatest per capita rates of AIDS are listed in Table 11-4. San Francisco, with more than 130 cases per capita, is the city most severely affected. San Francisco also continues to have the highest annual per capita incidence of AIDS. The impact on New Jersey and Florida cities as well as New York City also is reflected in these per capita figures.

SHIFTING DEMOGRAPHICS

The epidemic is shifting from one affecting middle-class white men to one affecting low-income minorities and drug users.

During the first years of the AIDS epidemic, male-to-male sexual contact was by far the major source of HIV infection. Among AIDS cases reported before 1985, some 64 percent fell into the homosexual/bisexual risk group.[10] During the past several years, the growth in both the number and the proportion of AIDS cases infected via intravenous drug use has presaged the future importance of this risk group in the epidemic. Intravenous drug use was the sole risk factor for 26 percent of cases reported in the first half of 1991, as compared to 17 percent of cases in 1982.[3,10] Accompanying this change, dramatic increases are occurring in the rate of AIDS among minorities and women.

Transmission associated with drug use. As of July 1991, 58,879 cases of AIDS had been reported among drug users, their sexual partners, and their children.[3] This number includes 11,823 who report both homosexual contact and drug use. About a third of newly reported cases are related to drug use. Because of the long latency period of HIV, however, most of the persons acquiring HIV infection during the past several years have not yet developed symptoms of AIDS and are not included in AIDS statistics. Current transmission of HIV is believed to be occurring to an even greater extent among drug users and their contacts.

Minorities. Among adult AIDS cases reported since the beginning of the epidemic, 28 percent have been black and 16 percent Hispanic, a total of 44 percent. Of cases reported during the past year, however, almost half (49 percent) were black or Hispanic.

Most of the people exposed to HIV via drug use have been minority. Of AIDS cases for whom drug use is the sole risk factor, four out of five are black or Hispanic. Homosexual contact has also been an important source of infection for minorities. Among Hispanic AIDS cases, slightly more were infected by homosexual contact than by drug use (41% vs. 40%). Among blacks, 36 percent were infected by homosexual contact as compared to 39 percent by drug use. However, drug use is the dominant risk factor among new cases.

Women. Currently about 10 percent of adults with AIDS are women.[3] As with minorities, the proportion of women is increasing. In 1985, women represented fewer than 7 percent of cases.[10] During the past year, 12 percent of cases diagnosed were women, more than 5,000 people.

Table 11-2

Population Rates of AIDS

	New Cases (Rate per 100,000)	Total Cases (Rate per 100,000)	Total Cases	Percent Growth (1 Yr)
DC	121.6	501.3	3,026	24
PR	50.6	163.7	5,819	31
NY	43.2	213.5	38,536	20
FL	37.3	127.6	16,914	29
NJ	31.4	148.8	11,575	21
CA	24.4	112.9	34,282	22
MD	21.3	75.3	3,638	28
NV	18.3	60.6	752	30
TX	18.0	74.0	12,773	24
GA	17.9	73.7	4,849	24

Source: CDC, July 1991.

Table 11-3

Total AIDS Cases by City

City	Total Cases
New York	33,490
Los Angeles	12,054
San Francisco	10,463
Houston	5,317
Miami	5,303
Washington D.C.	5,172
Newark	4,811
Chicago	4,457
Philadelphia	3,776
Atlanta	3,725

Source: CDC, July 1991.

Almost half of women infected are intravenous drug users. Another third are infected by sexual contact. While sexual contact with a drug user is the source of risk for most of these women (21 percent of total female cases), sex with a bisexual partner or a partner of unspecified risk are also important sources of infection.

A majority of women with AIDS are black (52 percent) or Hispanic (21 percent). For black women, drug use is directly or indirectly responsible for three out of four cases. Among Hispanic women, sex with a drug user is of relatively great importance. Fully 30 percent of Hispanic women are infected by sexual contact with a drug user, as compared to only 15 percent of infected white women and 20 percent of black women.

Activist groups argue that government agencies have inadequately addressed women's issues in research, treatment, and educational programs related to AIDS.[11] Natural history studies of women are now in progress, but were begun relatively recently. A clinical trial of zidovudine (AZT) for pregnant women has raised an additional set of concerns about women's health when the health of the fetus also is involved.

As more women become infected, gender differences in the course of HIV/AIDS have become the subject of increasing attention. Manifestations of HIV specific to women may include cervical disease and persistent vaginal candidiasis.[12,13] Pelvic inflammatory disease may also be increased among HIV-positive women but has proven difficult to diagnose. These and other manifestations of HIV among women are likely to be the focus of epidemiologic and treatment research during the 1990s.

Children with AIDS. Slightly fewer than 2 percent of all people diagnosed with AIDS have been children under the age of 13, a total of 3,140 cases since 1981.[3] Although small, this risk group has grown rapidly in the past few years, surpassing earlier projections of pediatric cases. By 1988, HIV/AIDS had become the ninth leading cause of death nationally among children between the ages of one and four years. In New York state, it is the leading cause of death among black children in this age range.[14]

A majority of children contract HIV *in utero* from mothers who either are themselves intravenous drug users or who have had sexual contact with drug users. Some 59 percent of children with AIDS are in this risk group. The proportion is higher among minorities; HIV infection is associated with drug use in 64 percent of black and Hispanic children as compared with 42 percent of white children with AIDS. Children under 5 years old with AIDS are predominantly black and Hispanic, 82 percent as of July 1, 1991.[3]

Table 11-4

Population Rates of AIDS by City

City	New * AIDS Cases (per 100,000)	Population (millions)	Total Cases	Total AIDS Cases (per 100,000)
San Francisco	130.9	1.6	10,463	647.6
Miami	81.4	2.0	5,303	269.5
New York	78.2	8.6	33,490	390.6
Jersey City	76.0	0.6	1,965	355.6
San Juan	67.5	1.7	3,650	213.9
Fort Lauderdale	66.8	1.3	3,030	237.0
Newark	51.6	1.8	4,811	264.4
West Palm Beach	44.8	0.9	1,624	181.9
Houston	35.6	3.4	5,317	158.3
Orlando	34.6	1.1	948	85.4
New Orleans	32.3	1.2	1,657	133.8
Washington D.C.	32.5	4.0	5,172	129.6
Atlanta	31.8	2.9	3,725	128.5

* New is June 1990 to June 1991.
Source: CDC, July 1991.

A majority of children with AIDS live in four states, New York, Florida, New Jersey, and California. About three-fourths of children with AIDS lived in these states in 1986. Now, although the number of children in each of these states has increased, Puerto Rico, Texas, Massachusetts, and Pennsylvania also have significant numbers of cases (Table 11-5).

Most children born with HIV infection will develop AIDS within the first few years of life. As more women of childbearing age become infected, health care providers in affected states will be dealing with an increasing number of young children with AIDS. Providers will face issues of how and where to treat these infants and toddlers, many of whom are abandoned or whose parents cannot realistically care for them. In a Harlem Hospital study, half of the HIV-infected children of IV drug-user mothers were "boarder babies" — living at the hospital for lack of another place to go. For these babies, in contrast to non-infected babies, foster placements are difficult to find. Length of stay for boarder babies in the Harlem Hospital was nearly four times as long as for other pediatric patients with AIDS.[15]

A growing number of HIV-infected children will also be reaching school age. While the public is now more willing to allow children with AIDS in schools,[16,17] sympathy has focused on children like Ryan White, who contract AIDS following transfusion or as a result of treatment for hemophilia. About one in five pediatric AIDS cases were in these risk groups early in the epidemic, but fewer than one in ten children developing AIDS during the last year were infected by blood or blood products.[3,18] While the children of drug users are less likely to enter suburban American schools, they also are much less likely to receive national attention to their education — or have major legislation bear their name, as was the case with Ryan White.

MEDICAL PERSONNEL

The growing role of drug use in the AIDS epidemic will impose substantial stresses on health care providers. Physicians and nurses will face the challenge of providing care for a difficult patient population with complex needs, often with inadequate resources. In cities with large numbers of AIDS patients, shortages of physicians and nurses willing to care for AIDS patients are likely; walkouts and lawsuits are possible.

Treating "undesirable" patients. The ethical responsibility of health care professionals to care for AIDS patients — and the conditions for that responsibility — have been discussed since early in the epidemic. A certain consensus exists that just as physicians in past epidemics have cared for patients at some risk to themselves, health care professionals are obligated to care for AIDS patients. As Schwarz comments, "The duty to treat is so fundamental to the concept of a caring profession that its absence violates the premises underlying the doctor-patient relationship and the meaning of being a physician."[19] Public opinion supports this view. In a 1985 survey, 87 percent of Americans said that all hospitals should be required to care for AIDS patients. Although a majority supported a physician's right to choose whether to treat a person with AIDS in 1983, by 1990, 75 percent said doctors should not refuse care.[5]

The views of health care workers on this subject are more conflicted. Most physicians feel a moral responsibility to treat. Fifty-five to 65 percent of physicians in a national study agreed that physicians and nurses could not ethically refuse to care for an HIV-positive patient. Seventy to 80 percent of the nurses surveyed agreed.[20] A California study found that a slight majority of nurses (54 percent) believe they should be allowed to refuse care, but fewer indicated that they would do so.[21] In a study of nursing students, 97 percent said they believed AIDS patients were entitled to care, but only a third were willing to provide care to AIDS patients.[21]

The ethical dilemma posed by AIDS has been complicated by the stigma attached to its current victims. Many physicians, like many other Americans, believe that AIDS patients "deserve" to be ill. In surveys of physicians, one-third to one-half of respondents report being angry with homosexuals and believing that they have brought AIDS upon themselves.[19,22]

These negative attitudes often are softened by direct experience with AIDS patients, especially in the case of homosexuals. Gay patients have been described as well-educated, well-groomed, interested in their treatment and having supportive friends/family.[23] In San Francisco, where the large majority of AIDS patients are gay, physicians reported more career satisfaction and intellectual

Table 11-5

Pediatric AIDS Cases

State	Percent of Cases	Cumulative Percent
NY	28	28
FL	14	42
NJ	10	52
CA	7	59
PR	6	65
TX	4	69
MA	3	72
PA	3	75

Source: CDC, July 1991.

stimulation after starting to treat AIDS patients, despite increased stress.[19] This change in attitude can have concrete effects. Health care workers more accustomed to dealing with AIDS seem to treat patients more humanely — touching, giving back rubs, and having more verbal interaction.[23]

The attitude changes that accompany familiarity with AIDS patients are less likely to apply when the patients are intravenous drug users. In one survey 38 percent of nurses and physicians said they felt less sympathetic toward IV drug users since AIDS, while only 5 percent said they felt more sympathetic.[20] Drug users tend to be demanding and difficult patients. As Fox et al. explain, "[Nurses] report difficulties in establishing good nurse/patient relations with IV drug users who have carried into the hospital context distrusting attitudes and manipulative behaviors characteristic of street drug culture."[24] Health care professionals generally come from a different socio-economic background than intravenous drug users with AIDS. While gay AIDS patients are generally white with above-average education — like 9 out of 10 registered nurses — many intravenous drug users are poor, minority, have a high school level of education or less, and may have a criminal record.[24]

In addition, health care workers often must cope with illegal drug use in the hospital setting. Even for recovered drug users, AIDS often is associated with relapse into drug use.[35] In New York's Beth Israel Medical Center, where the proportion of drug-user AIDS patients grew from 35 to 65 percent in two years, the vice president described the following situation:

> When large numbers of substance abuse patients inhabit a hospital, pushers begin strolling the halls. Wheeling and dealing goes on in the corridors and stairwells. Patients are "shooting up" ...[25]

If drug users were previously regarded with a measure of contempt, AIDS has added an ingredient of fear. As Bosk describes, "Whereas frustration and anger in some cases (especially when drug users were manipulative or physically threatening) and indifference in others used to constitute much of the response to drug-using patients, fear of AIDS has added a difficult dimension."[23]

Personnel shortages. The fear and discomfort felt by health care workers dealing with AIDS patients may undermine the ability of the health care system to provide adequate care. Significantly, only 29 percent of physicians and nurses report that the rewards of working with AIDS patients are worth the effort.[22] Physicians and nurses may decide not to work in cities, hospitals, and specialties that treat large numbers of AIDS patients.

In the case of registered nurses, recent shortages will allow them to avoid positions they dislike. A number of surveys document their current reluctance to care for AIDS patients:[21]

◆ In a California survey, 23 percent of nurses indicated they absolutely would not accept a job caring for AIDS patients and 10 percent would accept only reluctantly;

◆ 36 percent of nursing students in one study said they would refuse to provide care to AIDS patients;

◆ 17 percent of nursing students surveyed at a midwestern school would quit their job rather than care for an AIDS patient.

In hospital AIDS wards such as those in San Francisco, adequate nursing care has not been a problem. Many of these units, which allow nurses greater autonomy, have waiting lists of nurses waiting for openings.[24] But these wards have been populated by well-educated gay male patients; working with intravenous drug user AIDS patients may be less gratifying to most registered nurses.

The supply of medical residents able to care for AIDS patients will likely be affected. Some observers believe young physicians are already beginning to shy away from specialties such as internal medicine.[26] A survey in New York City hospitals found that 25 percent of medical and pediatric residents would not treat AIDS patients if they had a choice. Of the medical residents surveyed, 36 percent indicated that they would be choosing a career path less likely to involve AIDS patients.[27] As Bosk explains,

> AIDS seems to have changed the balance for many who might have tolerated or welcomed the opportunities to care for the underserved. For a medical student contemplating a residency, what was previously a chance to gain relative autonomy quickly in an institution with many substance-abusing patients may have become predominantly unwelcome exposure to a dreadful illness.[23]

OUTPATIENT CARE

The changing demography of AIDS patients will make it more difficult to provide cost-effective home and outpatient care for those who are seriously ill.

For homosexual AIDS patients, volunteers — friends, family members, or members of AIDS volunteer organizations — have provided an important component of patient care. Some 8,000 volunteers at the Gay Men's Health Crisis in New York have provided services including attendant care, housekeeping, meal preparation, and transportation to up to one-third of New York's AIDS patients.[28] These volunteer contributions substitute for paid nursing and attendant care. A Los Angeles study valued non-medical volunteer services received by a cohort of homosexual AIDS patients at $2,000 to $3,000 per patient.[29]

Intravenous drug users generally lack this type of community-based support. Families and friends of drug users usually do not have the financial resources of the homosexual community. AIDS itself, competing with inner-city problems of drugs and crime, is often not recognized as a significant threat.

Volunteer AIDS agencies have purposefully expanded their activities to minority communities, but are perceived as being oriented to gay white males. As one health care worker described, "Many people have complained not that they couldn't receive services and information, but that they didn't feel comfortable."[30]

Without these informal systems, many AIDS patients lack the services that would enable them to stay at home. Physicians facing the choice of discharging patients to an inadequate home situation often maintain them in acute care facilities longer than medically necessary. A one-day survey of 20 New York hospitals found that 256 hospitalized HIV/AIDS patients did not require acute care services; 38 were specifically identified as being in the hospital because they lacked "a suitable home environment."[31] While many of these patients were homosexuals without adequate support networks, a disproportionate number were drug users.

As survival with AIDS increases, the placement of AIDS patients will become a more acute problem. Home care services will represent a greater component of AIDS patients' health care at the same time that the number of patients requiring these services is increasing. A lack of home care support will also interfere with patients' ability to use outpatient therapy, which would substantially reduce their health care costs. As a result, there will be a growing demand for new multi-service "halfway" houses for AIDS patients.

ECONOMIC IMPACT

Health care systems and individual hospitals caring for substantial numbers of AIDS patients will incur large deficits. However, unlike communities facing natural disasters, the cities and hospitals struggling with AIDS can expect little federal assistance.

The problems of financing care for AIDS patients are already well known in hospital systems dealing with large populations of AIDS patients. Most AIDS patients do not have private insurance. Patients initially covered through their employment often lose benefits once they are unable to work. For drug users, reliance on Medicaid or public hospitals is primary, as many have no private coverage to begin with. A 1986 survey of New York hospitals found that 63 percent of AIDS patients with drug use risk factors were hospitalized in public facilities, while only 30 percent of other AIDS patients were hospitalized in these facilities.[32]

Medicaid pays for the largest proportion of AIDS care nationwide, an estimated 40 percent of AIDS patient costs.[33] The proportion varies widely across states. In the southern states where eligibility is restrictive, Medicaid covered 18 percent of AIDS hospital admissions in 1987, as compared with more than half of admissions in the Northeast and West.[34] Medicaid payment falls short of the full cost of services. At San Francisco General Hospital, Medi-Cal covers an estimated 66 percent of its patients' total costs; the proportion elsewhere varies by state and by hospital.[35]

As a result of deficits from Medicaid patients as well as indigence, hospitals in all parts of the country lose money treating AIDS patients. For public hospitals, which treat predominantly low income AIDS patients on Medicaid or without insurance, the average loss per facility was more than $600,000 in 1987. Private hospitals in the northeast, with about 40 percent Medicaid admissions and 10 percent "self-pay," lost an average of $200,000.[34] The largest AIDS-treatment center in the Boston area, Deaconess Hospital, predicted a $1 million loss from its AIDS services in 1988, attributing the increasing financial burden to the declining portion of patients with private insurance.[36]

With more AIDS patients, longer survival, and a larger proportion of poor patients, the burden on hospitals providing AIDS care can be expected to increase dramatically as the epidemic progresses. In a 1987 hospital survey, 5 percent of hospitals were providing care for more than half of AIDS patients. As these hospitals fill to capacity, new solutions will be required. Capital costs for new inpatient beds are estimated at $200,000 per bed in New York City.[37] Less expensive long term care beds and increased reliance on outpatient care may be able to relieve the shortage to some extent. Currently, however, the shortage of long-term care beds in cities like New York is more acute than for hospital beds, and Medicaid covers only a small fraction of hospital outpatient costs.[34,37]

The challenge of providing a therapeutic environment for clients with extensive psychosocial needs — in addition to medical needs — is daunting. Optimal nursing and social support requires counseling, referral, and coordination of social services, many of which are not available. The people infected during the "second" HIV epidemic, as the rise in infection among minority populations has been called, share the obstacles to obtaining health care faced by other poor and uninsured patients. Some do not seek needed services even when they are quite debilitated because they lack the means to pay.[30] Lack of trust — justified or not — and cultural differences with health care workers interfere with care. Withdrawal symptoms or unpleasant interaction with hospital staff have led drug-using patients to sign out of hospitals against medical advice.[38]

The ultimate question is whether cities and hospitals will be able to produce the needed resources, or whether, as some warn, "IV drug users may be abandoned to cope with their diseases with only minimal outpatient assistance or with none at all."[38] AIDS, unlike natural disasters that affect discrete areas of the country, has received equivocal support at the federal level. Debate over the Ryan White Comprehensive AIDS Resources Emergency Act (P.L.101-381) embodies many of the issues that may become central to AIDS legislation during the 1990s. This measure was designed to provide funds for a variety of AIDS health care services and treatment to hard-hit cities, states, and health care providers. It met with opposition from rural legislators and interest groups concerned with other health care issues.[39,40] Although a landmark in targeting funds for AIDS health care services, the Ryan White Act provides only a fraction of the funds originally intended. Future AIDS funding efforts will likely meet with similar competition for pieces of the health care pie.

TESTING PROVIDERS

Intense media coverage of the case of Kimberly Bergalis, apparently infected with HIV by her dentist, has resulted in a public furor over the testing of health care workers. Patients will want their doctors, nurses, and dentists to be tested for HIV, and they will want to be informed of results. Patients will demand recourse against institutions which knowingly allow infected workers to continue to practice.

Close to 5,000 health care workers have been diagnosed with AIDS since the beginning of the epidemic. Only one, dentist David Acer in Florida, is thought to have transmitted HIV in the health care setting. Five patients are believed to have acquired HIV from Dr. Acer after undergoing invasive dental procedures.[41,42]

Despite the low risk of infection from health care worker to patient, this case has raised strong public concern. The reasons are easy to imagine. Unlike exposure through voluntary behaviors, exposure to an infected physician or dentist is perceived to pose an involuntary risk. Unlike other sources of risk in the health care setting (*i.e.*, transfusion), the source of this risk is identifiable. There is a particular irony in being infected by persons entrusted with improving health.

A *Newsweek* poll documented strong public sentiment in support of testing health care workers to prevent transmission in the health care setting.[43] Ninety-four percent of respondents believed that all physicians and dentists should be tested. Ninety percent supported testing of all health care workers.

Three out of five physicians and nurses surveyed nationally are also in favor of testing.[20] Revised CDC guidelines recommend that physicians who perform "exposure prone" procedures be tested, but would rely on voluntary testing — a position supported by groups including the American Medical Association and the American Dental Association, which oppose mandatory testing.[44,45] Shortly after the release of the CDC guidelines, however, the Senate passed legislation requiring testing for surgeons and dentists performing specific high-risk procedures, and stipulating fines or prison terms for those continuing to practice if HIV positive.[46]

For HIV-infected health care workers, the disclosure of positive test results raises the immediate possibility of losing their job many years before they become ill. Two-thirds of respondents to the *Newsweek* survey stated they would discontinue all treatment from a practitioner after learning that he or she was HIV positive. About half believed that infected health care workers should be forbidden to practice. Health care workers facing this possibility have chosen to hide their status, continuing work until they become symptomatic. In several cases when employers and co-workers have known, they have supported this choice.[26,43]

The legislation regarding health worker testing has not yet been finalized, but debate on this issue will likely result in more stringent guidelines for HIV-infected health care workers in the near future. The issue of alternative career options will need to be addressed, especially for health care workers infected on the job.

TESTING PATIENTS

Health workers will respond to the risks of caring for large numbers of AIDS patients and to public demands for screening of providers by insisting that some or all patients be tested.

Anxiety among health care providers about the risk of infection is widespread.[19,22] The fear of becoming HIV infected, in addition to affecting health care workers' attitudes toward working with known AIDS patients, has led to a demand for patient screening to identify patients not known (by them) to be HIV positive. Although health care workers are advised to use universal precautions, the argument is that a high level of vigilance is difficult to maintain at all times. Indeed, both nurses and physicians indicate that they are much less likely to use gloves when drawing blood from patients with unknown HIV status than from HIV-positive patients.[20]

Although only 44 health care workers have been infected in health care settings, risky exposures are commonplace. In one study, 4 percent of patients who had blood drawn in an inner-city emergency room and whose HIV status was unknown were found to be HIV positive.[47] In another study, about 5 percent of physicians and nurses reported having been stuck with a needle used on a patient they knew or suspected was HIV positive.[20] Blood contact occurred during 30 percent of surgical procedures observed at an Atlanta hospital; 7 percent of these exposures were percutaneous injuries.[48]

About half of nurses and 44 percent of physicians in a 1991 survey favor HIV testing for all patients admitted to the hospital.[20] Three-fourths of nurses and physicians favor compulsory HIV testing for surgical patients and pregnant women. A majority of respondents believe that physicians should be able to order an HIV test without a patient's consent.

Public opinion supports health care workers' right to know a patient's HIV status. A 1991 survey found more than 80 percent of Americans favor routine HIV screening of patients at the time of routine medical examinations and hospital admissions.[5] A 1991 *Newsweek* poll found 97 percent of respondents believed patients should be required to inform physicians, dentists, and other health care workers if they are HIV positive.[43] Nearly nine out of ten in a separate survey stated that it should be illegal for HIV positive persons to withhold that information from their health providers. Most respondents also indicated that they would be willing to be tested by their health provider or during a hospital admission.[5]

Given this unequivocal public support and the increasing attention to transmission in the health care setting, some form of patient screening is likely to become a reality. Indeed, the Senate has already adopted an amendment requiring states to allow HIV testing of patients undergoing invasive procedures without consent, which is currently required in most states.[49] Informally the practice may already be widespread. As one physician notes, "In many institutions, blood is illegally and surreptitiously drawn on patients to find out their status."[43]

The prospect of legalized patient screening raises both ethical and technical issues. Which patients will be screened? If screening occurs at the discretion of the physician, will discrimination occur against minority or young male patients? If patients test positive, will there be an effort to deny elective forms of treatment? Will providers be able to decline responsibility under some conditions, such as when they are pregnant? Will patients be informed of their test results? Will hospitals be liable for the distress associated with false positive test results? Will patients or providers cover the costs of screening?

PREVENTION

In order to stem the epidemic, the public will become more supportive of controversial education and prevention programs. These include condom education, television advertisements for condoms and needle exchange programs.

Condoms. Early in the AIDS epidemic, many feared that AIDS education efforts would be hampered by the same controversy that has long surrounded public sex education. However, the risk of AIDS appears to have made an impact on attitudes towards sex education. Seven out of ten Americans want the government to provide them with more AIDS information.[50] An overwhelming majority, 94 percent, support AIDS education in the schools, and about 80 percent want that education to include information about condoms. A similar proportion think AIDS instruction should begin in grade school, and about 40 percent think it is acceptable to teach about condoms at that time.[51] Virtually all respondents say instruction about condom use should have been discussed by the time a student completes junior high school or middle school.

The public is divided over the question about the distribution of condoms in schools. Surveys conducted in 1988 and 1990 showed that about 4 in 10 Americans favored this practice. Approval among black and Hispanic respondents was greater than among white respondents.[51,52]

Discussion of condoms on television has been limited to public service announcements. Major television networks have consistently resisted airing paid condom advertisements, usually citing the objections of viewers and pressure from advertisers.[5] A 1990 survey found that almost two-thirds of Americans think condoms should be advertised on television. Half of the respondents would approve of condom commercials at any time of day, while the other half would prefer evening hours.[51]

Needle Exchange. Although the public has consistently supported expansion of drug treatment as a means of halting AIDS, programs that target active illicit drug users have been controversial. In particular, needle exchange programs, which provide clean needles and syringes to drug users in return for used equipment, have been seen as condoning or encouraging drug use.

Despite evidence refuting any increase in drug use associated with needle exchange,[53,54] such programs have met with a range of political and technical obstacles. A needle exchange experiment begun in New York City in 1988, was terminated in early 1990 with a change in city administration.[55,56] Illegal exchange efforts in Boston and Hartford resulted in arrests of program staff. Portland's Outside In program was delayed for months while insurance arrangements were negotiated.[57] At the federal level, a 1990 bill prohibited funding of any organization involved in distributing injection equipment.[58]

Although needle exchange is still far from an established program, it is becoming a more acceptable prevention strategy. More than two-thirds of respondents in a 1991 survey thought that needle exchange was an effective means of preventing the spread of AIDS.[59] Public support for these programs has increased from 40 percent in 1988 to 51 percent in 1991.[60,61] However, approximately even numbers say they strongly oppose or strongly favor needle exchange, a division reflected in the often acrimonious debates on this subject.

Legal challenges have been an important source of support for needle exchange programs. In cases in Connecticut, California, Massachusetts, and New York, individuals and groups prosecuted for distributing needles without a prescription (a practice illegal in 11 states) have been acquitted. In one case, a juror was so compelled by the evidence supporting needle exchange that he later formed an advocacy group for legalization of these programs.

Legal needle exchange programs have now been established in several communities including Tacoma and Seattle WA, Portland OR, and Boulder CO. Illegal programs such as San Francisco's Prevention Point distribute thousands of needles and syringes every month, tacitly permitted by local authorities. To have a substantial impact in preventing HIV transmission nationwide, these programs would need to be more accessible to drug users. It remains to be seen whether needle exchange will be transformed from pilot programs to a mainstay of AIDS prevention.

THE NIMBY SYNDROME

Despite concern for the epidemic, Americans will continue to resist the location in their neighborhoods of vitally needed drug treatment centers and AIDS care facilities.

Demand for drug treatment was greater than supply even before the AIDS epidemic, and the shortage of slots continues to be an important limit to the effectiveness of drug treatment as an AIDS prevention measure. Although data on treatment facilities are scarce, a 1989 survey estimated that 67,000 drug users were on waiting lists.[62]

In theory, the vast majority of the American public is in favor of increasing drug treatment efforts, expressing more confidence in drug treatment as a remedy for drug abuse than in criminal sanctions.[5] However, Americans are unenthusiastic about locating drug programs in their own neighborhoods.[63] The NIMBY (not-in-my-backyard) syndrome has become a major obstacle for siting the badly-needed new programs. As one New York report describes, "The regulatory system in place at the state and federal levels is ... not designed to quickly implement program expansion ... delays in program start-ups are caused by community opposition to the siting of treatment facilities, spurring legal actions by community planning boards, counties, towns, and others."[64]

AIDS care facilities are also unpopular. In one survey which asked respondents to rank the desirability of having various facilities in their neighborhood, a group home for AIDS patients was one of the least desirable choices. Only a factory, garbage landfill, or prison received a lower ranking.[65]

DRUG POLICIES

AIDS advocacy groups have prompted significant changes in the testing and approval processes for new drugs. However, policies for paying for experimental drugs, some of which have become standard treatments, have not yet been developed. Shifts in the demographic composition of AIDS patients will increase pressures to include more women and minorities in clinical trials.

AIDS Drugs. The AIDS epidemic brought a shift in the groups and alliances concerned with drug (pharmaceutical) regulation. In the past, consumer groups have favored strong, conservative regulation. AIDS activists, however, argued that an excessively cautious drug approval process was delaying access to potentially life-saving treatments. They demanded that new drugs be approved faster and that patients have access to drugs before approval.

In the wake of demonstrations and congressional hearings, the Food and Drug Administration (FDA) responded with several new measures.[66,67] An existing mechanism for allowing access to drugs during clinical trials, the treatment IND, was formalized in 1987 for patients facing life-threatening illness.[68] Import restrictions were relaxed, permitting AIDS patients to obtain unapproved drugs for their personal use.[69,70] Cooperation between the FDA and drug companies was improved.

Despite activists' initial misgivings, recent experience suggests that the FDA has become more responsive to the concerns of AIDS patients. The drug dideoxyinosine (ddI) was reviewed in record time, and the FDA advocated "creativity" in evaluating evidence on its effectiveness.[71] However, early access to new drugs may bring its own problems. Medical researchers criticized the ddI trials for their poor scientific quality. With inadequate data, the FDA may release drugs which have harmful effects not justified by their benefits. Patients may take harmless but ineffective drugs when they could be using better drugs. In theory, drugs that prove to be ineffective or undesirable should be withdrawn from the market.[72] In practice, however, the mechanisms for withdrawing drugs have been used only under extreme circumstances. A final but not insignificant concern is the question of who will pay for experimental drugs or drugs approved with marginal evidence of effectiveness.

Clinical Trials. To date, participation of drug users and minorities in clinical trials for AIDS drugs has been limited. Only 11 percent of patients in the AIDS Clinical Trials Group (ACTG) have been current or former drug users,[13] and fewer than 15 percent have been non-white.[73]

Clinical trials groups have made an effort to enroll more minorities, but the barriers to their inclusion are deep-rooted. For patients who are active drug users, lifestyle clearly hampers their ability to comply with treatment regimens. A more decisive barrier is that many minority patients do not have the resources — time, transportation, child care — to adhere to the strict routine required by the trials.

Female AIDS patients face an additional set of barriers. Now that clinical trials have become a means of treatment, policies excluding pregnant women (or potentially pregnant women) from trials in order to safeguard the fetus have become an unwanted obstruction. In addition, little is known about manifestations of HIV particular to women.

Modes of treatment developed for compliant male patients with adequate family and community support will be less appropriate for patients diagnosed during the 1990s. During the first years of the epidemic, establishing drug safety and efficacy in standardized circumstances overshadowed goals of making trials or treatment regimens more compatible with AIDS patients' lifestyles. Concerted efforts to include a greater variety of patients will make drug trials more complex and more expensive to administer.

CONCLUSION

At the end of the first decade of AIDS, many of the issues raised at the outset remain unresolved: how to change people's risky behavior; how to treat and care for people with AIDS; how to pay for their care; how to protect those at risk but not yet infected. The 1990s will witness an evolution in the AIDS epidemic which will magnify these problems rather than alleviate them. A larger proportion of people diagnosed with AIDS each year are the poor and disenfranchised. Fewer are middle-class white men. This shift will have far-reaching implications:

◆ More of the people developing AIDS in the 1990s will be poor, black or Hispanic, and politically marginal. In addition to AIDS, they will frequently lack family or other sources of support; many will be coping with drug addiction.

◆ New AIDS cases will be diagnosed increasingly in urban centers already struck by the nation's most severe social problems — drug abuse, crime, poverty — and accompanying demands on city services. These cities, most already experiencing budget deficits, will have few resources to spare for new programs.

◆ AIDS patients will continue to seek care at financially pressed public facilities already contending with AIDS and drug use. Medicaid, currently the largest payer for AIDS, will assume a greater burden.

Although AIDS has been called a national disaster, it has not inspired the same level of public support. Because the epidemic is concentrated demographically and geographically, many Americans lack a personal connection to AIDS. Much of the public — and indeed many health professionals — express little sympathy for those who have contracted AIDS via homosexual contact, and even less for drug users. While nearly half of those surveyed in New York City have a family member, friend, or acquaintance with AIDS, most people in the rest of the country know no one who has been affected. They perceive little or no danger of becoming infected themselves. Although they believe AIDS to be a serious health problem, therefore, many Americans may be reluctant to "bail out" the cities, people, and institutions beset by the epidemic during the 1990s.

Americans clearly have responded to AIDS. They have learned about its modes of transmission. More people support AIDS education in schools and other prevention programs such as needle exchange and contact tracing. They are concerned about their risk of becoming infected in the health care setting, even though the risk is very slight. At the same time, however, programs targeting groups at great risk are hampered by inadequate funding and the resistance of local residents to the siting of programs in their community.

As discussed in Chapter 8, Americans are unwilling to commit substantial resources to improving the conditions of the poor and minorities in our society. It remains to be seen whether the nation can develop and maintain a coordinated response to AIDS, as it, too, becomes a problem of the disenfranchised. Until we answer this question, we can be sure that AIDS will be a major health problem in the 1990s, but an exceptional burden for the communities and health care providers of the "second epidemic."

Supported by the Center for Policy and Education of the Harvard AIDS Institute, and the Agency for Health Care Policy and Research, Grant HSO6379-02.

REFERENCES

1. Gottlieb MS, Schanker HM, Fan PT, Saxon A, Weisman JD, Pozalski I. Pneumocystis Pneumonia— Los Angeles. *Morbidity and Mortality Weekly Report.* 1981; 30:250-252.

2. Centers for Disease Control. The HIV/AIDS Epidemic: The First 10 Years. *Morbidity and Mortality Weekly Report.* 1991; 40:22:357-364.

3. Centers for Disease Control. *HIV/AIDS Surveillance Report.* July 1991:1-8.

4.   Vermund ST. Changing Estimates of HIV-1 Seroprevalence in the United States. *The Journal of NIH Research*. July 1991:3:77-80.

5.   Blendon R J, Donelan K. Public Opinion and AIDS: Lessons for the Second Decade. 1991; *Unpublished.*

6.   Lambert B. Halving of Estimate on AIDS Is Raising Doubts in New York. *The New York Times*. July 20 1988.

7.   Hay JW. The Good News About AIDS. *New York Newsday*. May 18 1989.

8.   Hay JW. AIDS Epidemic: Falling Short of Projections? *Texas Tribune*. Nov 9 1989.

9.   Brookmeyer R. Reconstruction and Future Trends of the AIDS Epidemic in the United States. *Science*. 1991. 253:37-42.

10. Miller HG, Turner CF, Moses LE. *AIDS: The Second Decade*. National Research Council. National Academy Press. Washington, D.C. 1990.

11. ACT UP. Women's Treatment Agenda. 1991.

12. Centers for Disease Control. Risk for Cervical Disease in HIV-Infected Women — New York City. *Morbidity and Mortality Weekly Report*. 1990; 39:47:846-859.

13. College of Public and Community Service, Multicultural AIDS Coalition. *Searching for Women: A Literature Review on Women, HIV and AIDS in the United States*. University of Massachusetts-Boston, May 1991.

14. Centers for Disease Control. Pediatric HIV Infection on the Increase. *HIV/AIDS Prevention*. July 1991.

15. Hegarty JD, Abrams EJ, Hutchinson VE, Nicholas SW, Suarex MS, Heagarty MC. The Medical Care Costs of Human Immunodeficiency Virus-Infected Children in Harlem. *Journal of the American Medical Association*. 1988; 260:13:1901-1905.

16. Louis Harris and Associates. The Harris Poll, April 21, 1991. (Storrs CT: Roper Center for Public Opinion Research).

17. Louis Harris and Associates. September 1985. (Storrs CT: Roper Center for Public Opinion Research).

18. Centers for Disease Control. Update: Acquired Immunodeficiency Syndrome — United States, *Morbidity and Mortality Weekly*. 1986; 35:2:17-21.

19. Schwarz MR. Physicians' Attitudes Towards AIDS. in DE Rogers, E Ginzberg, *Public and Professional Attitudes Toward AIDS Patients*. Westview Press, San Francisco, 1989.

20. Colombotos J. Messeri P, Burgunder M, Elinson J, Gemson D, Hynes M. Physicians, Nurses and AIDS: Preliminary Findings from a National Study. 1991; unpublished.

21. Gee G. Nurse Attitudes and AIDS. in DE Rogers, E Ginzberg, *Public and Professional Attitudes Toward AIDS Patients*. Westview Press, San Francisco, 1989.

22. Wallach JJ. AIDS Anxiety Among Health Care Professionals. *Hospital and Community Psychiatry*. 1989; 40:5:507-510.

23. Bosk CL, JE Frader. AIDS and Its Impact on Medical Work: The Culture and Politics of the Shop Floor. *The Milbank Quarterly*. 1990; 68:Suppl 2:257-279.

24. Fox RC, Aiken LH, Messikomer CM. The Culture of Caring: AIDS and the Nursing Profession. *The Milbank Quarterly*. 1990;68:Suppl 2:226-256.

25. Killip T. Hospitals in NYC: A System Under Stress. in DE Rogers, E Ginzberg, *Public and Professional Attitudes Toward AIDS Patients*. Westview Press, San Francisco, 1989.

26. Neel JR. AIDS Risk to Health Workers Debated. Boston Globe. August 8, 1988.

27. Link RN, Feingold AR, Charap MH, Freeman K, Shelov SP. Concerns of Medical and Pediatric House Officers About Acquiring AIDS From Their Patients. *American Journal of Public Health*. 1988; 78:4:455-459.

28. Kobasa SCO. AIDS and Volunteer Associations: Perspectives on Social and Individual Change. *The Milbank Quarterly*. 1990; 68:Suppl 2:280-294.

29. Pascal A, Bennett CL, Bennett RL, Cvitanic M. The Costs and Financing of Care for AIDS Patients: Results of a Cohort Study in Los Angeles. *New Perspectives on HIV-Related Illnesses: Progress in Health Services Research*. Conference Proceedings. National Center for Health Services Research and Health Care Technology Assessment. May 17-19 1989.

30. Graham R. Among Minorities, Response to AIDS Lags. *Boston Globe*. June 19 1990:1.

31. New York State Department of Public Health. *AIDS in New York State Through 1988*. New York. 1988.

32. New York City Interagency Task Force on AIDS. *New York City Strategic Plan for AIDS*. May 1988.

33. Pascal A, Cvitanic M, Bennett C, Gorman M, Serrato CA. State Policies and the Financing of Acquired Immunodeficiency Syndrome Care. *Health Care Financing Review*. Fall 1989:11:1:91 104.

34. Andrulis DP, Weslowski VB, Gage LS. The 1987 U.S. Hospital AIDS Survey. *Journal of the American Medical Association*. Aug 11 1989:262:6:784-794.

35. Brunetta L. Paying the Bills: Medicaid and Hospitals Cover Much of the Cost. *AIDS Patient Care*. Feb 1988; 7-10.

36. Knox RA. AIDS Care System is Showing the Strain. *Boston Globe*. 1988:233:87.

37. Gross G. McIlvaine A, Nogan BA, Radinsky E. The Fiscal Implications of AIDS. *Citizens Budget Commission Quarterly*. Summer 1988; 8:3:1-7.

38. Friedman SR, Des Jarlais DC, Sterk CE. AIDS and the Social Relations of Intravenous Drug Users. *The Milbank Quarterly*. 1990; 68:Suppl 1:85-110.

39. Firshein J, Ed. Panel Won't Fund New AIDS Law, Votes Big Boost for Alzheimer's. *Medicine and Health*. 1990: 44:36:3.

40. Firshein J, Ed. Senators Try To Fund AIDS Care Bill. *Medicine and Health*. 1990; 44:39:1.

41. Centers for Disease Control. Possible Transmission of Human Immunodeficiency Virus to a Patient During an Invasive Dental Procedure. *Morbidity and Mortality Weekly Report*. 1990; 39:29: 489-492.

42. Centers for Disease Control. Update: Transmission of HIV Infection During Invasive Dental Procedures — Florida. *Morbidity and Mortality Weekly Report*. 1991; 40:23:377-380.

43. Kantrowitz B, Springen K, McCormick J, Reiss S, Hager M, Denworth L, Bingham C, Foote D. Doctors and AIDS. *Newsweek*. July 1 1991; 49-57.

44. Kong D. CDC Sets AIDS Policy for Health Workers. *The Boston Globe*. July 16 1991.

45. Goldsmith MF. Physicians and Dentists Tell the CDC: Avoid Quick Fix for a Tough Problem. *Journal of the American Medical Association*. 1991; 265:10:1221-1222.

46. Pianan E. Amendment Requires AIDS Disclosure. *The Washington Post*. July 19 1991.

47. Kelen GD, Fritz S, Qaqish B, Brookmeyer R, Baker JL, Kline RL, Cuddy RM, Goessel TK, Floccare D, Williams KA, Sivertson KT, Altman S, Quinn TC. Unrecognized Human Immunodeficiency Virus Infection in Emergency Department Patients. *New England Journal of Medicine*. 1988; 318:25:1645-1650.

48. Panililio AL, Foy DR, Edwards JR, Bell DM, Welch BA, Parrish CM, Culver DH, Lowry PW, Jarvis WR, Perlino CA. Blood Contacts During Surgical Procedures, *Journal of the American Medical Association*. Mar 27 1991; 265:12:1533-1537.

49. Firshein J. Another HIV Test Measure Clears Senate. *Medicine and Health*. 1991. 45:30:3.

50. ABC News. June 1990 (Storrs CT: Roper Center for Public Opinion Research).

51. KRC Communications Research and *The Boston Globe*. National attitudes towards AIDS, June 1990. Boston MA: The Boston Globe.

52. Kane Parsons. January 1988. (Storrs CT: Roper Center for Public Opinion Research).

53. Foreman J. Needle Exchanges Are Found To Foster Caution by Addicts, *Boston Globe*, June 7 1989.

54. Hart GJ, Carvell ALM, Woodward N, Johnson AM, Williams P, Parry JV: Evaluation of Needle Exchange in Central London: Behaviour Change and Anti-HIV Status Over One Year, *AIDS* 1989; 3:261-265.

55. Lambert B: New York To Begin Free-Needle Plan for Drug Addicts, *The New York Times*. Aug 12 1988.

56. Purdum TS: Dinkins to End Needle Plan For Drug Users, *The New York Times*. Feb 14 1990.

57. O'Neill P. Start-Up Due for Needle Exchange. *Oregonian*. Jan 6 1989.

58. American Psychological Association: Congress Approves Bleach Distribution Research, *Science Agenda*, 1990; 3:1:14.

59. Gay Men's Health Crisis, June 1991. (Storrs CT: Roper Center for Public Opinion Research).

60. CBS/New York Times. September, 1988. (Storrs CT: Roper Center for Public Opinion Research).

61. Media General/Associated Press. May, 1989. (Storrs CT: Roper Center for Public Opinion Research).

62. Office of Technology Assessment. *The Effectiveness of Drug Abuse Treatment: Implications for Controlling AIDS/HIV Infection*. OTA BP-H-73. 1990.

63. Des Jarlais DC, Friedman SR. Transmission of Human Immunodeficiency Virus Among Intravenous Drug Users. in VT DeVita, S Hellman, SA Rosenberg (eds), *AIDS: Etiology Diagnosis, Treatment and Prevention*, J.B. Lippincott, Philadelphia, 1988; 385-395.

64. New York Department of Health. AIDS: New York's Response, A 5-Year Interagency Plan. January 1989.

65. Daniel Yankelovich Group. Public attitudes toward people with mental illness. A report to the Robert Wood Johnson Foundation. April 1990. Princeton NJ: Robert Wood Johnson Foundation.

66. House of Representatives, Committee on Government Operations: Therapeutic Drugs for AIDS: Development, Testing, and Availability, U.S. Government Printing Office 87-433, Washington D.C., 1988.

67. House of Representatives, Committee on Energy and Commerce: Parallel Track Proposal for Clinical Drug Development — July 20 1989, U.S. Government Printing Office 101-97, Washington D.C., 1990.

68. Young FE, Norris JA, Levitt, JA, Nightingale SL: The FDA's New Procedures for the Use of Investigational Drugs in Treatment, *Journal of the American Medical Association*. 1988; 259:15:2267-2270.

69. Boffey PM: FDA Will Allow AIDS Patients to Import Unapproved Medicines, *New York Times*, July 24 1988, 1.

70. Edgar H, Rothman DJ: New Rules for New Drugs: The Challenge of AIDS to the Regulatory Process, *The Milbank Quarterly*. 1990; 68:Suppl. 1:111-141.

71. Chase M. DDI Decision Heralds a New FDA Activism. *The Wall Street Journal*. July 22 1991.

72. Siegel JE, Robert MJ. AIDS Drugs & the Cost of Regulation: Reforming FDA Policy. *Regulation*; in press.

73. Cotton P. Is There Still Too Much Extrapolation From Data on Middle-aged White Men? *Journal of the American Medical Association*. Feb 1990; 263:8:1049-1050.

CHAPTER 12

Conclusion and Forecast for the Future

Robert J. Blendon and Jennifer N. Edwards
Harvard School of Public Health

Our aim in writing this book was to answer one seemingly simple question: What are we, as a society, likely to do about the crisis in health care over the next several years? Our conclusion may both shock and disappoint many readers. We do not find a revolution about to occur. While citizens of this country have decided that fundamental change in our health care system is needed, they are immobilized by their disagreement over the form such changes should take. Until some middle ground is reached, our health care system is likely to follow along its current trajectory — the problems worsening, with minor incremental improvements made periodically. We do not mean to imply that important changes will not occur in health care in the next few years; but, if they do, they will be not be the result of a single, national legislative action.

To help those readers who wish to make plans for their own or their institution's future, we have made 18 specific predictions about our health care system's evolution over the next few years, based on the major findings in each of the preceding chapters. We have grouped them around a series of key issues and institutions.

THE NATIONAL HEALTH INSURANCE DEBATE

Prediction 1: A debate over the need for a national health plan, at least partially financed by new taxes, has begun. This controversy will not be resolved quickly but will carry on over a three to five year period.

In our society, major health care reform will require three conditions be met: (1) the public and leaders of key interest groups must recognize the need for fundamental change, (2) they must agree on a path to achieving change, and (3) there have to be strong political leaders who are committed to bringing the problem to closure.

At the moment, only the first condition has been met. Our surveys show near universal agreement among the public, major employers, and union leaders that the health care system needs to be fundamentally changed. In particular, there is a consensus that national legislation is needed to control health care spending and guarantee universal access to basic health care for everyone. The support for reform is significant, even if it means a moderate increase in taxes.

However, there is no agreement among the public and key interest groups on the type of national health plan the country should adopt. The specifications of a reform policy will require years of discussion and debate before a consensus is likely to emerge. Medicare was first introduced as legislation by President Kennedy in 1960 and was debated hotly for five years before it was enacted. In its final form, it included a number of important provisions that represented compromises between the views and priorities of the elderly, taxpayers, employers, unions, physicians, and hospitals. A similar process of accommodation and compromise between major groups will take time to evolve.

Last, strong political leadership has just begun to emerge on this issue. The Senate majority leader and the Chairman of the House Ways and Means Committee for the first time in 15 years are sponsoring a form of a national health plan.

On the other hand, the Bush Administration lags far behind with little interest in promoting national health care reform. The President has placed his prestige and political future on being the foreign policy President. The polls to date show his gamble to avoid domestic problems and focus overseas has been a dramatic success. At the moment, he looks like a shoo-in for re-election in 1992, subject only to unknown health problems or a major scandal.

The most likely outcome is the President will be re-elected and have to contend with a Democratic Congress in 1992 that is eager to make health care reform a national political issue. Health care reform is one of the few domestic issues that affect the middle class, the largest group of voters, and thus will ultimately activate the leadership necessary to enact a major program.

Prediction 2: At the end of what will seem like a long, contentious national debate, legislation will be enacted that requires employers to provide private insurance coverage for their employees (or pay a tax); with the government accepting the responsibility for providing subsidized insurance for the poor and those not in the labor force.

Regardless of the merits of an all-governmental program such as is found in Canada and Germany, or that could be achieved by extending Medicare to our entire population, the opposition of the major interest groups to such a program remains too strong. As shown by our surveys, no major interest group, with the exception of organized labor, now favors an all-governmental program. The public's view, which could have swayed the national debate if it had clearly favored one approach over another, remains divided between an all-public and a mixed private-public financing system. The third strike against a publicly financed plan is the Bush Administration. There is no precedent for a conservative Republican President to support the enactment of all-government program when a prominent, private sector alternative is available. To date, the Congress has overturned few of President Bush's vetoes and has, instead, sought compromise legislation.

In addition, because of a continuing lack of consensus on a number of policy questions, the legislation ultimately enacted will attempt to resolve all of our health care system problems at once. Rather, it will be a national health plan that postpones making difficult, controversial choices about cost containment and major structural reforms. The plan is likely to be phased in over several years to avoid increasing the federal deficit and instigating a taxpayer backlash, as was seen with the Medicare Catastrophic Care Act.

MEDICARE AND THE ELDERLY

Prediction 3: The elderly will remain the most powerful group shaping the nation's health care policy. In the period ahead, they will use their enormous clout to pressure Congress to expand long term care coverage under Medicare and add a new outpatient prescription drug benefit. However, this will take a number of years to come to fruition.

Senior citizens have on their health care agenda for the 1990s more comprehensive coverage of nursing homes, home care, and prescription drugs. They will not let public financing of these benefits die with the repeal of the Medicare Catastrophic Care Act.

When given a choice of how they would like long term care benefits to be financed, seniors show an overwhelming preference for expanding the Medicare program rather than encouraging the development of private long term care insurance. However, with national attention heavily focused on the federal budget deficit, some lingering sensitivities on Capitol Hill from the repealed

271

Medicare Catastrophic Care Act, and some resistance to paying the necessary taxes, we expect more Congressional interest around the less expensive of the two options — expanding coverage of prescription drugs.

> *Prediction 4: In the next few years, Medicare cost containment strategies will diverge even more dramatically from private sector employers' policies. The federal government will rely almost exclusively on physician and hospital price controls to reduce their outlays, while employers will emphasize competitive managed care plans and benefit reductions.*

Why will this be so? Price controls for doctors and hospitals are the most acceptable form of cost containment to senior citizens. As a result, these payment controls will be tightened over time. On the other hand, employers who are developing successful means of controlling costs could also help set policy.

Despite the apparent advantages for policymakers, capitated plans are not very popular with people over age 65. Only 6 percent of Medicare beneficiaries are now enrolled in HMOs. The majority of the elderly report they are not interested in joining an HMO because it restricts their choice of general practitioner and specialists. The elderly also oppose strategies that control costs by increasing cost sharing, but the opposition here is not as great as efforts to change their current medical care arrangements.

Lastly, we find senior citizens strongly opposed to efforts to place limits on the services available to elderly patients: rationing. The elderly do not approve of rationing by age or by the potential outcome of the treatment.

> *Prediction 5: The right to die question will be the medical ethics issue of the mid-1990s.*

There is a rapidly growing consensus among the elderly and Americans in general, that individuals suffering from terminal illnesses, or their families, should have the option of requesting that certain medical care interventions be discontinued. An overwhelming majority of the public favor withdrawing life-sustaining treatment from a terminally ill patient if requested by the individual or the family. A slightly smaller majority favor the much more controversial concept of allowing doctors to end the life of a patient with an incurable disease if so requested. The public does not view these as potential cost-savings measures, but as quality of life considerations. These perceptions are under-scored by the belief that such personal decisions should be made by patients, families and physicians, not by legislators, courts, or third party insurers.

These views will increasingly be reflected in decisions by juries in court trials, referendum votes in key states, and public pressures on legislatures to enact more permissive legislation.

EMPLOYERS

Prediction 6: Over the next several years, large employers will be intensifying their health care cost containment activities. However, because of their concern for the morale of their workforce they will avoid the tough decisions that might save them considerable sums of money.

Our survey of employers finds containing employee benefit costs ranks below maintaining the quality of their labor force as a corporate priority. As a result, we find large employers' plans for controlling their health care costs being focused on the softer choices and not the harder ones that could be more cost saving.

In our minds, the softer choices include raising co-insurance and deductibles and the introduction of more incentives to encourage employers to enroll in what has been nicknamed "litely" managed care plans. The intent of these programs is for employees to get medical care in the most cost-effective way without interfering in most of the decisions made by physicians on behalf of their patients. These programs include utilization review of expensive outpatient claims; offering a less costly HMO or PPO (usually a network or IPA model); negotiating discounts for employees with local hospitals and doctors; and encouraging the use of generic drugs.

On the other hand, we find little interest from large employers in adopting tougher corporate cost containment policies that would substantially alter the health care available to employees and their families by limiting choices to less costly providers and sites of care. These policies would include: (1) the use of gatekeeper primary care physicians, whom employees must see to get a referral to a medical specialist, (2) a requirement that all employees must enroll in a tightly managed care plan, such as a group model HMO, or (3) that the employee's choice of physicians and hospitals would be limited to a select list based on their lower prices or charges. Similarly, we find little interest in corporate rationing of high-cost medical technologies for their employees.

Prediction 7: Contrary to some earlier press reports, few leaders of large corporations today favor the adoption of an all-government system of national health insurance, similar to that found in Canada. However, if private sector cost containment activities fail in the next few years, a significant share of corporate leaders will be prepared to rethink their position on this issue.

Today eight out of ten corporate executives report they oppose the enactment of a Canadian-like national health plan. But this finding understates the level of frustration building in the corporate community. As the debate stretches out over the years, many corporate leaders may be prepared to consider a much more central role for government health financing. More than one-half of corporate leaders reported that if private sector cost containment activities were not

273

working to contain costs in a few year's time, they would consider a government-controlled national health insurance system. Our bottom line prediction is that today's corporate position on a national health plan differs significantly from that to be found in 1994.

HOSPITAL CARE

Prediction 8: The much ballyhooed revolution in American hospital care has not happened and is not likely to occur in the near future. We do not see large numbers of hospitals joining "Supermeds," for-profit chains, or the medical-industrial complex; nor do we see hospitals playing a much smaller role in the U.S. health care system.

We have not seen a significant downsizing of the hospital industry in the 1980s. What we have seen is a large number of mergers and formal affiliations between hospitals that are very different from the "Supermed" envisioned some years ago. Instead of national systems, the hospital systems that have developed are likely to be smaller, regional, and less formal in membership affiliation.

Merger mania has had its day, and either formal or informal consolidation into systems also may be slowing. The data indicate the organizations interested in consolidating have, for the most part, already done so. Data also suggests that the promised economies of scale and marketing advantages of large hospital chains have proven to be somewhat illusory.

Prediction 9: The word for hospitals of the mid-1990s will be growth, not shrinkage.

The aging of the population, plus the continued development of more sophisticated medical technologies and clinical procedures (implants, transplants, laser surgery, etc.) aimed at improving the quality of life for those with chronic illnesses, will start hospital admissions climbing once again.

In addition, hospitals will remain the dominant institution in our health care system because of their aggressive expansion into outpatient care. Hospitals, not free-standing centers, will continue to be the largest providers of emergency and outpatient care.

Prediction 10: For a small group of hospitals, the above forecast will have no relevance. Directors of these Mother Theresa-like hospitals will see themselves as being in another America. Their future will be characterized by more uninsured patients, lower reimbursement rates from Medicaid, and more inadequately insured AIDS patients — all pointing to greater deficits and financial constraints.

The combination of a conservative President, a continuing federal deficit, and no immediate enactment of a national health plan means little improvement in financial aid for those hospitals caring for medically indigent patients with the most serious health and social problems. These institutions can expect layoffs, staff burnout, long queues of patients waiting for care, and postponement of purchases of needed new equipment.

Prediction 11: A gradual shift in the bargaining power of American hospitals is occurring and will continue into the future.

Cost control pressures have become more pervasive; discounts and fixed government payments are replacing traditional hospital charges as the predominant source of hospital revenue. As a result, senior managers are losing autonomy to third party payers, HMOs, employees, and even patients. At the same time, hospital executives are gaining more clout in setting the agenda for practicing physicians, drug companies, and medical suppliers.

Prediction 12: Nonprofit hospitals will face increasing challenges to their tax exempt status in the 1990s and will lose many of these confrontations in the courts, legislatures, or in referendums.

The stampede during the last decade to make the hospital look like a Fortune 500 company will have an unforeseen economic consequence. The public now believes that not-for-profit institutions behave like for-profit businesses. In the years ahead, state and local officials, starved for new sources of revenues, are likely to translate this "hospitals are businesses" sentiment into limits on hospitals' tax exempt status, additional restrictions on access to tax exempt financing, and mandates that hospitals provide a fixed percentage of their revenue to treat medically indigent patients.

Prediction 13: By the mid-1990s, hospitals and other health care organizations will experience shortages of workers. Unlike during the 1980s, the shortfall in labor supply will reduce access to a much wider range of health care personnel than just nurses.

The rate of growth in the national labor force will decrease sharply during the 1990s. The slower growth in the labor force will mean all employers — especially those providing health care services that have been a major employer of new workers during the past two decades — must search harder for new workers. Wages are likely to go up sharply and people with lower qualifications will make up more of the new hires.

In addition to shortages, the health care workforce will be much more culturally diverse than in the past, creating numerous challenges for health care managers. Legal and illegal immigration to the United States will continue to rise. In all, nearly 25 percent of new workers in each year of the 1990s will be recent immigrants with very different orientations to the workplace.

PHYSICIANS

Prediction 14: The growth in the number of new doctors will continue to outpace the increase in the general population. As this trend continues, it will compel more doctors to take steps to more effectively compete with other physicians. It will also lead employers and government to be more aggressive in their efforts to restrain doctors' incomes.

It is now more than a decade since the likelihood of a physician surplus was predicted. From an economic perspective, the signs of this occurring have been slow in coming. However, there are changes stemming from the increasing supply of doctors that are likely to multiply in the years ahead. The proportion of physicians offering evening and weekend hours and those advertising for patients is likely to grow. Similarly, dislike it as they may, more doctors will feel pressure to contract with managed care plans and HMOs in the future.

Likewise, as thousands of new doctors open their offices and seek incomes similar to their predecessors, both government and employers will be more concerted in their efforts to curtail the historic growth in doctors' incomes. This will involve the more aggressive search for fee discounts, review of admission and testing decisions, and efforts to establish fixed targets for their physician outlays.

Prediction 15: In the future, physicians are going to be willing to come to the bargaining table and offer an historic national compromise. The medical profession will for the first time actively campaign for the enactment of a universal health plan, even if it involves more restrictions on their fees. The trade-off — the legislation must significantly reduce physicians' risk of malpractice suits and lessen their administrative hassles with insurers.

Malpractice is seen by doctors as the most serious threat to their autonomy and professional well being. The reform efforts that have been enacted by many states have slowed the growth in liability claims, but they have not significantly relieved the anxiety of the medical community on this issue. Only more sweeping legislation could do this. With the trial lawyers so influential in legislatures across the country, such reform would need to be part of a larger, more popular legislative program.

Similarly, the managed care revolution, coupled with the growing restriction on insurance payments will increase the time and costs physicians must spend in administrative insurance related efforts.

Taken together, these two issues will lead physicians to offer national decisionmakers an historic trade-off. We have already seen a sign of their willingness to move in this direction by the publication of a special theme issue of *The Journal of the American Medical Association* on the problems of the uninsured and underinsured. A proposal for national health reform prepared by the AMA was a major component of the issue.

> *Prediction 16: In the future, medicine will remain an attractive career option in comparison to other professions. However, because of increased competition from other doctors and growing government and insurer intervention, physicians, particularly younger ones, will express increasing dissatisfaction with their role as doctors in our society.*

Despite all the health care changes occurring, medicine will remain an attractive choice for college graduates. It is not that medical practice itself will be as appealing as it was in earlier years; rather the pressures from the baby boom and a slowly growing economy will make other career alternatives less attractive both financially and in terms of personal reward.

Although medicine may be seen as the better career choice, physicians will be increasingly burdened with outside intervention in their medical decision making as employers' efforts to manage their costs expand. The level of paperwork and oversight involved in getting reimbursed for the care physicians provide will multiply, increasing their dissatisfaction with medical practice.

AIDS AS A NATIONAL DISASTER

> *Prediction 17: By 1994, almost 400,000 people will have been diagnosed as having AIDS and a quarter of a million individuals will have died.*

In order to stem this epidemic, Americans will become more supportive of implementing controversial education and prevention programs. These include condom education, television advertisements for condoms, and needle exchange programs.

Also growing from the intense media coverage of Kimberly Bergalis, apparently infected with HIV by her dentist, the public will demand compulsory testing of health care workers. Patients will want their doctors, nurses, and dentists to be tested for HIV, and they will want to be informed of results. Patients will demand recourse against institutions that knowingly allow infected workers to continue to practice.

> *Prediction 18: The victims of the AIDS epidemic, now in its second decade, are shifting from middle-class, gay, white men to low-income minorities and illegal drug users. The changing demographics of AIDS will affect hospitals and health professionals treating a large number of these patients.*

The growing role of drug use in the AIDS epidemic will impose substantial stresses on health care providers. Physicians and nurses will be faced with the challenge of providing care to a difficult patient population with complex needs and, often, inadequate resources. In cities with large concentrations of cases, there are likely to be shortages of physicians and nurses willing to provide care to AIDS patients. Walkouts, strikes, and lawsuits are conceivable.

This new class of AIDS patients will create numerous financial dilemmas for hospitals. Many of the new AIDS patients are uninsured; need expensive treatment and care that is excluded by many insurance policies; have no friends and relatives to care for them at home; or are covered by Medicaid — a plan with below average reimbursement levels. Health care systems and hospitals caring for substantial numbers of AIDS patients will suffer from large deficits and will have many patients who have no home to which they can be discharged. However, unlike communities facing other natural disasters, the cities and hospitals struggling with AIDS can expect little federal assistance because of the political lack of concern and constraints resulting from the federal deficit.

LOOKING AHEAD

In concluding, we have highlighted a few, but not all, of the key groups and important issues facing the health care system. In future volumes, we will take a more in-depth look at a variety of issues and groups, including the role of small businesses in the health care reform debate, the future of the insurance industry, the impact of cost containment on the availability of new medical technology, how the views of American doctors concerning the practice of medicine compare to their foreign counterparts, and the role of the states in solving local and regional health care problems. In addition, we will go back and see if this year's forecasts are holding true and whether or not there is a need to change our predictions.

The most significant finding of this work is that there has been a shift in Americans' beliefs about the need for health care system reform. Based on individual experiences, the public and major health care leadership groups have reached this same conclusion. Health care reform is not a passing interest — this consensus has stayed with us through the Gulf War and the Recession. In fact, the current situation has become a crisis in many peoples' minds.

Were we a country with a strong, centralized government, we would be able to act on this change quickly and decisively. However, our political system is one that makes sweeping changes only after a wide consensus has been reached. What our book shows is that we, as a country, have started down the road to finding this consensus. Changes are being implemented by employers, doctors, hospitals, and others. But as we said in the beginning, forecasters tend to overestimate the time in which changes can be accomplished. For meaningful reform to occur, groups of people will have to understand the need for compromises. We hope this book will be a step down the road to that understanding.

INDEX

Independent Practice Associations (IPAs), 130, 159, 273

Insurance, health. *See health insurance.*

Interest rates, 46-48

Italy, right to health care, 187

Japan,
        capital stock, 46
        health care spending, 176

Journal of the American Medical Association (JAMA), 277

Kentucky, national health insurance survey, 188

Labor force,
        demographic changes, 32, 41-45, 275
        immigrant workers, 42-44
        shortages, 275
        tenure rates, 45
        women workers, 42, 44-45
        worker productivity, 48-49

Labor unions. *See union leaders.*

Los Angeles Times survey, 179, 186
        national health insurance, 188, 189

Long term care,
        consumer preference, 88, 89, 90-91
        insurance benefit, 111, 218
        insurance, public support for, 180, 201-02, 206, 271-72

Malpractice, 156-57, 163, 229
        reform, physician support for, 163, 239, 276

Managed care, 23, 116, 126, 161, 180, 273, 276
        alternative to national health insurance, 236
        consumer satisfaction with, 95
        cost control measure, 165, 203-04, 206, 272
        interest group survey, 229, 236
        "litely" managed care, cost containment, 115, 119, 273
        relationship with hospitals, 130-39

Margins, hospital, 21
        Medicare, 21
        patient, 20

TABLES AND FIGURES